Table 8.1 p. 214
Table 7.9 p. 190

p.135 FOPDT

CHEMICAL
PROCESS
CONTROL

CHEMICAL PROCESS CONTROL

James B. Riggs

Department of Chemical Engineering

Texas Tech University

Ferret Publishing

Printed in the United States of America

ISBN 0-9669601-0-6

Ferret Publishing

2609 24th Street

Lubbock, Texas 79410 USA

1-806-747-3872

Table of Contents

PART I: INTRODUCTION

PART II: PROCESS DYNAMICS

PART III: PID CONTROL

PART IV: ADVANCED PID CONTROL

PART V: CONTROL OF MIMO PROCESSES

Preface

Over the past 15 years, process control engineering has emerged as a major technical specialty for chemical engineers. As a result, more and more chemical engineers are developing careers in the process control field. The objective of this text is to provide a framework for teaching undergraduate students the fundamentals of process dynamics and feedback systems while also teaching these students the critical skills necessary to function as process control engineers in industry.

An industrial process control engineer needs to be able to tune and troubleshoot control loops, make process control design decisions and understand the terminology of the profession. It is important to teach these skills in an undergraduate control class if we are going to produce engineers who are productive when they begin work, but these skills by themselves can be limiting without a fundamental understanding of process dynamics and feedback systems. In addition, much of the terminology of the process control profession is strongly tied to the theoretical analysis of control systems. Professional terminology is crucial if control engineers are going to be able to convey their ideas and sell their approaches to their peers, their boss, and the process operators. (A summary of additional terminology is listed at the end of each chapter and the first time that a new term is used, it appears in bold letters in the text.) Clearly, there needs to be a proper balance between teaching industrially relevant process control skills and developing a fundamental understanding of process control theory.

This text is my attempt at this challenging balancing act. Moreover, I have attempted to clearly delineate within this text between material that directly relates to the industrial practice of process control and theoretical material that is presented for the fundamental understanding of process control systems and for the introduction to important terminology. For example, it is important for a student to understand that even though transfer functions (Chapter 4) are an important approach to analyzing and understanding the dynamic behavior of feedback systems, they are rarely directly used by industrial control engineers to analyze the behavior of their control loops. The material in this text that is primarily oriented toward control theory is contained in Chapter 4 (Laplace Transforms and Transfer Functions), Chapter 5 (Idealized Dynamic Behavior), Chapter 8 (Frequency Response Analysis) and a large part of Chapter 6 (PID Control). On the other hand, Chapter 2 (Control Loop Hardware and Troubleshooting) is largely descriptive and is directly related to industrial control practice. But in general, most of the remaining chapters contain elements of both theory and practice. That is, the fundamental understanding of feedback systems and the analysis tools developed in theoretically oriented chapters are used to guide the study of control approaches relevant to industrial practice.

Certain industrial leaders in the field of process control have called for academia to put the "process" back into process control. That is, they would like for academia to teach process control with a process point of view. Industrial process control engineers use their knowledge of the entire process that they are working on along with their knowledge of control systems to solve control problems. Control engineers that do not understand the process are vulnerable to developing control solutions that appear fine to them, but in fact work against the overall objectives of the process. Moreover, this situation can result in serious safety problems.

In Chapter 3 (Dynamic Modeling), dynamic models of the actuator, the process, and the sensor are developed and combined to model the dynamic behavior of several process systems. Dynamic models for a thermal mixer, a composition mixer, a level in a tank, two continuous stirred tank reactors (CSTR's), and a heat exchanger are developed and used throughout the text. This approach to process modeling is quite simple and computationally efficient while exposing the student to process dynamics not unlike those demonstrated by industrial processes. The addition of sensor noise (Section 3.5) provides additional realism to these simple simulators. The exercises at the end of the chapters call for the student to use the simulators for a variety of functions including controller tuning and the application of advanced PID techniques. This approach provides the student with valuable hands-on dynamic and control experience and is quite different from the classical approach which is based on using transfer functions to study these problems. Also, the actuator/process/sensor view of process systems is used in Chapter 6 to evaluate the feedback behavior of a number of control loops commonly encountered in the chemical processing industries and provides an important process based view of control systems.

Chapter 7 presents an approach to process controller tuning which is based upon using an evaluation of the process nonlinearity and the magnitude of the disturbances affecting the process to determine the appropriate tuning criteria. This approach is developed by analyzing a nonlinear CSTR to demonstrate that process nonlinearity and disturbance magnitude can combine to produce unstable feedback behavior. Moreover, chemical engineering examples are used to introduce and demonstrate advanced PID techniques such as cascade, ratio, and feedforward (Chapter 9), inferential control and scheduling of controller settings (Chapter 10), and configuration selection for the control of multiple input/multiple output processes (Chapter 12).

Finally, the approach taken in this text is not to exhaustively cover the full range of process control topics, but rather to focus on material that will develop a fundamental understanding of feedback systems and develop the skill set required for an industrial process control engineer. It is my hope that this text will inspire more students to enter the important and interesting field of chemical process control.

James B. Riggs   August 1998
Lubbock, Texas

Note to Instructors

Teaching process control is a challenging task because it is generally the first time that the students have been exposed to dynamic behavior and it is difficult to keep the study of this field from becoming abstract to the student. One approach that I have found helpful in this regard is to use laboratory demonstrations of hardware to show the different types of hardware involved, process dynamics, and feedback behavior. It has been my observation that students tend to have an easier time learning technical material when they can physically see this equipment in operation. Our process control laboratory is a fluid flow/heat transfer process that uses industrial-type hardware with a laboratory distributed control system (DCS). Alternatively, a laboratory unit operation process without industrial hardware can be used to demonstrate process dynamics by having the instructor operate the process as the controller. In the latter case, control valves and a range of sensors donated by industry can be put on display for the student to examine.

The classical approach to homework problems for process control is based on developing analytical solutions for control problems using simplified transfer function models of a process which generally do not consider the dynamics of the sensor or actuator system. As a result, the student gets a steady diet of tedious partial fraction expansions in order to arrive at the analytical solutions. The approach taken here is to use discussion questions and exercises with process simulators for homework problems. That is, simplified simulators that involve models of the actuator, process, and sensor along with software models for PID controllers, filters, autotune testing, and several advanced PID control functions are included on a diskette with the text. In this manner, the student is able to have a hands-on experience with process dynamics, tuning, and advanced PID control.

Finally, I have found that it is important to expose the students to the components that make-up a feedback control loop (Chapter 2) before they study modeling and feedback behavior so that they understand how a feedback loop is actually implemented industrially. Unfortunately, there are several terms and approaches that are discussed in Chapter 2 that are not yet fully understood by the student. For example, significant portions of the troubleshooting material is concerned with controller tuning which is addressed in Chapter 7. As a result, I have found it necessary to return to Chapter 2 near the end of the course to reemphasize the important aspects of control hardware and troubleshooting after exposure to the full range of process control topics.

Note to Students

In this text, two general types of material will be presented to you: theoretical and industrially oriented. The theoretical material, which is largely based upon Laplace transforms, is presented to provide a fundamental understanding of the dynamic behavior of feedback control systems. In addition, much of the terminology used by control engineers is based upon the theoretical analysis of process control systems.

The industrially oriented material involves an analysis of the hardware that actually makes up industrial control loops, presentations of a wide range of control approaches, and using a model-based approach to understand control loop behavior. The model-based approach analyzes the dynamic behavior of the components of a process control loop: controller, actuator, process and sensor. **It is important to keep track of what is theoretical material which is intended for fundamental understanding and what material is directly related to the industrial practice of process control.**

The accompanying diskette contains simulators of a number of simple processes. Each program contains the dynamic model of the process (i.e., actuator/process/sensor) and software for a variety of controllers. In order to complete the homework exercises, the simulators can be used by enabling and disabling certain sections of the program and applying the proper tuning parameters. These programs are available as either FORTRAN or MATLAB files.

Download the software for this text from the following website:

http://www.pcoc.ttu.edu/riggs_book/software

Acknowledgments

It is not possible to complete a project like this without a lot of help from a variety of sources. Ken Junk from Fisher Controls provided very valuable information on control valves and troubleshooting and editorial feedback on the chapter on control loop hardware. Greg McMillan from Monsanto supplied information and guidance on the material on industrial sensors. Jack Watts and Mike Nichols from Phillips Petroleum and Scott Flathouse from Celanese supplied a wide range of failure modes for the components of industrial control loops. Jim Downs from Tennessee Eastman and Scott Boyden from Aspentech suggested several important topics that were included. Bob Ellis of Aspentech provided editorial feedback and Charley Cutler reviewed the material on Dynamic Matrix Control.

Dominique Bovin of EPFL provided very detailed editorial feedback as well as a number of suggestions for additional topics and examples. Larry Ricker from University of Washington identified several examples that were added to the text. Chang Bock Chung from Chonnam National University provided extensive editorial feedback. Several portions of this text were influenced by collaboration with Russ Rhinehart. H. R. Heichelheim, who is a professor emeritus from Texas Tech, performed the copy editing for this text.

My graduate students (Andrei Bobkov, Satish Enagandula, J. Govindhakannan, Kishor Gudekar, Haitao Huang, Xuan Li, Rodney Thompson, and Meisong Yan) enthusiastically provided editorial feedback. In addition, Joe Anderson, Scott Hurowitz, and Marshall Duvall provided examples from their research projects. The material on Dynamic Matrix Control is based largely on the approach developed by Scott Hurowitz. Joe Anderson and Marshall Duvall taught me how to overcome the software and hardware problems associated with desktop publishing.

Most importantly, my wife, Brenda, did the word processing for this text and acted as a consultant for my problems with Corel Ventura.

Dedicated to my wife, Brenda, and our children, Michelle, James Michael, and Matthew

PART I

INTRODUCTION

Chapter 1

Introduction

1.1 Chemical Process Control

Chemical Process Control (CPC) is concerned with operating a plant such that the product quality and production rate specifications are met in a safe and reliable manner. In order to attain these objectives, various flow rates are, in most cases, adjusted in order to maintain operation (e.g., important levels, pressures, temperatures, and compositions) near the desired operating points. CPC is part of the larger field of automatic control which ranges from controlling aircraft to controlling robots to controlling the critical systems in a computer.

The Chemical Processing Industries (CPI, i.e., the companies that operate refineries and chemical plants) over the past 15 to 20 years have been in a transition from a relatively young industry that was largely driven by innovation in new products and new processing approaches to a more mature industry where the technology of the industry is changing much more slowly. In earlier times, new products, such as nylon and Teflon®, were developed and new process designs, such as fluidized catalytic cracking (FCC) and plastic processing technologies were developed. These innovative products and processing approaches provided a major economic advantage to their developers. The resulting profit margins associated with these technological breakthroughs far outweighed the incremental benefits of optimal or near optimal operation. For example, the addition of an FCC unit, which converts low valued gas oils to high valued gasoline, to a refinery provided much higher profit margins than the additional incremental benefit of optimal operation of the FCC unit. Optimal operation of an FCC unit is economically important but it pales in comparison to the economic incentive of adding an FCC unit to a refinery in the first place. Today all refineries have FCC units; therefore, for a refinery to remain competitive, it must be concerned with the optimal operation of the FCC unit. CPC is an integral part of attaining the most efficient operation of an FCC unit and most other processes in the CPI.

In addition, during the 1970's and 1980's, significant advancements in instrumentation and process computers made possible the rapid development that has been observed in CPC. In the 1960's, the chemical engineering staff of a company was largely made up of process engineers and design engineers. During the 1970's and 1980's, CPC consulting companies and control experts within operating companies

3

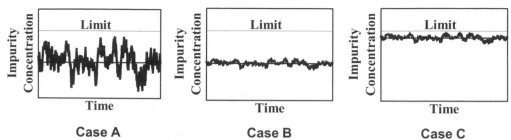

Figure 1.1 Comparison between impurity measurements and the upper limit on the impurity in a product for the original control system (case A), the improved control system with the original impurity setpoint (case B), and the improved control with new setpoint (case C).

were able to demonstrate that improved process control can provide very significant economic return usually with relatively low capital investment. As a result, today a typical chemical engineering staff of an operating company in the CPI is made up of process engineers and process control engineers. Now design services are normally provided by consulting companies.

CPC is intimately involved in the effort to meet the operational objectives of the process while striving for the most efficient operation of the plant. Minimizing product variability is many times a key operational objective and is directly affected by the performance of the process control system. In fact, the performance of an overall process control system is many times expressed in terms of the variability in the products produced by the process. Figure 1.1 shows the measurement of the impurity in a product for the original control system (case A). Case B represents the performance of a new control system. Note that the controller corresponding to case B produces a product with less variability in the impurity than results for case A; therefore, case B is referred to as producing a lower variability product than case A. For many products, low variability is an important product specification. If a product does not meet its product variability specifications, the resulting product can be low-valued with low demand while product that meets the variability specification can be high-valued with high demand. In addition, since case B has lower variability, the average impurity level can be moved closer to the impurity specification (case C). Many times operating closer to the limit allows greater production rates or lower utility usage both of which result in a more efficient operation of the process. Other types of operational limits are encountered resulting from environmental regulations, capacity limits on equipment, and safety limits. In a similar manner, operating close to these limits can also be economically important. Figure 1.2 shows the impurity distribution or frequency of impurity measurements for the three cases shown in Figure 1.1.

1.2 Everyday Examples of Process Control

Process control is commonplace in our everyday life. Several examples are considered here in our effort to introduce the concept of process control as well as introduce some of the terminology of the field. The terminology introduced here will

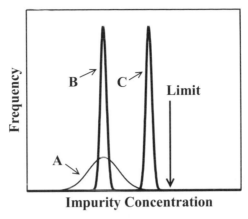

Figure 1.2 Frequency distribution for cases presented in Figure 1.1.

be frequently used throughout the remainder of the text.

Controlling the Water Temperature of a Shower. Everyone is familiar with the problem of controlling the water temperature of a shower when you first get in the shower or after something has changed the water temperature (e.g., water heater starts running out of hot water). Assume that the valve (faucet) on the cold-water line is manipulated to control the shower water temperature.

Consider the case in which the water heater is starting to run out of hot water. As the heater starts to run out of hot water, the hot water temperature will decrease. As a result, the person in the shower will begin to close the valve on the cold water line in order to maintain the desired shower temperature.

Let's analyze this process from a process control point of view. In this case, the shower is the **process**. The person's skin "senses" the water temperature, and is therefore, referred to as the **sensor**. Controlling the water temperature is the objective of the control operation; therefore, the water temperature is the **controlled variable**. The desired water temperature is called the **setpoint**. The flow of cold water into the shower head is used to control the shower water temperature and is referred to as the **manipulated variable**. The valve on the cold-water line and the person's hand are used to change the cold water flow rate and are referred to as the **actuator** which is known industrially as the **final control element**. Note that in this case the actuator changes the manipulated variable. The person in the shower senses the temperature and combines this with past experience with the cold water valve to determine how much to turn the valve; therefore, the person in the shower is acting as the **controller**. Adjusting the cold water flow rate based on the sensed shower water temperature is an example of **feedback control** or **closed loop control**. The combination of the sensor, setpoint, controller, actuator, and process comprise the feedback control loop. When a change in the valve on the cold water line is made and the shower water temperature is allowed to move to a new steady-state condition without any further changes in the cold water valve, the resulting time behavior of the shower water temperature is called the **open loop response** of the process. Therefore, an open loop test does not involve feedback from the measured controlled variable.

A changing hot water temperature is called a **disturbance** to the process since it is not directly controlled and it affects the shower water temperature. Another disturbance can occur when someone flushes a nearby toilet if adequate supply pressure is not available for the cold water. In this case, after the toilet is flushed, the shower water temperature will increase sharply. When you hear someone flushing the toilet, if you adjusted the cold water flow before the shower water temperature increases in an effort to reduce the resulting temperature increase, that would be an example of **feedforward control** which involves compensating for known disturbances. If you step out of the shower when you hear someone flushing a toilet to avoid being burned by the hot water, that would be an example of **override control**.

For a poorly designed shower, when the valve on the cold water line is turned, it may take several seconds before the shower water temperature changes. This can result when the velocity of water in the cold water line is low and/or when the piping from the hot and cold water mixing point to the shower head is excessively long. As a result, when a change in the cold water valve is made, the person in the shower must wait until the effect on the shower water temperature has occurred before making another adjustment to the valve. The time delay between a change in the cold water valve and a change in the shower water temperature is the **deadtime** of the process and deadtime makes feedback control more difficult.

Return to the case in which the hot water heater is running out of hot water. As the hot water temperature decreases, the cold water flow rate must also decrease in order to maintain the desired shower water temperature. Eventually, the cold water flow rate will go to zero at which point the shower water temperature will equal the hot water temperature. But as time goes on, the hot water temperature, and as a result, the shower water temperature will drop below the desired level. Since the cold water flow rate cannot be negative, a zero flow rate for the cold water represents a **constraint** or limit to the process.

An old valve on the cold water line can exhibit significant "sticking". That is, if the valve is opened a small amount, no change in the flow will result. If additional small changes are made, eventually a large change in the cold water flow rate will result causing a significant change in the shower water temperature. Then if the valve is closed in small steps, a number of steps will be required before the cold water flow rate will decrease and the resulting decrease in the shower water temperature will be a relatively large change. A sticking valve affects the flow rate metering precision that one can attain and is referred to as **valve deadband.** Since the valve affects how accurately the manipulated variable is controlled, significant valve deadband can affect how precisely the controlled variable is controlled, i.e., variability in the shower water temperature.

To this point, we have considered that the cold water flow rate is used to control the shower water temperature, which is an example of a

Single-Input/Single-Output (SISO) process since one manipulated variable (the flow rate of cold water) is used to control one controlled variable (the shower water temperature). Assume now that it is desired to control both the shower water temperature and the shower water flow rate using the cold water flow rate to control the temperature and the hot water flow rate to control the shower water flow rate. This is an example of a **Multiple-Input/Multiple-Output (MIMO)** process since there are two inputs (the hot and cold water flow rates) and there are two outputs (the shower water temperature and total shower flow rate). Note that if the cold water flow rate is changed while controlling the shower water temperature, the shower water flow rate will also change. Likewise, if the hot-water flow rate is adjusted to control the total shower flow rate, the shower water temperature will also change. This is an example of **coupling** between control loops in a MIMO process. Instead of using the cold-water flow rate to control the shower water temperature and the hot-water flow rate to control the shower flow rate, the hot-water flow could be used to control the shower water temperature and the cold-water flow rate could be used to control the shower water flow rate. In addition, other manipulated variables can be used, e.g., the ratio of the cold water flow rate to the hot-water flow rate. The **pairing of manipulated and controlled variables** has a very significant effect upon the control performance for MIMO processes (Chapter 12).

Controlling the Water Temperature in a Bathtub. The process is the water in the bathtub. The setpoint is the desired bath water temperature. The sensor is the person's hand that is immersed in the bath water to sense the water temperature. Also, the person's hand is used to measure the temperature of the water added to the tub. The manipulated variable that is used to control the temperature of the water in the bathtub is the temperature of the water entering the bathtub and the actuator is the valve on the hot water line and the person's hand. The person is the controller for this process. This process is called a semi-batch process since water enters the tub but does not exit. The shower is an example of a continuous process.

Note that there are two separate control loops: the control loop for the tub water temperature and the control loop for the temperature of the water entering the tub. If a person samples the tub water and finds that it is too hot, they must reduce the temperature of the water entering the tub. This is an example of **cascade control** since the control loops are applied in tandem, i.e., the setpoint for the temperature controller on the water entering the tub is set by the tub water temperature controller. As the setpoint for the temperature of the water entering the tub is changed, the valve on the hot water line is adjusted.

When adjustments are required for the tub temperature, it takes some time for a correction in the measured temperature to result. The "inertia" of the process is referred to as the **lag** of the process and depends on the volume of water in the tub and the volumetric flow rate of water into the tub.

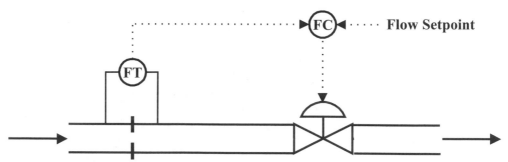

Figure 1.3 Schematic of a flow control loop. FT- flow transmitter and FC- flow controller.

Driving a Car. Consider a person driving a car. The objective (i.e., setpoint) is to keep the car in its lane on the road. The sensor is the person's eyes and the controlled variable is the position of the car on the road. The manipulated variable is the steering wheel/power steering system/front wheel system while the actuator can be thought of as the person's hands and arms that turn the steering wheel. Loose steering (i.e., the steering wheel can be moved back and forth without changing the direction of the car) represents deadband in the actuator. The controller is the person driving. Curves in the road are also disturbances and driver anticipation of the curve is feedforward control. Wear on the tires, a worn suspension, or fouled spark plugs represent very slow disturbances to this process. When the driver sees that the car is drifting to the center or the shoulder of the road and the corrective action is feedback control.

Cruise Control on an Automobile. The sensor for the cruise control unit can be two magnets attached to the drive shaft in combination with an electrical coil that generates a current that is directly proportional to the revolutions per minute that the drive shaft is turning which in turn is directly proportional to the speed of the automobile. The setpoint for the cruise control unit is provided when the driver pushes the "set" button when the automobile reaches the desired speed. The setpoint for the controller is actually the electrical current that was being generated by the sensor when the set button was pushed. The controlled variable is the generated electrical current from the sensor which correlates directly with the speed of the automobile. The actuator is the throttle position on the engine while the manipulated variable is the flow of gasoline to the engine. Hills or a loss of power produced by the engine represent disturbances to the cruise control unit. Since changes to the throttle position are directly proportional to the error from setpoint, the cruise controller is a **proportional-only controller**. When a steep hill is encountered, a small but persistent error from the specified automobile speed will result. This constant error from setpoint is referred to as **offset**. If the driver pushes the resume button when the automobile far below the setpoint speed, the throttle will fully open and the maximum flow rate of gasoline to the engine will result. This is an example of a **saturated manipulated variable** since the manipulated variable of the process is at its highest level.

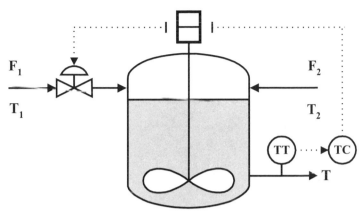

Figure 1.4 Schematic of a CST thermal mixer. TT - temperature sensor/transmitter and TC - temperature controller.

1.3 Chemical Engineering Process Control Examples

Flow Controller. The most common control loop in the CPI is a flow controller (Figure 1.3). The sensor in this system is usually a combination of an orifice placed in the line and a device that measures the pressure drop across the orifice which is directly related to the flow rate.   The actuator is the control valve.   The flow controller compares the measured flow rate with the specified flow rate and accordingly opens or closes the control valve.   A more complete analysis of flow controller operation is presented in Section 6.6.

Continuous Stirred Tank (CST) Thermal Mixer. Figure 1.4 shows a schematic for a continuous stirred tank thermal mixer for two feed streams at different temperatures.   The setpoint is the desired product temperature and the controlled variable is the product temperature. The manipulated variable could be the flow rate of one of the feed streams to the mixer and the actuator would be the control valve on the corresponding feed stream.   The sensor is a temperature sensor/transmitter located in the product line. The temperature controller compares the measured temperature with its setpoint and makes changes to the control valve on feed flow to the mixer. Disturbances to the process include changes in the temperature of the feeds to the CST. The volume of the mixer divided by the total volumetric flow rate to the mixer is the **residence time** or the average time that an element of feed spends in the mixer assuming that the liquid level in the CST is held constant. For this process, the **time constant** of the process is equal to the residence time. The time constant is a measure of how fast the temperature in the mixer can change. As a rule of thumb, one can assume that it takes approximately four time constants to observe the full effect of a step change of an input to a process under open loop conditions.

Continuous Stirred Tank Composition Mixer. In a manner similar to the CST thermal mixer, the CST composition mixer mixes two streams with different

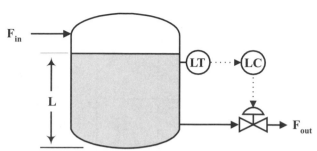

Figure 1.5 Schematic of a level in a tank. LT - level sensor/transmitter and LC - level controller.

concentrations of components. The setpoint is the concentration of the product produced by the mixer and the manipulated variable is the flow rate of one of the streams. The actuator is the control valve on the manipulated feed stream. The sensor is a composition analyzer that analyzes samples taken from the product line. Normally, gas chromatographs (GC's) are used as on-line analyzers and they provide new composition measurements typically every three to ten minutes. The time between new measurements is referred to as **analyzer deadtime** or **analyzer delay**. The controller compares the measured composition of the product with its setpoint and makes changes to the control valve on the feed flow to the mixer. The residence time and time constant of this process would be equal to the volume of liquid in the mixer divided by the total volumetric feed rate to the mixer assuming that the liquid level in the mixer is held constant.

Level Control in a Tank. Figure 1.5 shows a schematic for this case. The setpoint is the desired level in the tank and the controlled variable is the level in the tank. The manipulated variable is the exit flow from the tank and the actuator is the control valve on the outflow line. The sensor is the level indicator on the tank and changes in the inlet flow rate are disturbances to the process.   The level controller compares the measured level with the setpoint for the level in the tank and makes a change to the control valve on the exit flow from the tank.

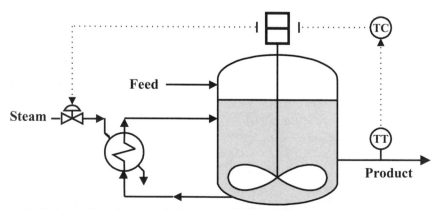

Figure 1.6 Schematic of an endothermic CSTR. TC - temperature controller and TT- temperature sensor/transmitter.

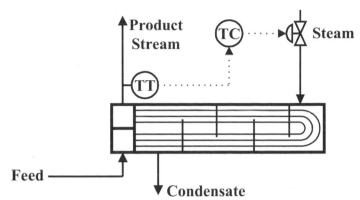

Figure 1.7 Schematic of a steam heated heat exchanger. TC - temperature controller and TT - temperature sensor/transmitter.

Endothermic Continuous Stirred Tank Reactor. An endothermic CSTR is shown schematically in Figure 1.6. The controlled variable is the temperature of the product leaving the reactor and the manipulated variable is the feed rate of steam to the heat exchanger. The sensor is a temperature sensor/transmitter that measures the temperature of the product stream leaving the reactor. The controller compares the measured value of the product temperature with its setpoint and makes changes to the control valve on the steam to the heat exchanger.

Stirred Tank Heater. Figure 1.6 also represents a stirred tank heater if no reaction occurs in the tank. In this system, the material in the tank is heated by passing it through the heat exchanger. The controlled variable is the temperature of the product leaving the tank and the manipulated variable is the flow rate of steam to the heat exchanger. The actuator is the valve on the steam line and the sensor is the temperature sensor/transmitter which is placed in the product line. The temperature controller compares the measured value of the product temperature with its setpoint and makes changes in the control valve on the steam to the heat exchanger.

Heat Exchanger. Figure 1.7 shows a schematic of a steam heated heat exchanger. The feed enters the heat exchanger and flows through the tube side of the tube bundle receiving heat from the steam. The controlled variable is the temperature of the stream leaving the heat exchanger and the manipulated variable is the flow rate of steam.   The actuator is the valve on the steam line and the sensor is the sensor/transmitter which measures the temperature of the stream leaving the heat exchanger. The temperature controller compares the temperature of the stream leaving the heat exchanger with its setpoint and makes changes in the control valve on the steam.

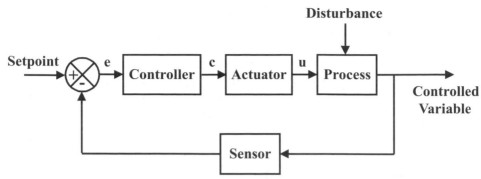

Figure 1.8 Block diagram of a generalized feedback system. e is the error from setpoint, c is the controller output, and u is the manipulated variable.

1.4 Block Diagram of a General Feedback Control System

Figure 1.8 shows a block diagram representation of a generalized feedback control system. Note that each of the previous examples can be represented by this diagram. That is, each of the examples has a controller, an actuator, a process, and a sensor, in that order, along with feedback of the measured value of the controlled variable to the controller. In addition, each of the examples is affected by disturbances as well. Note that the sensor reading is compared with the setpoint and the controller chooses control action based upon this difference. The actuator system is responsible for making changes in the level of the manipulated variable. The "process" for a control loop is only the part of the system that determines the value of the controlled variable from the inputs. The overall process can be based upon a number of processing units.

This block diagram of a feedback control loop will be used in Chapter 6 to qualitatively evaluate feedback control behavior. Note that the symbol $\otimes$ in Figure 1.8 represents an addition function. The negative sign on the measurement of the controlled variable results in forming the difference between the setpoint and the measured value of the controlled variable which is referred to as the **error from setpoint**. A block diagram of an open loop process would involve only the actuator, process, and sensor without the feedback of the measurement of the controlled variable to the controller.

1.5 Types of Controllers

Manual Control. When operators act as the controller, this is referred to manual control. Operators typically make changes in manipulated variable levels and wait to see where the process will settle before making the next manipulated variable change. In this manner, the operator adjusts the manipulated variable in a conservative fashion by using a series of steady-state or near steady-state steps. The time between manipulated variable changes is set by the **open loop settling time** of the process, i.e., the time for the process to reach a new steady-state operating point after a single step change in the manipulated variable level has been applied to the process. Consider manual control for a single change in a disturbance. Operators will see the initial effect of the disturbance and make their estimate of the needed change in the manipulated variable. Then they will watch the response of the process (i.e., observe for approximately one open loop settling time). After the process has settled or nearly settled, they will make another adjustment to the manipulated variable level and observe. It typically takes several adjustments to return the process to the desired setpoint. Obviously, when the process is subjected to frequent disturbance upsets, operators will be continually making changes to the process and observing the results in an effort to keep the controlled variable near its setpoint.

PID Controllers. The most common controller in the CPI is the PID controller which is the primary emphasis of this text. The PID controller has proportional, integral, and derivative action (Chapter 6) and it is applied at a much higher frequency (i.e., applied much more frequently) than manual control. As a result, properly implemented PID controllers provide marked performance improvement over manual control. For a single disturbance, a properly tuned PID controller will typically return the process to or near setpoint in approximately one open loop settling time. For a series of disturbances, the PID controller significantly outperforms manual control in terms of the resulting variability about setpoint.

Advanced PID Controllers. PID controller performance can be enhanced by a number of techniques including cascade control, ratio control, feedforward control, scheduling of controller tuning, decouplers, and antiwindup (Chapters 9 to 12). These techniques are designed to assist PID controllers with regard to more effectively handling disturbances, process nonlinearity, coupling, etc.

Model-Based Controllers. Controllers that directly use process models to determine the control action can handle process nonlinearity, disturbances, coupling, and complex dynamics if the model used in the controller accurately represents these features. There are a variety of model based controllers (Chapter 13) where the major classifications are linear and nonlinear model-based controllers. Also, there are a number of different types of controllers within each of these classifications. Model-based controllers can offer significant performance improvement over PID controllers in certain cases when properly implemented and maintained.

1.6 Responsibilities of a Chemical Process Control Engineer

Overview. From an overall point of view, the process control engineer is responsible for using his process control skills and process knowledge **to make money** for the operating company. Specifically, the process control engineer is responsible for seeing that a plant that was generally not designed with regard to process control performance operates safely, reliably, and efficiently while producing the desired product quality. The control engineer does this by transferring the variability that would otherwise go into important controlled variables to manipulated variables and less important controlled variables. In order to meet these objectives, it is essential that process control engineers use a complete knowledge of the process in order to attain the most desirable performance of the process.

Controller Design. The control engineer is responsible for selecting the proper mode of the controller (P-only, PI or PID) depending upon the characteristics of the process. That is, the P-only controller uses only proportional feedback action, the PI controller uses proportional and integral action, and PID uses proportional, integral, and derivative action and each of these controller options has advantages when applied in the proper situation. In addition, the control engineer is responsible for applying advanced PID versions (cascade, ratio, feedforward, etc.) to the cases where they will offer significant advantages. Therefore, the control engineer must understand the advantages and disadvantages of the advanced PID techniques as well as understand the control-relevant aspects of the process in question, e.g., the proper pairing of manipulated and controlled variables. The control engineer may also be responsible for specifying the type of sensors and control valves.

Controller Tuning. Selecting the values of the controller settings (e.g., choosing the amount of proportional, integral, and derivative action to be used by a PID controller) is critically important for the proper functioning of a controller. Controller tuning is generally a compromise between controller performance and controller reliability (Chapter 7). For certain systems, the controllers can be tuned aggressively resulting in very tight control while others require much more conservative controller settings. Controller tuning is obviously needed for implementing new controllers, but is more frequently required for existing control loops due to changes in the behavior of the process or for changes in the magnitude or type of disturbances affecting the process.

Controller Troubleshooting. Even a properly designed and tuned controller may not function properly. For example, an erratic sensor or an improperly functioning actuator can seriously undermine the performance of a controller. Excessive disturbance levels can also be the sources of unacceptable controller performance. It is the responsibility of the control engineer to identify the reasons for improperly functioning control loops and correct them as much as possible (Chapter 2).

Documentation of Process Control Changes. Any significant change to a process, including changes to the process controls, requires approval by a safety review committee for most companies in the CPI. Before approving changes in the controls for a process, the safety review committee typically requires that a process change data sheet be completed which describes the proposed process changes and is approved by the operational and management authorities for the affected area of the plant. The process control engineer is responsible for completing the process change data sheet, obtaining the approval signatures, and presenting the process modifications to the safety review committee. In addition, the process control engineer usually serves on the safety review committee in order to assess the effects of process modifications on the process control systems.

Types of Process Control Engineers. There are, in general, several levels of responsibility that control engineers are assigned to. For example, for an entry level assignment, process control engineers might have the responsibility for the process control tasks for an area of the plant. These engineers would be responsible for the day-to-day operation of the control loops in their area (i.e., tuning and troubleshooting). Control engineers with five or more years experience or with graduate training in process control may be responsible for larger, more challenging control projects throughout the plant. These control engineers would be involved in the design, tuning, and troubleshooting for the controllers. Finally, corporate level control engineers typically are stationed at corporate engineering headquarters and are involved in long term control projects at a variety of plant sites. These engineers typically have a Ph.D. degree in chemical process control or have worked their way up the ranks to be recognized as one of the company's top process control engineers. For each of these job levels, effective process control engineers use their knowledge and experience on control systems combined with a thorough understanding of the chemical processes that they are working with to deal with process control problems. The key point here is that **for process control engineers to perform effectively, they must have a thorough knowledge of the process behavior and the operational objectives and constraints of the process**.

1.7 Operator Acceptance

A major issue in effectively functioning as a process control engineer is **operator acceptance**. Operator acceptance depends upon developing process control solutions that work effectively in an industrial setting as well as getting along with the operators. The quickest way to ensure that your control work will not be accepted by the operators is to deal with them in an arrogant and condescending manner. For example, if you come into the control room with an arrogant attitude, a significant number of operators will take it upon themselves to make sure that you are not successful in their plant. Regardless of how well your controller functions on the process, if you have offended the operators, they will see that your controller does not stay on-line. Remember that at 2 a.m., they are the "kings" of the process.

That said, the best way to interact with the operators is to give them the respect that they deserve and seek their advice and input whenever you start a control project. Remember that they are observing the process day in and day out. They may not correctly know why certain things happen in the process but you can count on them knowing what happens and under what conditions. As a result, operators are a valuable resource of operating experience.

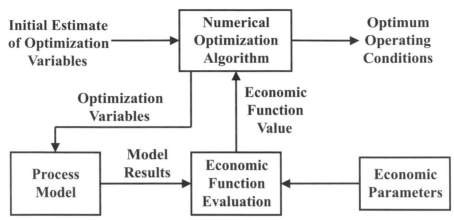

Figure 1.9 A logic flow diagram of a process optimization procedure.

With regard to implementing controllers that function well in an industrial setting, the control engineer must ensure that the proper controller type (Chapters 6, 9, and 10) has been chosen for the process in question and that the controller is properly tuned (Chapter 7). Bumpless transfer (Chapter 11) and anti-windup (Chapter 11) should be used as well. Validity checks and filtering should also be applied to sensor readings. In this manner, controllers can provide good control performance in a highly reliable fashion. That is, the best controllers are the ones that meet their control objectives, stay in service unless there is a sensor or actuator failure and respond "gracefully" when the actuator or sensor failures occur.

1.8 Interfacing Process Control and Process Optimization

Process optimization is concerned with operating the plant so that the operation results in producing the highest rate of profit generation for the operating company. For example, for many reactor systems, as the reactor temperature is increased the conversion of the reactants increases, but the ratio of products to byproducts (i.e., selectivity) decreases; therefore, there is an optimum reactor temperature that provides the best economic tradeoff between conversion and selectivity. The economic optimum temperature is related to a number of process variables (e.g., feed rate, feed composition, reactor volume) as well as economic parameters (e.g., product values, separation costs, feed costs).

Figure 1.9 shows a logic flow diagram for a typical process optimization algorithm. The optimization process starts with an initial estimate of the optimum operating conditions which in the case of the reactor example is the initial estimate of the optimum reactor temperature. The numerical optimization algorithm passes the initial estimate of the optimum operating conditions to the model equations (Chapter

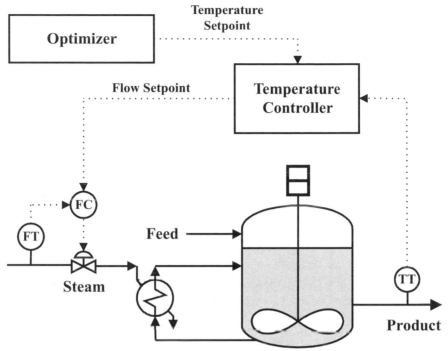

Figure 1.10 Schematic of an endothermic CSTR with regulatory control, supervisory control, and optimization. FC- flow controller; FT- flow sensor/ transmitter; TT-temperature sensor/transmitter.

3) where all the conditions of the process are calculated. For the reactor example, the production rate of products and byproducts would be calculated along with the utility usage for the process using material and energy balances around the reactor. The model results are then combined with economic parameters to calculate the rate of profit generation. The following general equation represents the usual calculation approach used to evaluate the economic function value:

$$\Phi = \sum P_i V_i - \sum F_i V_i - \sum U_i C_i$$

where Φ is the rate of profit generation or the value of the economic objective function, P_i is a production rate of a product or byproduct, V_i is the value per unit mass of a feed, product, and byproduct, F_i is a feed rate, U_i is a utility rate (e.g., steam flow rate), and C_i is the corresponding unit cost for utility usage. In this manner, the numerical optimization algorithm chooses values of the optimization variables, and in the case of the reactor example, the reactor temperature, until the optimal economic function value is identified. That is, each time a new reactor temperature is chosen by the optimization algorithm, the model equations are solved and the product and byproduct rates are used to determine the corresponding value of the economic objective function. Once the optimum value of Φ is identified, the optimization calculation is finished.   The corresponding values of the optimum operating conditions (i.e., the optimum optimization variables) are typically applied to the process as setpoints for a number of controllers on the process.

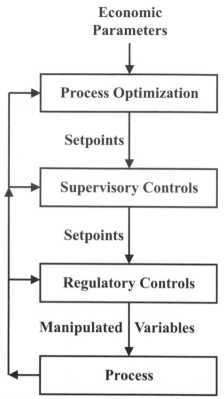

Figure 1.11 A block diagram showing the interactions between process optimization, supervisory control, and regulatory control.

Figure 1.10 shows how optimization can be applied to an endothermic CSTR. Note that the result of the numerical optimizer, optimization model, and economic objective function is the optimum reactor temperature. This temperature becomes the setpoint for the reactor temperature controller which is referred to as a **supervisory controller**. The output of the supervisory controller is the setpoint for the flow controller on the steam which is referred to as a **regulatory controller**. Generally, composition and temperature control loops serve as supervisory controllers while pressure, level and flow control loops are used as regulatory controllers. In summary, process optimizers determine the setpoints for the supervisory control loops which in turn select the setpoints for the regulatory control loops which adjust valves on the process. This hierarchy of optimization/supervisory control/regulatory control is shown schematically in Figure 1.11. Note that the connection from the process to the regulatory controls, supervisory controls, and the process optimizer represents the flow of process measurements to each of these functions.

1.9 Illustrative Example of a Process Control System

Figure 1.12 shows a schematic of a control system on a distillation column. The purpose of this section is not to overwhelm the student with the complexity of

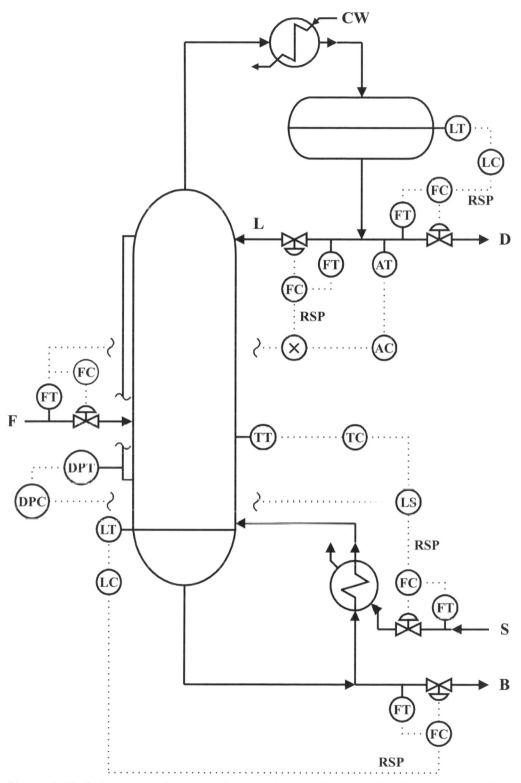

Figure 1.12 Schematic of a control system applied to a distillation column. F-column feed rate, D- distillate flow rate, L- reflux flow rate, B- bottoms flow rate, S- steam flow rate, CW- cooling water.

material that has not yet been studied, but to demonstrate from an overall point of view the set of process control skills that will be addressed in the remaining chapters of this text.

The overall objective of the control configuration shown in Figure 1.12 is to maintain the composition of the distillate product, D, and the bottoms product, B, at their respective setpoints in the face of process disturbances (e.g., feed flow rate and feed composition changes). In addition, when the column is fed more feed than it can separate, it is desired to maintain the purity of the distillate product at the expense of the bottoms product. Table 1.1 lists the symbols for the various control components (e.g., sensor/transmitters and controllers) that are used in this text.

There are five controlled variables for this column: the composition of the distillate product, the temperature of a tray in the stripping section, the level in the accumulator, the level in the reboiler, and the feed flow rate to the column. The operator selects the setpoints for the level controllers on the accumulator and the reboiler, the temperature controller, and the distillate composition controller as well as the setpoint for the column feed rate controller. Also, there are four manipulated variables: the flow rate of the distillate product, the reflux, the bottoms product, and the steam to the reboiler. For the control configuration shown in Figure 1.12, the flow rate of reflux is used to control the composition of the distillate product while the steam flow rate is adjusted to control the tray temperature in the stripping section, which leaves the distillate and bottoms flow rates to control the levels in the accumulator and reboiler, respectively.   Chapter   12   addresses   selecting   the   proper manipulated/controlled variable pairings.

The flow rates of the reflux, distillate, bottoms, and steam are each controlled by their respective flow controllers (FC). The setpoints for each of these flow controllers are provided by the corresponding supervisory controllers. For example, the remote setpoint (RSP) for the flow controller on the distillate is set by the level controller (LC) on the accumulator. This is referred to as a remote setpoint since the setpoint for the flow rate controller on the distillate is determined "remotely" by the level controller. This is an example of cascade control which is analyzed in Chapter 9. In this manner, the flow rates of the four manipulated variables are adjusted to meet the column control objectives.

The measured feed rate to the column multiplies (×) the output from the composition controller on the distillate product in order to set the flow rate for the reflux flow controller. As a result, when a feed rate change occurs, the remote setpoint (RSP) for the reflux rate flow controller will be automatically changed to maintain the specified reflux to feed ratio which is set by the distillate composition controller (AC). This is an example of ratio control which is presented in Chapter 9.

The composition control loop on the bottoms product involves a tray temperature controller (TC). For this column, the temperature of the indicated tray correlates strongly with the composition of the bottoms product. Since this measured tray temperature responds much faster than the laboratory analysis on the product stream, the tray temperature controller is used to select the remote setpoint (RSP) for the steam flow controller (FC). The setpoint for the tray temperature controller (TC) is set by the operator based upon the laboratory analysis of the bottom product composition; therefore, these TC and FC loops in tandem are another example of cascade control. In addition, using a tray temperature for composition control is an example of inferential control which is presented in Chapter 10.

Table 1.1
Definition of Symbols for Control Diagrams.

AC - analyzer controller (i.e., composition controller)

AT - analyzer transmitter (i.e., composition analyzer/ transmitter)

DPC - differential pressure controller

DPT - differential pressure sensor/transmitter

HS - high select (this element selects the larger of two or more inputs)

LC - level controller

LS - low select (this element selects the lower of two or more inputs)

LT - level sensor/transmitter

PC - pressure controller

pIIC - pH controller

pHT - pH sensor/transmitter

PT - pressure sensor/transmitter

RSP - remote setpoint (i.e., the setpoint calculated by another controller)

TC - temperature controller

TT - temperature sensor/transmitter

$\otimes$ - summation block (minus signs for an input compartment denote subtraction)

+ - addition function (i.e., two inputs are added to yield the output)

$\times$ - multiplication function (i.e., two inputs are multiplied to yield the output)

This control configuration is designed to prevent the column from flooding as the feed rate to the column is increased. The onset of flooding is marked by a sharp increase in the pressure drop across the column. A differential pressure controller (DPC) sets the steam flow rate necessary to prevent flooding. The low select (LS) chooses the lower steam flow rate setpoint (RSP) between the differential pressure controller (DPC) and the tray temperature controller (TC) and sends the result to the steam flow controller (FC) as its remote setpoint (RSP). When operation is not near the flooding constraint, the DPC will set a steam flow rate that is considerably larger than the tray TC; therefore, the LS will use the output from the tray TC as the setpoint for the steam flow controller. When flooding is approached, the LS will choose the output from the DPC since it will be lower than the tray TC. This is an example of override/select control which is covered in Chapter 10.

The proper mode for the PID controller for each of the controllers in this system should be selected (Chapter 6) and each controller should be tuned to meet the operational objectives of the process (Chapter 7). Bumpless transfer and anti-windup strategies should be applied in order to provide smooth and reliable service for each control loop. Solving day-to-day operational problems on these control loops will require a thorough knowledge of the components that comprise each of the feedback loops as well as a knowledge of control loop troubleshooting techniques (Chapter 2).

It should be clear that there are a number of critical skills that are required to design, implement, and maintain process control systems. The remainder of this text is devoted to the study of these items from a fundamental and practical point of view.

1.10 Summary

CPC is concerned with operating a plant so that the operational objectives are met in a safe and reliable manner. CPC directly affects the variability of the products, and therefore, affects product quality, production rates, and utility usage. In addition, CPC is a prerequisite for process optimization.

A single control loop combines a controller, an actuator, and a sensor with the process to maintain the controlled variable at its assigned setpoint. Disturbances enter the process and require the control system to take action to absorb their effect in order to keep the controlled variable near its setpoint.

PID controllers are the most commonly used controllers in the CPI. Nevertheless, in the extremes, manual control and model-based control are also widely used in industry.

The process control engineers are primarily responsible for controller design, controller tuning, and controller troubleshooting. For process control engineers to be successful, they must be able to work effectively with the operators and they must rely upon their process understanding to guide their application of process control techniques.

1.11   Additional Terminology

Actuator - the system that changes the level of the manipulated variable. The actuator system usually involves a control valve and associated equipment.

Analyzer deadtime - the time from process stream sampling to analyzer reading availability.

Analyzer delay - the time from process stream sampling to analyzer reading availability.

CPC - chemical process control.

CPI - chemical processing industries (i.e., chemical plants and refineries).

Cascade control - manipulation of a regulatory controller setpoint by a supervisory controller.

Closed-loop control - use of the measured value of the controlled variable to select the manipulated variable level.

Constraint - a limit on process operation.

Controlled variable - the process variable that the control loop is attempting to maintain at its setpoint.

Controller - unit which adjusts the manipulated variable level in order to keep the controlled variable at or near its setpoint.

Coupling - the interaction between control loops for a MIMO process.

Deadtime - the time difference between a manipulated variable change and significant process change.

Disturbance - a change to an input to the process that is not a manipulated variable.

Error from setpoint - the difference between the measured value of the controlled variable and its setpoint.

Feedback control - use of the sensor reading and the setpoint value to select the level for the manipulated variable for a process.

Feedforward control - a controller that makes adjustments to the manipulated variable level based upon measured disturbances in an effort to absorb the effect of the disturbance.

Final control element - the system that changes the level of the manipulated variable. The final control element usually involves a control valve and associated equipment.

Lag - the property of a process that keeps it from making instantaneous changes.

Manipulated variable - the process variable, usually a flow rate, that is adjusted in order to keep the controlled variable at its setpoint.

MIMO - multiple input/multiple output process, i.e., a process with two or more inputs and two or more outputs.

Offset - a persistent error between the measured value of the controlled variable and its setpoint.

Open loop response - the measured value of the controlled variable as a function of time after a step change in the manipulated variable value without feedback control.

Open loop settling time - the time for the controlled variable to attain 95% of its ultimate change after a step change in the manipulated variable.

Operator acceptance - having the operators routinely use a controller, i.e., operator trust in reliable and effective controller operation.

Override control - the arrangement of control loops in order to prevent the violation of safety, environmental, or operational constraints.

Pairing of manipulated and controlled variables - for MIMO processes, selecting which manipulated variable is to be used to control which controlled variable.

Process - the system whose outputs are affected by its inputs.

Process optimization - selecting the setpoints for key controllers such that the process produces the highest rate of profit generation.

Proportional-only controller - a feedback controller that makes changes to the manipulated variable value that are proportional to the error from setpoint.

Regulatory controller - the lowest level of controls, usually flow controllers, pressure controllers and level controllers.

Residence time - the average time that an element of feed spends in the process.

Saturated manipulated variable - a manipulated variable that is at its maximum or minimum level.

Sensor - the device that measures a process variable.

Setpoint - the desired or specified value for the controlled variable.

SISO - a single input/single output process.

Supervisory controller - the controllers that are responsible for meeting the setpoints applied by the optimizer or the operator, usually temperature or composition control loops.

Time constant - a measure of how fast a process changes for a change in an input.

Valve deadband - the maximum positive and negative change in the signal to the final control element that does not produce a measurable change in the flow rate in question.

1.12 Questions and Exercises

1.1 Identify a control process that you interact with daily. Choose an example that is different from the ones presented in the text. Identify the controller, actuator, process, and sensor and draw a block diagram for the control loop.

1.2 Give an everyday example for each of the following terms. Use examples different from those presented in the text.
    a. Disturbance
    b. Deadtime
    c. Process constraint
    d. Coupling

1.3 Choose an industrial process control system that you have been exposed to. Identify the controller, actuator, process, and sensor and draw a block diagram for the control loop.

1.4 Summarize the difference between manual, PID, advanced PID, and model-based control. How are they similar?

1.5 What things would cause an operator not to use a control loop? List as many reasons as possible.

1.6 What are the primary responsibilities of a process control engineer? Give an example of each one that you identify.

1.7 Identify a SISO process and a MIMO process used in industry.

1.8 Explain how process control is different from process optimization. Give an industrial example of each to substantiate your analysis.

1.9 Consider a distillation column that separates propane from butane. The overhead product from the column, which is largely propane, is used as fuel while the bottoms product, which is largely butane, is a much more valuable product since it is a component blended directly into the gasoline pool. The greater the separation produced by the distillation column (i.e., the lower the mole fraction of butane in the overhead propane product and the lower the mole fraction of propane in the butane product), the larger the fraction of the butane removed in the process, but at the expense of requiring a larger steam usage. Consider how optimization, supervisory control, and regulatory control would be applied to this column.

  a. Write an equation for the economic objective function for this case. Remember that the butane that leaves with the propane is valued as fuel and the propane in the butane does not yield gasoline in the reformer reactors but is valued as fuel grade propane.

  b. Draw a control schematic of this column (i.e., similar to Figure 1.10) showing the connection between optimization, supervisory control, and regulatory control. Assume that the reflux flow rate is used to control the butane in the overhead product and the steam flow to the reboiler is used to control the propane in the bottoms product. In addition, assume that the flow rate of the reflux and the steam to the reboiler are controlled by flow control loops.

1.10 Identify an example of how you use optimization in your everyday life. List the degrees of freedom (the things that you are free to choose) and clearly define the process and how you would determine the objective function.

1.11 Explain in your own words how the overhead product composition is controlled for the distillation column shown in Figure 1.12.

1.12 Explain in your own words how the bottom composition is controlled for the distillation column shown in Figure 1.12.

1.13 For Figure 1.12, list each of the following items
  a. All controlled variables
  b. All manipulated variables
  c. All sensors
  d. All cascade control loops
  e. All process constraints

Chapter 2

Control Loop Hardware and Troubleshooting

2.1 Introduction

In order to apply control to a process, one measures the controlled variable and compares it to the setpoint and based upon this comparison typically uses the actuator to make adjustments to the flow rate of the manipulated variable. The industrial practice of process control is highly dependent upon the performance of the actuator system (final control element) and the sensor system as well as the controller. If either the final control element or the sensor is not performing satisfactorily, it can drastically affect control performance regardless of controller action. Each of these systems, i.e., the actuator, sensor, and controller, are made up of a number of separate components; therefore, the improper design or application of these components or electrical or mechanical failure of one of these components can seriously affect the resulting control performance of the entire control loop. This chapter will describe the components that comprise a typical feedback control loop used in the CPI by providing an overview of the proper design approaches that should be used and performance levels that should be expected for these components. The description of these devices will focus on their control-relevant aspects. Finally, troubleshooting approaches and control-loop component failure modes are discussed. This chapter is intended as an introduction to these subjects. The complete handling of these subjects would require several textbooks.

Figure 2.1 is a schematic of a feedback control loop for a temperature controller on the CST thermal mixer (Figure 1.4). Note that this feedback control loop is made up of a controller, a final control element, a process, and a sensor. Figure 2.2 is a schematic of the hardware that comprises this feedback temperature control loop as well as the signals that are passed between the various hardware components. Note that the sensor system in Figure 2.1 corresponds to the thermowell, thermocouple, and transmitter in Figure 2.2 while the actuator system in Figure 2.1 corresponds to the control valve, I/P converter, and instrument air system in Figure 2.2. Likewise, the controller in Figure 2.1 is made up of the A/D and D/A converters, the DCS, and the operator console in Figure 2.2. The abbreviations used in this paragraph are described in the next several sections.

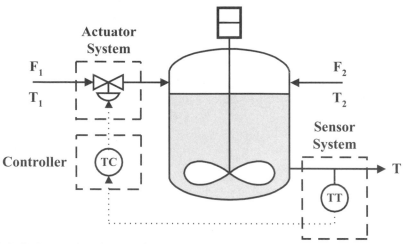

Figure 2.1 Schematic of the CST thermal mixer showing the actuator system, sensor system, controller, and the process.

A thermocouple is used to measure the temperature inside the mixing tank and is placed in thermal contact with the process fluid leaving the mixing tank by a thermowell in the product line. The thermocouple generates a millivolt signal that is proportional to the temperature inside the thermowell. The temperature transmitter converts the millivolt signal generated by the thermocouple into a 4-20 ma analog electrical signal. When the thermocouple/transmitter system is calibrated properly and when the thermowell is properly designed and located, the value of the analog signal will correspond closely to the temperature in the mixing tank.   The thermocouple/thermowell/temperature transmitter comprises the sensor system for this process.

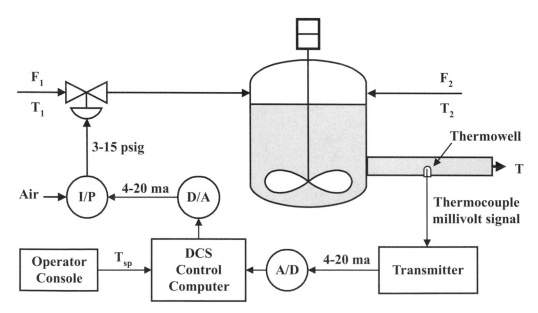

Figure 2.2 Schematic of the control system on the CST thermal mixer showing each component along with the various signals.

The 4-20 ma analog signal from the temperature transmitter is converted into a digital reading by the **analog-to-digital (A/D) converter**. The output of the A/D converter is a digital measurement of the temperature that is used in the control calculations. The operator console shown in Figure 2.2 allows the operator or control engineer to observe the performance of the control loop and to change the setpoint, T_{sp}, and controller tuning parameters for this loop. The value of T_{sp} and the digital value of the measured mixer temperature are used by the control algorithm in the **distributed control system**, (DCS, i.e., the control computer). The output from the controller is a digital signal that is converted into a 4-20 ma analog signal by the **digital-to-analog (D/A) converter**. Note that the DCS, D/A and A/D converters, and the operator consoles are typically located in a centralized control room while the remaining equipment resides in the field near the process equipment.

The 4-20 ma analog signal from the D/A converter goes to the **current-to-pressure (I/P) converter**. The I/P converter uses a source of instrument air to change the air pressure applied to control valve (3-15 psig) corresponding to the value of the analog signal. That is, if I is the value of the analog signal and P is the instrument air pressure delivered to the control valve,

$$\frac{I-4}{16} = \frac{P-3}{12}$$

This relationship is true as long as the analog signal varies between 4 and 20 ma and the pneumatic signal varies between 3 and 15 psig of instrument air. Changes of instrument air pressure to the control valve cause changes in the stem position of the control valve which result in changes in the flow rate to the process. These changes in the flow rate to the process cause changes in the temperature of the mixer which are measured by the sensor which completes the feedback control loop. The final control element consists of the I/P converter, the instrument air system, and the control valve.

Being able to effectively troubleshoot a control loop requires the knowledge of the components that actually implement the control loop as well as the signals that are passed between these elements. This chapter considers the design and control relevant aspects of the DCS, the actuator system, and several commonly encountered sensors as well as control loop troubleshooting.

2.2 Distributed Control System

Background. In the 1920's, pneumatic PID controllers were introduced and were in widespread use by the mid 1930's. Pneumatic controllers use bellows, baffles, and nozzles with a supply of air pressure to apply control action. That is, the pneumatic controller receives a pneumatic signal corresponding to the measured value of the controlled variable and acts on this signal with a bellows, baffle, and nozzle in conjunction with the instrument air system to produce a pneumatic signal that is sent to

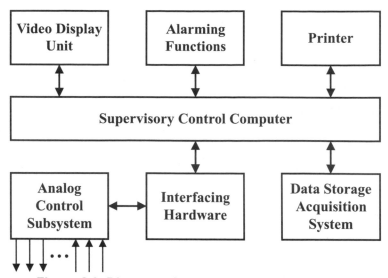

Figure 2.3 Diagram of a supervisory control system.

the control valve. For the early versions of pneumatic controllers, the controllers were installed in the field near the sensors and control valves. In the late 1930's, transmitter-type pneumatic controllers began to replace the field mounted pneumatic controllers because of the increase in size and complexity of the processes being controlled. For the transmitter-type pneumatic controllers, the sensor readings were converted into pneumatic signals (i.e., 3-15 psig) that were conveyed by metal tubing into the control room where the pneumatic controller determined the control action which in turn was pneumatically transmitted to the actuator on the process. Since the transmitter-type pneumatic controllers were typically located in a central control room, operators could conveniently address the overall control of the process using a number of controllers from a centralized location.

In the late 1950's, electronic controllers (i.e., electronic analog controllers) became commercially available. These devices use capacitors, resistors and inductors to implement control action. Since electronic transmitters were used (i.e., the output from the sensor was converted to a 4-20 ma signal and the 4-20 ma controller output signal was converted to a pneumatic signal by the I/P converter), the use of electronic analog controllers eliminated the need for long runs of metal tubing by using electrical wires which greatly reduced the installation costs and resulted in faster responding controllers. By 1970, the sales of electronic controllers exceeded the sales of pneumatic controllers in the CPI[1].

The first supervisory computer control system was installed in a refinery in 1959. A simplified schematic of a supervisory computer control system is shown in Figure 2.3. Note that this system offered data storage and acquisition as well as control loop alarms that previous control systems did not offer. In addition, the centralized computer could use the available operating data to determine the setpoints for certain

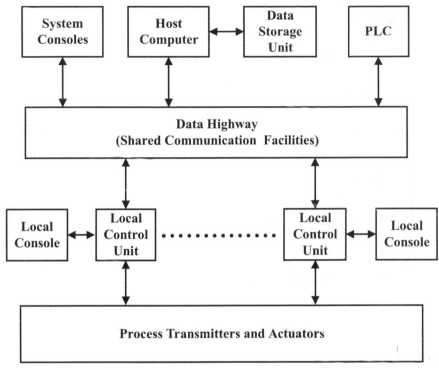

Figure 2.4 Generalized diagram of a DCS.

key control loops in an effort to obtain the most efficient operation of the plant (i.e., process optimization).

The biggest disadvantage of the centralized control computer approach was that if the control computer failed, the entire control system would be shut down. A redundant control computer was an expensive alternative and not always reliable. Due to the technological breakthroughs in computers and associated systems in the 1970's, a new computer control architecture was developed and introduced by vendors in the late 1970's. It was based on using a number of **local control units (LCU's)** which had their own microprocessors and were connected together by **shared communication lines** (i.e., a **data highway**) as well as connected to operator/engineer consoles, a data acquisition system, and a general purpose computer. This computer control architecture became known as a **distributed control system (DCS)** [Figure 2.4] since it involved a network with various control functions distributed for a variety of users.

The advantages of a DCS over a centralized control computer result from the use of microprocessors for the local control function. Even if a microprocessor were to fail only the control loops serviced by that LCU would be affected. A redundant microprocessor that performs the same calculations as the primary microprocessor (i.e., a hot backup) greatly increases the system's reliability. As a result, the probability that all the control loops will fail at the same time or even a major portion of the control loops will fail is greatly reduced compared to a centralized control computer. In addition, the DCS is much easier to expand. That is, to increase the number of control loops serviced by the DCS, only a primary and a redundant LCU need to be added. The modular nature of DCS's can be a major economic advantage for systems that undergo expansion. In comparing a DCS with electronic analog controllers, the application of conventional controls is generally equivalent, but implementing controllers is much easier and less expensive per loop using a DCS.

Structure of a DCS. A generalized schematic of a DCS is shown in Figure 2.4. A number of local control units (LCU's), which contain spared microprocessors, perform the control functions for the process in a distributed fashion. Each local control unit has several consoles attached to it. The consoles (**video display units, VDU's**), which utilize **cathode ray tubes** (**CRT**'s), have video displays that show process schematics with current process measurements. Operators and control engineers use these displays to monitor the behavior of the process, set up control loops, and enter setpoints and tuning parameters. Normally, these consoles have touch screen capability so that if operators want to make a change to a control loop, they touch the icon for the controller that they are interested in. Then a screen pops up that allows the operator to make the desired changes. On some DCS's, control loops can be conveniently set up by clicking and dragging on the tags for the desired sensor readings and the final control elements and connecting these to the type of controller that they choose. Since the local control unit is attached to the shared communications facility, a local display console can view schematics and current operating data for other parts of the plant but typically can make changes only to the control loops associated with its LCU. The local console can also be used to display historical trends of process measurements. In order to do this, the local console must access historical data in the data storage unit by using the data highway (i.e., the shared communication facilities).

Data acquisition is accomplished by transferring the process measurements through the LCU's into the data highway and into the host computer where the process data are passed on to the data storage unit. Note that the archived process data can be accessed from one of the system consoles or one of the local consoles. In control rooms that used analog controllers, data storage for important control loops was typically accomplished using a strip chart recorder which provided a record of previous measurements on a small roll of paper with different colors of ink to record different process measurements.

The data highway holds the entire DCS together by allowing each modular element and each global element to share data and communicate with each other. The data highway is composed of one or more levels of communication hardware and the associated software.

System consoles are directly attached to the data highway and can act as a local console for any of the local control units. In addition, system consoles can be used to change linking functions of the distributed elements.

The host computer is a mainframe computer that is used for data storage, for process optimization calculations, and for applying advanced process control approaches. Attached to the host computer is the data storage unit (usually a magnetic tape based system) where archived data are stored.

Approach. The goal of a DCS is to apply the control calculations for each control loop so fast that the control appears continuous. Since DCS's are based upon sequential processors, each control loop is applied at a discrete point in time and the control action is held constant at that level until the next time the controller is executed. The time between subsequent calls to a controller applied by the DCS is called the **controller cycle time** or the **control interval**. Unfortunately, **the fastest cycle times for controller calls within a DCS are typically in the range of 0.2 seconds while most loops are called only every 0.5 to 1.0 seconds. The regulatory control loops typically use control intervals in the range of 0.5 to 2.0 seconds while supervisory control is typically applied with control intervals of 20 seconds up to several minutes**. This controller cycle time does not present a limitation for slower control loops such as level, temperature, and composition control loops while it does present a limitation for fast control loops such as flow controllers and some pressure controllers. A real-time control system for the DCS is used to enforce a priority ranking of control functions. That is, certain high priority control loops are maintained at the expense of less important loops.

Since DCS's are based on digital controller calculations, a wide variety of special control options are available in self contained modular form and can be easily selected by "click and drag" action on some DCS's. In this manner, complex control configurations can be conveniently assembled, interfaced, and implemented. In addition, a variety of signal conditioning techniques can be applied to process measurements including filtering and validity checks.

Programmable logic controllers (PLC's). Programmable logic controllers have been used primarily in the CPI for controlling batch processes and for sequencing of process startup and shutdown operations. PLC's have been traditionally based on **ladder logic** which allows the user to specify a series of discrete operations, e.g., start the flow to the reactor until the level reaches a specified value, next start steam flow to the heat exchanger until the reactor temperature reaches a specified level, next start catalyst flow to the reactor, etc. A small PLC can be responsible for monitoring 128 separate operations while a large PLC can handle over 1000 operations. Today the distinction between PLC's and DCS's has become less clear since PLC's are being designed to implement conventional and advanced control algorithms and DCS's are being offered that provide control for sequenced operations. PLC's are typically attached to the data highway in a DCS (Figure 2.4) and provide sequenced control functions during startup, shutdown, and override of the normal controllers in the event of an unsafe operating condition.

Fieldbus Technology. The fieldbus approach to distributed control is shown in Figure 2.5. Note that it distributes control to intelligent field mounted devices (i.e., sensors, valves, and controllers with onboard microprocessors which are used for complex operations and diagnostics) using a high speed, digital two-way communication system that connects the field mounted devices with **Local Area**

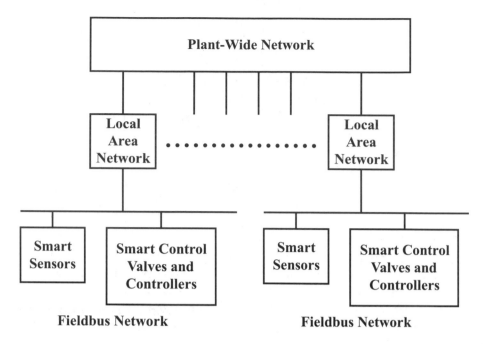

Figure 2.5 Schematic of the integration of the fieldbus with plant networks.

Networks (**LAN**'s), process automation systems, and the plant-wide network. This high speed communication system is similar to the data highway used by DCS's. Supervisory and advanced control are implemented in the LAN's while the regulatory control functions are handled by the field mounted devices on the fieldbus network. The advantage of the fieldbus design comes from the fact that a large number of field mounted devices can be attached to a single two wire communication line instead of running electrical wires from each sensor/transmitter to the centralized control room and from the control room to each final control element. This results in a significant reduction in the time and cost associated with system installation. Fieldbus technology is just beginning to be available commercially, but is expected to remove regulatory controls from DCS's and move them into the field in the future.

2.3 Actuator Systems (Final Control Elements)

The actuator system for a process control system in the CPI is typically comprised of the control valve, the valve actuator, the I/P transmitter, and the instrument air system. The actuator system is known industrially as the final control element. In addition, there is a variety of optional equipment that is designed to enhance the performance of the actuator system, such as valve stem positioners and instrument air boosters.

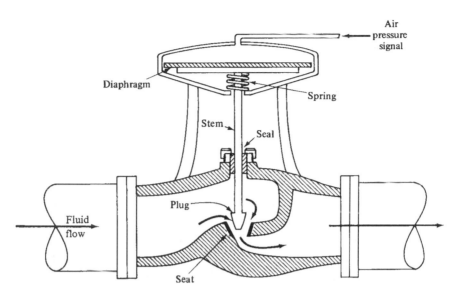

Figure 2.6 Schematic globe control valve. Reprinted with permission from the McGraw-Hill Publishing Company.

Control valves. The most common type of control valve in the CPI is the globe valve. Figure 2.6 shows a schematic of a globe valve. For globe valves, the closure member is called a **valve plug** which is positioned at the end of the **valve stem**. As the valve stem is lowered, the plug approaches the **valve seat** restricting the area for flow through the valve. When the plug makes contact with the valve seat, the valve is closed and flow through the valve is shut off. Globe valves are characterized by the fact that the plug travels perpendicular to the valve seat. The top of the valve stem is attached to a diaphragm and a spring which opposes the force of the instrument air on the diaphragm. As an example, consider Figure 2.6 for which as the instrument air pressure is increased, the diaphragm moves against the spring, moving the stem downward, thus moving the valve plug closer to the valve seat, reducing the flow through the valve. Likewise, when the air pressure is decreased, the flow through the valve increases. Therefore, changes in the instrument air pressure coming from the I/P converter are able to affect changes in the flow rate through the control valve.

Figure 2.7 shows a detailed cross-section of a globe control valve with a plug in a **cage-guided valve** arrangement along with notation indicating some of the key components of a control valve and valve actuator. The cage provides guidance for the plug as the plug is moved toward or away from valve seat. The cage also provides part of the flow restriction produced by the control valve. The packing reduces the leakage of the process stream into the environment but provides resistance to movement of the valve stem. The travel indicator indicates the valve stem position. Figure 2.8 shows the valve body assembly for a globe valve with an unbalanced plug. The unbalanced plug is subject to a static force directly related to the pressure drop across the valve and a shear force due to the fluid velocity past the plug. The greater these forces, the more force is required to close the valve and the less force that is required to open the valve. Note that for Figure 2.6, it requires more force to open than to close due to the pressure

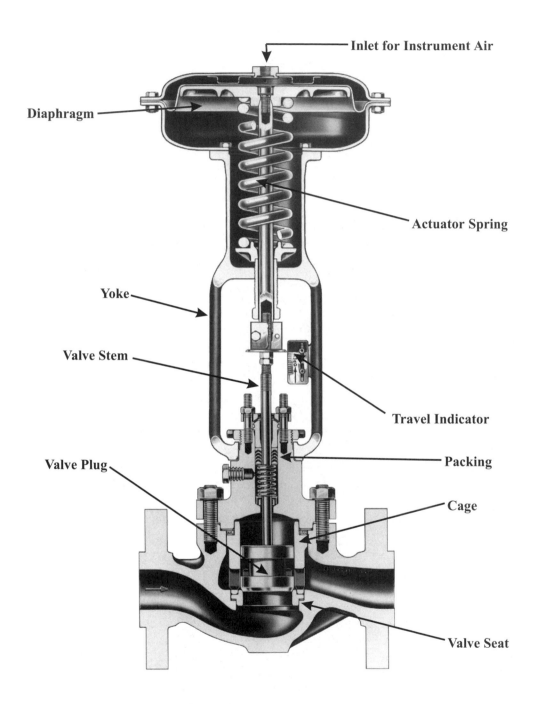

Figure 2.7 Cross-section of a globe valve with an unbalanced plug. Courtesy of Fisher Controls.

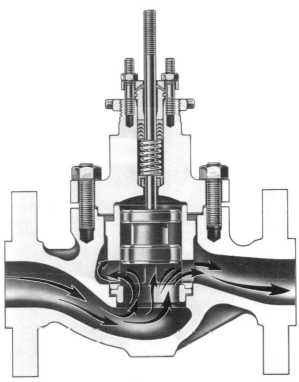

Figure 2.8 Cross-section of a globe valve body assembly with an unbalanced plug. Courtesy of Fisher Controls.

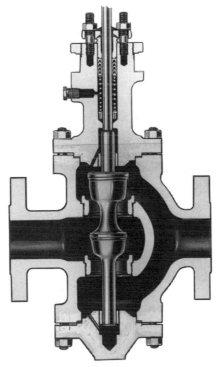

Figure 2.9 Cross-section of a globe valve body assembly with a balanced plug. Courtesy of Fisher Controls.

drop and shear forces on plug. Figure 2.9 shows the valve body assembly for a globe valve with balanced plugs. This valve is referred as having balanced plugs since the top and bottom of the plug are subjected to the same downstream pressure when the valve is closed thus the static force on the valve stem is low. In addition, the shear forces also cancel each other. Valves with balanced plugs are preferred because they tend to be faster responding than valves with unbalanced plugs and require smaller valve actuators, but they should only be used with clean liquids. For example, an unbalanced plug would be preferred for service with a liquid that tends to crystallize on any surface that does not have strong turbulence applied to it since the unbalanced plug would be less susceptible to deposits than a balanced plug.

Sizing of control valves is important since if the valve is oversized or undersized, it can significantly affect the precision of flow metering provided by the final control element. When the valve is oversized, the valve is not sufficiently open to allow the valve to accurately control the flow rate to a specified level. When the valve is undersized, the valve may be almost fully open so that accurate control is not possible or in certain cases the required flow cannot be met even when the valve is fully open. A simplified valve flow equation is given by

$$F_m = K C_v(x) \sqrt{(P_1 - P_2)/\rho} \qquad\qquad \textbf{2.1}$$

where F_m is the mass flow rate through the valve, K is a constant that depends on the units used in this equation, $C_v(x)$ is the valve coefficient which is dependent upon the stem position (x) [i.e., $C_v(x) = C_v^{max}$ when the valve is fully open and $C_v(x)=0$ when the valve is closed], ρ is the density of the fluid, P_1 is the upstream pressure, and P_2 is the downstream pressure. This equation is based upon an incompressible fluid under turbulent flow conditions with no attached fittings. In general, control valves should be designed so that the valve provides accurate metering of the flow over a wide operating range between almost fully open and almost closed. This will reduce the likelihood that the valve will be expected to operate nearly fully open or fully closed where control performance is generally poor. The proper size of the valve should be selected as well as the proper type of valve in order to provide a wide operating range.

Figure 2.10 shows how $f(x)$ varies with stem position for three types of valves: a quick opening valve, an equal percentage valve, and a linear valve where

$$f(x) = \frac{C_v(x)}{C_v^{max}}$$

This figure shows the **inherent valve characteristics** for these valve types which indicate how the flow rate through the valve varies with stem position for a fixed pressure drop across the valve. The design of the plugs, valve seats, and cages (where applied) determine the particular flow versus stem position that a control valve possesses. That is, the shape of the valve plug and the flow openings in the cage determine the shape of the flow restriction as the valve stem position is changed. For example for a quick opening valve, as the valve is opened from fully closed, the

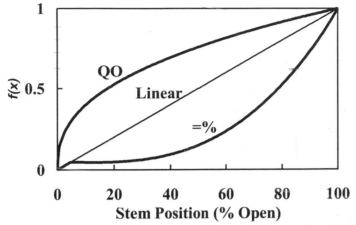

Figure 2.10 Inherent valve characteristics for a quick opening (QO), linear, and equal percentage valve (=%).

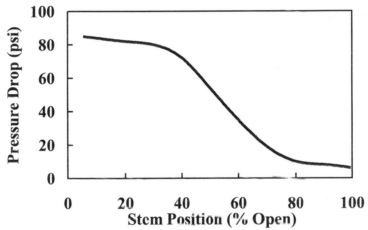

Figure 2.11 Pressure drop versus stem position for an equal percentage valve.

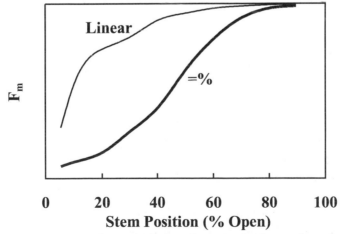

Figure 2.12 Installed valve characteristics for a typical equal percentage (=%) valve and linear valve.

cross-sectional area of the restriction of the valve increases much faster than the linear or equal percentage valves. From a process control standpoint, it is desirable to have a control valve that exhibits a linear relationship between flow rate and stem position over a wide range for the installed valve. Normally, the pressure drop across a valve changes as the flow through the process changes and does not remain constant (e.g., Figure 2.11). That is, as the flow through the line increases, the control valve opens and the pressure drop across the valve decreases; therefore, an equal percentage valve actually provides a much more linear **installed valve characteristic** than linear or quick opening valves as shown in Figure 2.12. Installed valve characteristics are characterized by the flow rate as a function of stem position for an installed valve. The linear installed valve characteristics for an equal percentage valve can be understood by recognizing that the largest pressure drop is available when the valve initially opens and an equal percentage valve has a relatively low inherent flow and the lowest pressure drop is available when the valve is almost completely open and an equal percentage valve has its highest inherent flow at this point. For this reason over 90% of the globe valves used in the CPI are equal percentage valves. From an examination of Figure 2.12, one can see that this equal percentage valve should be able to perform well for a stem position between 10% and 80% open. Butterfly valves are also used for flow control applications but generally have a significantly smaller range within which they perform well compared with globe valves. For applications where the pressure drop across the control valve remains relatively constant (e.g., control of the flow rate of condensing steam to a heat exchanger), linear valves are preferred. The flow rate of steam to a heat exchanger should provide a fairly constant pressure drop across the valve since the upstream steam supply pressure would remain relatively constant as would the pressure of the condensing steam within the heat exchanger. Quick opening valves are not usually used for feedback flow control applications but are used in cases where it is important to start a flow rate as quickly as possible (e.g., coolant flow through a by-pass around a control valve for an exothermic reactor).

An important characteristic of a valve is the **valve deadband** which is a measure of how precisely a control valve can control the flow rate. The deadband for a steering system on an automobile would be the maximum positive and negative turn in the steering wheel that does not result in a noticeable change in direction of the automobile. For a control valve, deadband is the maximum positive or negative change in the signal to a control valve that does not produce a measurable change in the flow rate. Valve deadband is caused by the friction between the valve stem and valve packing and other forces on the valve stem. Typically, industrial control valves have a deadband of 10% to 25%. Generally, the larger and the older the control valve, the larger the deadband. A properly functioning valve with a valve positioner typically should have a deadband less than 0.5%. Note that deadband is reported in percent and represents the maximum change that does not cause a measurable change in the flow rate through the valve.

Cavitation results when the liquid vaporizes and implodes inside the control valve. As a fluid flows through a control valve the pressure drops sharply near the restriction between the valve plug and the valve seat due to high velocity in this region. As the fluid passes the valve restriction region and enters a region with a larger cross-section, the pressure increases sharply (i.e., pressure recovery) due to the drop in the fluid velocity. If the pressure in the valve restriction region is less than the vapor pressure of the liquid, a portion of the liquid will vaporize and when the pressure recovers due to a drop in the velocity, the bubbles will violently collapse. Cavitation results in noise and vibration, reduced flow, and erosion of the body of the valve.

Valve Actuator. The valve actuator provides the force necessary to move the valve stem position and alter the flow rate through the valve. The valve actuator must provide the force necessary to overcome pressure forces, the flow forces, the friction from the valve packing, and the friction from the guide surfaces.

Figure 2.13 shows a cross-section of a typical **air-to-close actuator**. Note that the pressure of the instrument air acts on the diaphragm/spring system from the top causing the valve to close as the air pressure supplied to the valve actuator is increased. The diaphragm is constructed of an air impermeable, flexible material that allows the valve plug to move from closed to fully open as the instrument air pressure is increased from 3 to 15 psig. Note that the force generated by the instrument air pressure on the surface of the diaphragm is balanced by the force of the compressed actuator spring (Figures 2.7 and 2.13). An actuator with a control valve with an air-to-close valve actuator is also known as a **reverse acting final control element**. For an **air-to-open actuator**, the instrument air enters below the diaphragm so that as the air pressure is increased the valve stem moves upward opening the valve. An actuator with a control valve with an air-to-open valve actuator is also known as a **direct acting final control element**. Valve actuators generally provide a fail-safe function. That is, in the event of a loss of instrument air pressure, the valve actuator will cause the valve to fully open or fully closed. For example, an actuator with an air-to-open unit will fail closed and an air-to-close unit will fail fully open. In this manner, a valve actuator can be chosen such that the proper failure mode is obtained. For example, consider the valve on the cooling water to an exothermic reactor. Obviously, an air-to-close actuator would be selected so that the loss of instrument air pressure would cool down the reactor instead of allowing a thermal runaway.

I/P Transmitter. The I/P transmitter is an electromechanical device which converts the 4-20 ma signal from the controller to a 3-15 psig instrument air pressure to the valve actuator which in turn affects the valve stem position.

Optional equipment. Several devices are available for improving the overall performance of final control elements.

Valve positioners. The **valve positioner**, which is usually contained in its own box and is mounted on the side of the valve actuator, is designed to control the valve stem position at a prescribed position in spite of packing friction and other forces on the stem. The valve positioner itself is a feedback controller that compares the measured stem position with the specified stem position and makes adjustments to the instrument air pressure in order to provide the proper stem position. In this case, the setpoint for the valve positioner can be a pneumatic signal coming from an I/P converter or the 4-20 ma analog signal coming directly from the controller. Due to the

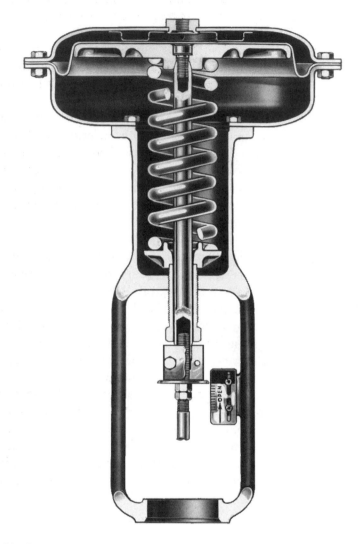

Figure 2.13 Cross-section of a valve actuator. Courtesy of Fisher Controls.

friction from the packing, it is not possible to move the valve stem position to a precise value. As a result, the valve positioner tends to open and close the valve bracketing the desired stem position. This high frequency, high gain feedback provided by the valve positioner can result in precise metering of the average flow rate. A valve with a deadband of 25% can provide flow rate precision of less than ±0.5% using a valve positioner. Valves with low levels of valve friction can control the average flow rate to a precision approaching ±0.1% using a valve positioner.

For flow control loops that are controlled by a DCS, a valve positioner is a necessity because the control interval for a DCS (i.e., 0.5 to 1.0 seconds) is not fast enough for most flow control loops. There are two general types of valve positioners:

pneumatic positioners and digital positioners. Pneumatic positioners receive a pneumatic signal from the I/P converter and send a pneumatic signal to the valve actuator. A more modern type of valve positioner is a digital positioner which receives the 4-20 ma analog signal directly and adjusts the instrument air pressure sent to the valve actuator. Digital positioners have the advantage that they can be calibrated, tuned, and tested remotely and they can also be equipped with self-tuning capabilities.

Booster relays. Booster relays are designed to provide extra flow capacity for the instrument air system which decreases the **dynamic response time** of the control valve (i.e., the time for most of a change to occur). Booster relays are used on valve actuators for large valves that require a large volume of instrument air to move the valve stem. Booster relays use the pneumatic signal as input and adjust the pressure of a high flow rate capacity instrument air system that provides pressure directly to the diaphragm of the valve actuator.

Adjustable speed pumps. Adjustable speed pumps can be used instead of the control valve systems just discussed. A centrifugal pump directly driven by a variable speed electric motor is the most commonly used form of adjustable speed pump. Another type of adjustable speed pump is based on using a variable speed electric motor combined with a positive displacement pump. Adjustable speed pumps have the following advantages compared with control-valve based actuators: 1) they use less energy; 2) they provide fast, accurate flow metering without additional device requirements; 3) they do not require an instrument air system. Their major disadvantage is capital cost particularly for large flow rate applications. Another disadvantage of adjustable speed pumps is that they do not fail open or closed like a control valve with an air-to-close actuator or with an air-to-open actuator, respectively. As a result, the CPI almost exclusively use control-valve based actuators except for low flow applications, such as catalyst addition systems or base injection pumps for wastewater neutralization which typically use adjustable speed pumps.

2.4 Sensor Systems

Sensor systems are composed of the sensor, the transmitter, and the associated signal processing (see Appendix B). The sensor measures certain quantities (e.g., voltage, currents, or resistance) associated with devices in contact with the process such that the measured quantities correlate strongly with the actual controlled variable value. There are two general classifications for sensors: continuous measurements and discrete measurements. Continuous measurements are, as the term implies, generally continuously available while discrete measurements update at discrete times. Pressure, temperature, level, and flow sensors typically yield continuous measurements while certain composition analyzers (e.g., gas chromatographs) provide discrete measurements.

Several terms are used to characterize the performance of a sensor:

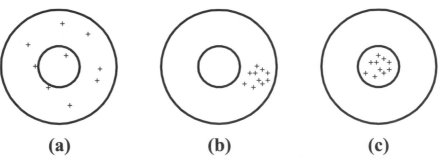

(a)   **(b)**   **(c)**

Figure 2.14 Targets which demonstrate the difference between accuracy and repeatability. (a) Neither accurate nor repeatable. (b) Repeatable but not accurate.   (c) Accurate and repeatable.

- **Span** is the difference between the largest measurement value made by the sensor/transmitter and the lowest.
- **Zero** is the lowest reading available from the sensor/transmitter, i.e., the sensor reading corresponding to a transmitter output of 4 ma.
- **Accuracy** is the difference between the value of the measured variable indicated by the sensor and its true value (see Figure 2.14). The true value is never known; therefore, accuracy is estimated by the difference between the sensor value and an accepted standard.
- **Repeatability** is related to the difference between the sensor readings while the process conditions remain constant (see Figure 2.14).
- **Process measurement dynamics** indicate how quickly the sensor responds to changes in the value of the measured variable.
- **Calibration** involves the adjustment of the correlation between the sensor output and the predicted measurement so that the sensor reading agrees with a standard.

   Smart sensors are available that have built-in microprocessor-based diagnostics. For example, smart pH sensors are available that are able to identify the buildup of coatings on the pH electrode surface and can trigger a wash cycle to reduce the effect of these coatings. In general, smart sensors are moderately more expensive than conventional sensors, but when they are properly selected and implemented, smart sensors can be an excellent investment due to greater sensor reliability and reduced maintenance.   Best practice[2] for instrument selection, for instrument installation, and to reduce maintenance costs has been identified for the CPI.

   A wide variety of sensors are available for measuring process variables[3]. Choosing the proper sensor for a particular application depends on the controlled variable that is to be sensed, the properties of the process, accuracy and repeatability requirements, and costs, both initial and maintenance. Following is a listing of the most commonly used sensors in the CPI that are used for feedback control.

Temperature measurements. The two primary temperature sensing devices used in the CPI are **thermocouples (TC's)** and **resistance thermometer detectors (RTD's)**.

Thermocouples. Thermocouples are based on the fact that two metal junctions (i.e., the contacting of two different types of metal wire) at different temperatures will generate a voltage and the magnitude of the voltage is proportional to the temperature difference. The cold junction of a thermocouple is normally at ambient temperature but is electrically compensated so that it behaves as if it were at a constant temperature. Therefore, the voltage generated by the hot junction inside a thermowell in contact with a process fluid varies quite linearly with the process temperature. Thermocouples are constructed of metal pairs including iron-constantan, copper constantan, chromel-alumel, and platinum-rhodium which is the most popular material of construction and results in the most accurate thermocouples. (Alumel, chromel, and constantan are trade names for alloys that are used to make these thermocouples.)

RTD's. RTD's are based on the observation that the resistance of certain metals depends strongly upon its temperature. A Wheatstone bridge or other type of resistance measuring bridge can be used to measure the resistance of the RTD element and thus estimate the temperature. Platinum and nickel are typically used for RTD's. Platinum has a much wider useful range (i.e., -200°C to 800°C) while nickel is more limited (-80°C to 320°C) but is less expensive than platinum. Each of these metals has a known temperature dependence for its resistance; therefore, calibration requires only applying the RTD to a known temperature condition. RTD's require a separate power supply.

Thermowells. Thermowells are typically cylindrical metal tubes that are capped on one end and protrude into a process line or vessel in order to bring the TC or RTD in thermal contact with the process fluid. Thermowells provide a rugged, corrosion resistant barrier between the process fluid and the sensor that allows for removal of the sensor while the process is still in operation. Thermowells that are coated with polymer or other adhering material can significantly increase the lag associated with the temperature measurement, i.e., significantly increase the response time of the sensor. For example, see Figure 2.15 which shows a typical thermowell and housing as well as several thermocouples.

Overall Comparison of TC's and RTD's. TC's are less expensive and more rugged than RTD's but are an order of magnitude less precise than RTD's. Typically, RTD's should be used for important temperature control points, such as on reactors and distillation columns.

Repeatability, accuracy and dynamic response. TC's typically have a repeatability of ±1°C while RTD's have a repeatability of ±0.1°C. Accuracy is a much more complex issue. Errors in the temperature reading can result from heat loss along the length of the thermowell, electronic error, sensor error, error from nonlinearity, calibration errors, and other sources[4].

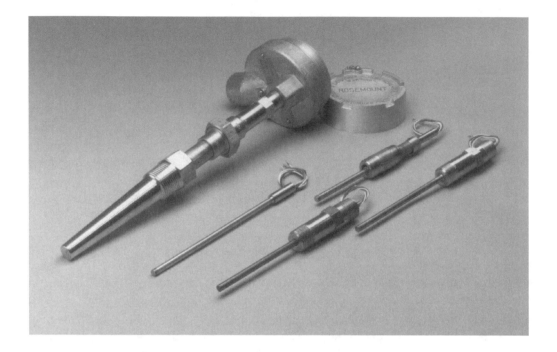

Figure 2.15 Photograph of hardware for measuring process temperature. Included are a thermowell and transmitter housing (left) and several TC's. Courtesy of Fisher-Rosemount.

The dynamic response time of a TC or RTD sensor within a thermowell can vary over a wide range and is a function of the type of process fluid (i.e., gas or liquid), the fluid velocity past the thermowell, the separation between the sensor and inside wall of the thermowell, and material filling the thermowell (e.g., air or oil). Typical well-designed applications result in time constants of 6-20 seconds for measuring the temperature of most liquids.

Pressure measurements. The most commonly used pressure sensing devices are strain gauges. Strain gauges are based upon the property that when a wire is stretched elastically, its length increases while its diameter decreases both of which increase the resistance of the wire. Serpentine lengths of elastic resistance wires can be bonded to the surface of an elastic element (diaphragm). When deformation of the diaphragm occurs as the result of a pressure increase, the wires elongate, and therefore, the resistance of these wires increases indicating an increased pressure reading. These pressure sensing devices actually measure the differential pressure across the diaphragm, but can be used to measure a process pressure in gauge pressure by allowing the low pressure side of the device to be exposed to atmospheric pressure. Another approach is to use a strain gauge to measure the effect of a pressure change on

Figure 2.16 Photograph of a differential pressure sensor/transmitter (DP cell). Courtesy of Fisher-Rosemount.

a coiled tube. The resistance of the strain gauge is usually measured using a Wheatstone bridge. Pressure sensors are very fast responding. Repeatability for pressure measurement is generally less than ±0.1%.

Flow measurements. The most commonly used flow meter is an orifice meter. An orifice meter uses the measured pressure drop across a fixed area flow restriction (an orifice) to predict the flow rate. The pressure drop across an orifice is usually measured using a **DP cell** (Figure 2.16). The pressure drop across an orifice plate, ΔP, is related to the volumetric flow, Q, by the following equation

$$Q = \frac{C_d A_2}{\sqrt{1-(A_2/A_1)^2}} \sqrt{\frac{2\Delta P}{\rho}}$$

where A_1 is the pipe cross-sectional area, A_2 is the cross-sectional area of the orifice, ρ is the density of the fluid, and C_d is the discharge coefficient. C_d is a function of the Reynolds number and the type of fluid, but typically is approximately 0.6. A straight run of pipe preceding the orifice meter is required. If not, an error as large as 15% can

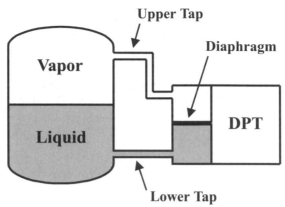

Figure 2.17 Schematic of a typical differential pressure level measurement system.

result in the predicted flow rate. Since the orifice meter is based upon a measured pressure drop, it is a very fast responding measurement. Orifice meters typically provide a repeatability in the range of ±0.3 to ±1%.

Other types of flow meters are used for flow rate control in special situations, including vortex shedding flow meters and magnetic flow meters. Vortex shedding flow meters are based on inserting an unstreamlined obstruction in the pipe and measuring the frequency of pulses created by the flow past the obstruction. The flow rate is directly related to the frequency of the pulses created by the obstruction. Magnetic flow meters can be used to measure the flow rate of electrically conducting fluids. Magnetic flow meters are based on the principle that a voltage is generated by an electronically conducting fluid flowing through a magnetic field. The magnetic flow meter creates a magnetic field using an electromagnet and measures the resulting voltage which is proportional to the flow rate in the pipe. The installation costs for vortex shedding flow meters and magnetic flow meters are much higher than for orifice meters, but their maintenance costs are usually much lower since they do not use pressure taps for their measurements. **Flow measurements**, whichever type is chosen, **are typically installed upstream of the control valve to provide the most accurate, lowest noise measurement**. Installing the flow sensor downstream will subject the sensor to flow fluctuations and even two phase flow which reduce the sensor accuracy and increase the measurement noise.

Level measurements. The most common type of level measurement is based upon measuring the hydrostatic head in a vessel using a differential pressure measurement. This approach typically works well as long as there is a large difference between the density of the light and heavy phases. This approach usually has relatively fast measurement dynamics since it is based on a pressure measurement. Level measurements typically have a repeatability of approximately ±1%.

Figure 2.17 shows how a differential pressure measurement can be used to determine the level in a vessel. This approach directly measures the hydrostatic head in the vessel. Because of plugging and corrosion problems, it may be necessary to keep the process fluid from entering the differential pressure transmitter. In addition, it is important to keep vapor from condensing in the upper tap and collecting in the low pressure side of the differential pressure transmitter. This can usually be accomplished by insulating the pressure tap and wrapping it with resistive heating tape.   There are other level measuring approaches that are based upon a variety of physical phenomena and are used in special cases. Float activated devices, which are similar to the level measuring approach used in the water reservoir in toilets, are sometimes used in the CPI.

Chemical composition analyzers. The most commonly used on-line composition analyzer is the **gas chromatograph (GC)** while recently there have been inroads made by infrared analyzers and ultraviolet and visible radiation analyzers. On-line composition measurements are generally much more expensive than temperature, pressure, flow rate, and level measurements with much lower reliability. The annual cost of an on-line composition analyzer can easily be in excess of $100,000 due to high capital costs and large maintenance costs. The decision to use an on-line composition analyzer is normally based on process economics due to its large associated cost. For example, for refineries and high volume chemical intermediate plants, on-line analyzers (usually GC's) are used extensively because 1) due to the large flow rates used in these large plants, process improvement due to on-line composition analysis easily justifies the application economically and 2) the measurement techniques are generally well established for this industry. On the other hand, for the specialty chemicals industry, much less use of on-line analyzers is made due to 1) lower production rates and 2) unavailability of reliable analyzers.

Gas chromatographs. GC's process a volatile sample through a small diameter (approximately 3/8 inch) packed column along with a carrier gas. As a result of different affinities of the sample components for the column packing, the various sample components have different residence times in the packed column. As each component emerges from the column, it passes through a detector process. The most commonly used detectors are thermal conductivity detectors and hydrogen-flame ionization detectors. Hydrogen-flame ionization detectors are more complicated than thermal conductivity detectors but are much more sensitive for hydrocarbons and organic compounds. Repeatability for GC's can vary over a wide range and is dependent on the particular system being measured.

Infrared, ultraviolet and visible radiation. These analyzers are based on the property that each compound absorbs specific frequencies of radiation and the greater the concentration, the higher the degree of absorption. In order to identify a component from among several components, only the absorption frequencies of the component of interest are required.

Sampling system. The sample system is responsible for collecting a representative sample of the process and delivering to the analyzer for analysis. Obviously, the reliability of the sample system directly affects the reliability of the overall composition analysis system. The transport delay associated with the sample system contributes directly to the overall deadtime associated with an on-line composition measurement. For example, an improperly designed sample system can result in one hour of transport time for the sample to be taken from the process and delivered to the analyzer while a properly designed system can result in a transport delay of 10 seconds or less. This difference in sampling deadtime can have a drastic effect on the performance of a control loop. Table 2.1 summarizes the dynamic characteristics and repeatability of control valve systems and several different types of sensors.

Transmitters. The transmitter converts the output from the sensor (i.e., a millivolt signal, a differential pressure, a displacement, etc.) into a 4-20 ma analog signal that represents the measured value of the controlled variable. Consider a transmitter that is applied to a temperature sensor. Assume that the maximum temperature that the transmitter is expected to handle is 200°C and that the minimum temperature is 50°C, then the span of the transmitter is 150 °C and the zero of the transmitter is 50°C. Transmitters are typically designed with two knobs that allow for independent adjustment of the span and the zero of the transmitter. Properly functioning and implemented transmitters are so fast that they do not normally contribute to the dynamic lag of the process measurement. Modern transmitters have features that, if not applied properly, can reduce the effectiveness of the control loop. For example, excessive filtering (see Appendix B) of the measurement signal by the transmitter can add extra lag to the feedback loop thus degrading control loop performance.

Table 2.1
Summary of Time Constants and Repeatability

	Time Constant (sec)	Valve Deadband or Sensor Repeatability
Control valve *	3 - 15	10 - 25%
Control valve w/valve positioner*	0.5 - 2	0.1 - 0.5%
Flow control loop w/valve positioner*	0.5 - 2	0.1 - 0.5%
TC w/ thermowell	6 - 20	±1.0 °C
RTD w/ thermowell	6 - 20	±0.1 °C
Orifice flow meter	<0.2	±0.3 - ±1%
Differential Pressure Level Indicator	<1	±1%
Pressure sensor	<0.2	±0.1%

* Based on globe valves.

2.5 Troubleshooting Control Loops

Chemical process control engineers spend a major portion of their time troubleshooting control loops. For example, an operator may point out that a particular loop has been behaving erratically and ask the control engineer to take a look at that loop. A more general problem can be that a final product has excessive variability in its impurity levels and the control engineer's job is to reduce the variability of the final product of a plant to an acceptable level. In this latter example, a number of control loops may require scrutiny. When one or more loops are found not to be performing properly, troubleshooting will be required to return them to proper operation or at least identify the source of the problem.

Troubleshooting control loops involves an overwhelming number of possible causes. Due to the dimensions of this problem, it is important to utilize a systematic approach when troubleshooting. Control loop troubleshooting is too often treated as an afterthought and performed haphazardly. This section will present an overall approach to troubleshooting as well as a detailed analysis of fault detection within the final control element, the sensor system, the control computer or DCS, and the process.

Overall Approach to Troubleshooting. The key to effective troubleshooting is expressed in the old adage, "Divide and conquer". That is, it is important to locate the area that is causing the poor performance: the final control element, the sensor system, the controller, or the process. The place to start is to test each system separately in order to determine if that portion of the control loop is operating properly or that it is not performing at the expected level. For example, the final control element can be evaluated by applying step tests to it. Input to the final control element, which is normally set by the controller, can be manually adjusted. The measured settling time of the manipulated variable (usually a flow rate in a flow control loop) should be 60 seconds or less for a valve without a positioner and 8 seconds or less if a valve positioner is used on the control valve. In addition, the deadband of the actuator system should be evaluated. If it is determined that the performance in these two areas is satisfactory, there is no need to evaluate the actuator system further. If not, the actuator system should be tested further. The next subsection addresses the types of problems occurring with actuator systems.

The controller tuning is very often the source of erratic control performance and can be corrected by simply retuning the control loop. Controller tuning involves selecting the values of the controller tuning parameters that provide good performance that is reliable. Controller tuning is the easiest thing to change but one should be aware that retuning the controller may mask the real problem with the control loop. When a component of the feedback system is not functioning properly and the controller is retuned, erratic behavior may not be present, but a sacrifice in control performance will result. Also, there can be cases where the wrong type of controller was applied. Controller tuning can be assessed by simply placing the control loop in manual (opening the control loop) and observing whether or not the measured value of the

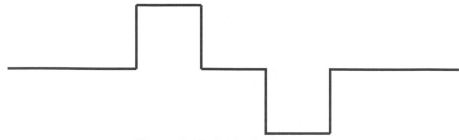

Figure 2.18 A block sine wave.

controlled variable lines out to a steady-state or near steady-state value. If it does, then controller tuning is probably part of the problem. If it does not, then inputs (disturbances) to the control loop in question are the primary source of the upsets.

The sensor system is a little less convenient to check. Using the DCS to trend the measured value of the controlled variable can be helpful to point out certain abnormalities. For example, the repeatability of the sensor can be estimated during a steady-state period. In general, to evaluate the sensor, one has to perform a detailed analysis of the sensor which usually involves independently measuring the controlled variable and comparing this result with the sensor readings as well as removing the sensor and calibrating it externally.

Next, the process should be evaluated with regard to its effect on controller performance. For example, excessive disturbances entering the process can be reduced by modifying upstream operations. Fouling or mechanical failure can create a situation in which it is not possible for the controller to maintain the controlled variable at its setpoint. That is, the control of the process may not be satisfactory because an unidentified constraint prevents normal control of the process.

Finally, the entire loop should be tested under closed loop conditions. First, the **closed loop deadband** should be determined, i.e., the largest positive and negative setpoint changes that can be implemented without causing measurable changes in the controlled variable. For this purpose, a block sine wave in the setpoints to the controller can be used as shown in Figure 2.18. Note that the setpoint is increased and after some time it is returned to its original level. Then the setpoint is reduced and once again after some time it is returned to its original level. The block sine wave calls for both positive and negative changes about the original setpoint. The procedure for determining the closed loop deadband is to apply a block sine wave with a small step height (e.g., 0.5%) and check to see if the measured value of the controlled variable tracks the setpoint. If it does, then the closed loop deadband is less than the variation provided for by the block sine wave. If the controlled variable does not track the setpoint, then the closed loop deadband is greater than the starting setpoint height and the setpoint height should be increased and the block sine wave setpoint test repeated. In this manner, the height of the block sine wave is increased until the controlled variable tracks the setpoint for positive and negative changes which will bound the deadband of the closed loop system. For Figure 2.19, the initial height of the block sine

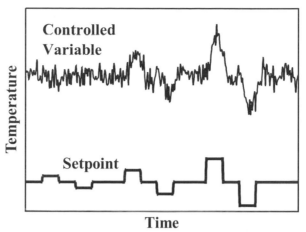

Figure 2.19 Results of a series of block sine wave tests to determine the closed loop deadband. Note that the setpoint and the measured value of the controlled variable are plotted on different scales.

wave was 0.1 °C. Note that a consistent change in the measured temperature was not observed. Next, the height of the block sine wave was increased to 0.2 °C. For this case, a small but noticeable increase and decrease in the temperature can be observed. The results for a 0.4 °C height for the block sine wave are also shown and tracking of the setpoint can be clearly seen. Therefore, for this example, the closed loop deadband for this system is between 0.1 and 0.2°C. If the closed loop deadband is excessive even though the components checked out individually, some element of the closed loop process is not functioning properly, e.g., A/D or D/A converter or transmitter. In addition, the dynamic response of the closed loop process can also be assessed from the results of the closed loop deadband test.

Another approach that can be useful in troubleshooting a control loop that had been performing well until recently is to determine what has changed recently in the process. For example, the controller could have been recently retuned. A new analyzer could have recently been installed. A new instrument technician could be responsible for calibrating and maintaining an analyzer. The feed to the unit could have significantly changed recently. These examples and many more could be directly related to the source of poor control loop performance. When something significant has changed recently, it can provide a valuable clue that allows quicker determination of the source of the problem with a poorly performing control loop.

Final Control Element. The final control element is made up of the instrument air system, the I/P converter, and the control valve (the valve and the valve actuator). If both the measured value of the manipulated variable and the controller output are recorded by the DCS or control computer, it is usually a simple task to plot the two on the same graph and determine if the actuator system is functioning properly. An estimate of the valve deadband should also be made. If it has been determined that the actuator system is not functioning properly, one should first determine if the instrument air pressure at the control valve is responding quickly after a step change in the signal to the final control element has been implemented in the DCS or in the control computer. If the instrument air pressure at the control valve increases sharply after the step test has been implemented, then the control valve is the source of the slow or erratic response.

In order to evaluate the performance of a control valve, the deadband of the control valve should be determined. The deadband is the largest change in the input to the actuator system that does not produce a measurable change in the flow rate. The deadband for valves with positioners typically ranges from 0.1 % to 0.5 % of the flow rate for properly implemented systems and depends on the size of the valves, the pressure drop across the valve, the fluid properties, etc. Deadband for an industrial valve without a positioner typically ranges from 10 % to 25% and even higher for older valves that have not been maintained. The deadband of an actuator system can be measured by applying a series of block sine waves in the signal to the actuator until the deadband is identified. For example, if a block sine wave with an individual step size

Table 2.2
Common Problems with the Final Control Element
• Excessive lag in the instrument air system. • Wrong type of instrument air connected to control valve. Some plants have high and low pressure instrument air. • Low instrument air pressure. • Wet or dirty instrument air. • Excessive deadband.* • Improperly sized control valve*. • Excessive resistance to movement of valve stem*. • Leak in diaphragm of control valve. • Debris is stuck in opening to control valve. • A plugged or obstructed instrument air line. • Plug/seat erosion in the control valve. • A by-pass line open or leaking. • Flashing and cavitation. • Improperly tuned valve positioner*.   * More frequently observed problems

0.1 % is applied to the actuator but no noticeable flow rate change is made, the deadband is greater than 0.1 %. Then a larger step size must be tested in a block sine wave until increases and decreases in the measured flow rate are observed. In this manner, the magnitude of the deadband can be bracketed. Table 2.2 lists a number of common problems with the components of the actuator system.

Sensor Systems. The sensor system is composed of the sensor, the transmitter, and the sampling system that allows the sensor to make its measurement. The sensor itself can be checked by applying the sensor to a standard or known condition. For example, a composition standard can be run through a gas chromatograph to verify the accuracy of the instrument or a thermocouple can be placed in boiling water to check its accuracy and dynamic response time. The evaluation of sampling systems can require more experience and/or analysis. For example, a low velocity in the sample line from the process stream to a gas chromatograph can result in excessive transport delay which can greatly reduce controller effectiveness.

In addition, one should be careful to determine if the sensor used is really measuring the controlled variable of the control loop. Differential pressure sensors are used for pressure, flow, and level measurements. They are particularly susceptible to plugging of the sensing lines that connect the differential pressure sensor to the process itself. Plugging of the sensing lines can result from the buildup of coatings or solids or from freezing of the fluid in the pressure taps (Figure 2.15). In addition, the calibration of a differential pressure sensor is quite sensitive to the conditions of the fluid in the sensing lines. For example, condensate buildup in lines that are supposed to be dry can lead to large calibration errors. Table 2.3 lists some commonly encountered sources of problems for sensor systems. For a complete analysis of the sensor system, an instrument engineer or other expert may be required. Table 2.1 lists the expected ranges for the repeatability and the time constant for several commonly used sensors in the CPI which can be used to identify a poorly performing sensor.

Table 2.3
Commonly Encountered Problems with Components of a Sensor System

Sensor	Common Problems
Transmitter	• Not calibrated correctly*. • Low resolution • Excessive signal filtering* • Slow sampling
Thermocouple/ RTD	• Off-calibration*. • Short in the electrical circuit/grounding problems. • Improperly located thermowell*. • Thermowell with excessive thermal resistance (e.g. stainless steel thermowells). • Partially burned out thermocouple. • Interference from heat tracing. • Buildup of material on the outside surface of the thermowell.

Table 2.3 **Commonly Encountered Problems with Components of a Sensor System**	
Pressure Indicators	• Plugged line to pressure indicator*. • Confusion about absolute pressure readings, gauge pressure readings and vacuum pressure readings. • Condensation in lines to pressure indicator*
Sampling System For GC	• Excessive transport delay for an analyzer. • Sample drawn from wrong process point. • Plugged sample system*. • Sample system closed off.
GC	• Out of calibration. • Plugging in the GC column. • Failure of electrical components in GC. • Excessive noise on measurement.
Flow Indicator	• Square root compensation applied for non-differential pressure type flow indicator. • Square root compensation not applied for differential pressure type flow indicators. • Square root compensation applied twice, i.e., once in transmitter and once in DCS. • Orifice plate installed backwards. • Damaged orifice plate. • Plugged line to differential pressure sensor*. • Flashing of liquids as they flow through an orifice meter.
Level Indicator	• Plugged line from process to DP cell*. • Leak in line to DP cell or in DP cell itself. • Boiling of liquid in line to or from DP cell due to a steam leak in the steam tracing line. • Solidification of liquid in line to or from process to DP cell due to failure in steam tracing. • Formation of emulsions which can confound interface level measurements. • Leak in float type level indicators. • Formation of foams which can interfere with level measurements.
*More frequently observed problems	

Controller/DCS System. The controller/DCS system consists of the controller with its tuning parameters, A/D and D/A converters, and the signal conditioning, i.e., filtering and validation. Each of these components requires separate evaluation. Table 2.4 lists possible problems with the controller/DCS system.

Process. The process can be examined directly by opening the control loop in question and observing the process behavior. If the open loop process exhibits oscillatory behavior, it would indicate a problem internal to the process. In addition, the noise level on the analyzer reading can be accessed under open loop conditions.

Changes in disturbance levels and process gain changes due to nonlinearity are a natural part of process control. Out of the ordinary disturbance levels can cause an otherwise properly tuned controller to oscillate or go unstable. It may be possible to reduce the magnitude of the disturbances to acceptable levels by modifying the upstream operations (e.g., tuning upstream controllers). Excessive disturbances, when not measurable, can be inferred by observing the range of the average manipulated variable levels.

Excessive fouling of heat exchangers or deactivation of catalyst can result in process gain changes that result in sluggish or unstable behavior. The question is whether these changes are preventable or are a real part of the problem that the controller should be expected to handle.

Process changes can also occur that require manipulated variable levels in excess of what is physically available. For example, after feed rate increases to a distillation column, the reboiler can be unable to provide enough heat transfer to maintain the purity of the bottom product. When the column is unable to maintain the purity of the bottom product, it is a physical limitation of the process and not the fault of the controller. Loss of steam pressure can also cause a constraint that can affect control loop performance. Downstream pressure changes can cause a loss of pressure

---

Table 2.4
Possible Problems with the Controller/DCS System

- Improperly tuned controller*.
- Wrong scaling for A/D and D/A converter.
- Improper or lack of pressure/temperature compensation for flow measurement.
- Improper selection of reverse acting or direct acting controller (Chapter 6).
- Too much or not enough filtering of the measured controlled variable*.
- Signal aliasing due to excessive control interval (see Appendix B).
- Poor resolution on A/D or D/A converters.
- Derivative action based on error from setpoint instead of based on measurement.

* More frequently observed problems

driving force that is normally used to transport the flow through a process line resulting in a constraint for the maximum flow rate. When adequate manipulated variable action is not available, a process constraint has been exceeded and constraint control techniques (Chapter 10) should be used. Therefore, it should be clear that a thorough understanding of the process is a prerequisite for control loop troubleshooting.

Example 2.1 Troubleshooting example

Following is a step-by-step troubleshooting process along with intermediate results for a temperature controller that was observed to result in sluggish closed loop performance.

Step 1: Determine the deadband of the final control element using a series of block sine wave tests. **Result:** The deadband of the final control element was less than 0.4% and the dynamic response time of the final control element was 2 seconds; therefore, the final control element was found to be functioning properly.

Step 2: Retune the temperature controller. **Result:** The controller settings did not change significantly; therefore, the controller tuning does not appear to be the problem.

Step 3: Evaluate the sensor. Check the repeatability of the sensor by observing the temperature measurements during a steady-state or near steady-state period. **Result:** The repeatability was less than 0.1 °C which is good for an RTD. An independent measurement of the temperature is made and compared with the sensor reading. **Result:** The sensor reading is observed to have excessive lag, i.e., a dynamic response time for the sensor was estimated to be about 5 minutes. It was determined upon further examination that there was an excessive air space between the RTD element and the surface of the thermowell. The proper installation of the RTD in the thermowell was made and the dynamic lag of the sensor was found to be in the proper range.   The controller was retuned and control performance was found to be significantly improved.

Example 2.2 Troubleshooting example

Following is a step-by-step troubleshooting process along with intermediate results for a reactor temperature controller that exhibits excessive reactor temperature excursions from setpoint. Reactor temperature control is achieved by manipulating the heat added to the feed to the reactor.   The reactor temperature controller is the supervisory controller and selects the setpoint for the flow controller on the steam to the heat exchanger for the feed to the reactor which is the regulatory controller. First, the performance of the flow controller on the steam line is evaluated.

Step 1: Perform a series of closed loop block sine wave tests on the steam flow controller. **Result:** The repeatability of the flow measurement was observed to be larger than it should be. It was determined that the differential pressure sensor had a partially plugged pressure tap. This problem was corrected and the flow controller was tested over the expected range of the flow rate of the steam. **Result:** It was observed that in the low flow rate range the flow control performance was poor. Upon examination of the control valve it was determined that an equal percentage valve was used while a linear valve should have been used since the pressure drop across the valve remains relatively constant. The valve plug and cage were replaced with ones that resulted in linear inherent valve characteristics and good controllability of the steam flow over the entire flow rate range was observed after the flow controller was retuned.

Step 2: Evaluate the temperature sensor on the product stream from the reactor. **Result:** It was determined that the repeatability and dynamic response of the temperature sensor was good.

Step 3: Retune the temperature controller on the reactor exit temperature. **Result:** After the temperature control loop was retuned, the variability in the reactor temperature from setpoint was observed to be a factor of three lower than was previously observed, thus meeting the operational objectives of this control loop.

Example 2.3 Troubleshooting Example

Following is a step-by-step troubleshooting procedure for a composition control loop on the overhead of a distillation column for which the variability of the impurity level in the overhead product was in excess of the product specifications. The output of the composition controller goes to a flow control loop on the reflux flow.

Step 1: Evaluate the deadband of the flow controller on the reflux. **Result:** The deadband of the flow control loop was found to be ±0.3% with a time constant of approximately 1.5 seconds; therefore, the flow control loop is functioning properly.

Step 2: Check the tuning for the composition controller. **Result:** Controller appears to be properly tuned.

Step 3: Evaluate the on-line GC. **Result:** The repeatability of the analyzer found to be ±2% by observing GC readings during a steady-state period. This repeatability is well within the product variability limits and is consistent with the analysis of this type of mixture. Upon further examination it was determined that there was excessive sample transport delay; therefore, the sample pump was replaced and the sample transport delay was reduced to an acceptable level. After this change and the retuning of the composition controller, the variability of the overhead product was reduced, but it was found to periodically exceed the product variability specifications.

Step 4: Evaluate the closed loop deadband for the composition control loop. **Result**: It was found that the deadband was acceptable but the dynamic response was slower than expected. Upon further evaluation it was determined that excessive filtering of the analyzer reading was being used. The proper level of filtering was applied and the composition controller was retuned. The resulting product variability was found to be well within the product specifications.

2.6 Summary

An industrial feedback control loop is made up of a controller, an actuator system, a process, and a sensor system. The sensor generates an output that is related to the controlled variable and the transmitter converts this reading into a 4-20 ma analog signal. The A/D converter converts the analog signal into a digital value for the sensor reading. The DCS accepts the digital sensor reading, compares it to the setpoint, and calculates the digital value of the controller output. The D/A converter converts this digital reading into a 4-20 ma analog signal which in turn is converted to a 3-15 psig instrument air pressure by the I/P converter. The instrument air pressure acts on the control valve which causes the manipulated flow to the process to change. This change to the process as well as other input changes cause the value of the controlled variable to change. The sensor reading changes and the control loop is complete.

The DCS is made up of a number of different elements and is held together by the data highway. The DCS is responsible for performing control calculations, providing displays of current and previous operating conditions, providing a means to modify control functions, archiving process data, providing process alarms, and performing process optimization calculations. The advantages of a DCS come from its low cost per control loop for large processing plants and its superior reliability.

The actuator system is made up of the control valve, the valve actuator, the I/P converter, and the instrument air system. Due to the valve deadband, a typical industrial control valve has a deadband of from 10% to 25%. If a valve positioner is installed, the deadband should drop to less than 0.5%. Depending on the design of the valve plug and valve seat, a control valve can have different inherent valve characteristics, i.e., different flow rate versus stem position behaviors for a constant pressure drop across the control valve. Equal percentage valves are used in about 90% of the control valve applications in the CPI while linear valves are used in the remaining cases in which the pressure drop across the valve remains relatively constant. The valve actuator determines whether or not the valve will fail open or closed when instrument air pressure is lost.

The sensor system is composed of the sensor, the transmitter, and the associated signal processing. TC's and RTD's are used to measure process temperatures and are implemented on processes using thermowells. RTD's are more expensive than TC's , but they provide much more precise temperature measurements. Pressure measurements are typically made using strain gauges in which the measured resistance of a portion of the strain gauge is proportional to the process pressure. Flow measurements are typically made from the pressure drop across an orifice plate. Level measurements are commonly based upon the differential pressure between two taps on the process vessel. GC's are used to measure product compositions on-line by passing a sample through a packed column and detecting the separated components as they exit the GC column.

The key to troubleshooting control loops is to independently check the actuator system, the sensor system, the process, and the control computer in order to isolate the source of the problem. The actuator system is the easiest to check since the flow measurement is generally available. The sensor system may require an instrument technician to determine whether or not it is functioning properly. Checking the control computer generally involves evaluating the controller tuning but can also involve A/D and D/A converters, sensor signal conditioning, or simple oversights. Finally, changes to the process (e.g., changes in the type or magnitude of disturbance) can also be the source of a poorly performing control loop.

2.7 Additional Terminology

A/D Converter - an analog to digital converter. Converts a 4-20 ma electrical analog signal into a digital reading that can be processed by the DCS.

Accuracy - the difference between the true value and the measurement.

Air-to-close actuator - a valve actuator that causes the valve to close as its instrument air pressure is increased (i.e., fails open).

Air-to-open actuator - a valve actuator that causes the valve to open as its instrument air pressure is increased (i.e., fails close).

Cage guided valve - a valve with a cage around the valve plug that guides the plug toward the valve seat.

Calibration - an adjustment of the correlation between the sensor output and the predicted measurement so that the sensor reading agrees with the standard.

Closed loop deadband - the maximum positive and negative change in the setpoint to a control loop that can be implemented without a noticeable change in the measured value of the controlled variable.

CRT - cathode ray tube. A computer console that allows the operators and engineers to access process operating conditions and adjust the process control activities of a DCS.

Control interval - the time period between adjacent calls to a controller from a DCS.

Controller cycle time - the time period between adjacent calls to a controller from a DCS.

D/A converter - a digital to analog converter. Converts a digital value from the DCS into a 4-20 ma electrical analog signal.

Data highway - communication hardware and the associated software in a DCS that allows the distributed elements of a DCS to exchange data with each other.

Deadband - the maximum percentage change in the input that can be implemented without an observable change in the output.

DCS - a distributed control system. A control computer that is made up of a number of distributed elements that are linked together by the data highway.

Direct acting final control element - a final control element with an air-to-open valve actuator.

DP cell - a differential pressure sensor/transmitter.

Dynamic response time - the time for a system to make most of its change after an input change has occurred.

GC - gas chromatograph. A composition analyzer that is based on separating the components of a mixture in a small diameter packed column.

I/P converter - an electromechanical device that converts a 4-20 ma electrical signal to a 3-15 psig pneumatic signal.

Inherent valve characteristics - the flow rate versus stem position for a fixed pressure drop across the valve.

Installed valve characteristics - the flow rate versus stem position for a valve installed in service.

LCU - local control unit. A microprocessor in a DCS that is responsible for performing control functions for a portion of a plant.

Ladder logic - a programming language used in PLC's to implement a sequence of actions.

LAN - a local area network.

PLC - programmable logic controller. A process computer typically used to apply a sequence of control actions, e.g., startup, shutdown, and batch operations.

Process measurement dynamics - a measure of the speed with which a sensor to responds to a change in the process.

RTD - resistance thermometer detector. A temperature sensor that is based on the known temperature dependence of a pure metal resistor.

Repeatability - an indication of sensor reading consistency.

Reverse acting final control element - a final control element with an air-to-close valve actuator.

Shared communication facility - communication hardware and the associated software in a DCS that allows the distributed elements of a DCS to exchange data with each other.

Smart sensor - a sensor that is equipped with a microprocessor that provides onboard diagnostics and/or calibration.

Span - the difference between the maximum and the minimum value of a measurement that can be made by a sensor/transmitter.

TC - thermocouple. A temperature sensor that is based upon the fact that metal junctions at different temperatures generate an electrical voltage.

VDU - video display unit. A computer console that allows the operators and engineers to access process operating conditions and adjust the process control activities of a DCS.

Valve Deadband - the maximum percentage change in the input that can be implemented without an observable change in the output.

Valve plug - the device in a valve that is responsible for restricting flow through the valve.

Valve positioner - a device that adjusts the instrument air pressure to a control valve in order to maintain a specified value for the stem position.

Valve seat - the portion of the valve that the valve plug rests against when the valve is fully closed.

Valve stem - a rod that connects the diaphragm in the valve actuator with the valve plug so that as the air pressure acts on the diaphragm the plug provides more or less restriction to flow through the valve.

Zero - the lowest sensor/transmitter reading possible, i.e., the sensor reading corresponding to a transmitter output of 4 ma.

2.8 References

1. Lucas, M.P., *Distributed Control Systems*, Van Nostrand Reinhold Company, New York, p. 4 (1986).

2. McMillan, G. K., G. E. Mertz, and V. L. Trevathan, "Troublefree Instrumentation", *Chemical Engineering*, pp. 80-88 (Nov 1998).

3. Liptak, *Instrument Engineers Handbook*, Chilton, Philadelphia, (1995).

4. McMillan, G.K. *Advanced Temperature Control*, Instrument Society of America, pp. 133-155(1995).

2.9 Questions and Exercises

2.1 Choose an industrial process control loop and make a drawing similar to Figure 2.2 for your system and list all signals on your diagram.

2.2 For Figure 2.2, what hardware is located in the field and what hardware is located in the control room?

2.3 What hardware comprises the final control element?

2.4 What is the difference between the actuator system and the final control element? What is the difference between the actuator system and the valve actuator?

2.5 Why have DCS's replaced analog controllers and supervisory control computers in the CPI? Why is fieldbus technology likely to begin replacing DCS's in the future? Can you identify a pattern?

2.6 Using Figure 2.4, explain how process data are stored and later displayed on a system console.

2.7 What is a PLC and how is it different from a DCS? How are they alike?

2.8 From a process control standpoint, indicate how you would size a control valve.

2.9 How would you choose between selecting a globe valve with an unbalanced plug and one with a balanced plug?

2.10 Why are globe valves generally used for flow control applications?

2.11 What is the difference between inherent and installed valve characteristics?

2.12 Why are equal percentage valves generally selected over linear and quick opening valves?

2.13 Explain how cavitation occurs and what it causes.

2.14 What physical characteristic of the process determines whether a valve actuator is air-to-open or air-to-close?

2.15 Identify a case where an air-to-close valve actuator should be used and explain your reasoning.

2.16 Why has an increased usage of DCS's resulted in a greater use of valve positioners?

2.17 Under what conditions are adjustable speed pumps preferred over a flow control loop using a control valve?

2.18 From a process point of view, which is generally more important for a sensor, accuracy or repeatability? Explain your reasoning.

2.19 When is the dynamic response time of a sensor important to a process control system and when is it not important?

2.20 What are the two most important differences between TC's and RTD's ?

2.21 Why is a straight run of pipe preceding an orifice meter required?

2.22 Why are flow measurement devices usually located upstream of the control valve?

2.23 Consider a pressure sensor/transmitter that reads 80 psig when the transmitter output is 8 ma and reads 100 psig when the transmitter output is 10 ma. What is the zero and span of this pressure sensor/tranmitter?

2.24 What determines whether or not an on-line analyzer should be installed?

2.25 Summarize the recommended approach to troubleshooting a process control loop.

2.26 What are the most frequently observed problems with the actuator systems?

2.27 What is the most common problem with sensors which are based on a differential pressure measurement?

2.28 Explain how you would determine whether or not a sensor system is functioning properly.

2.29 What is the most common problem with the DCS/controller system?

2.30 How can you determine if large disturbances are entering a process?

2.31 In a manner similar to Examples 2.1, 2.2, and 2.3, present a troubleshooting study and results for

a. A level controller that is malfunctioning due to plugged line to the differential pressure cell in the level indicator.

b. A pressure controller that is malfunctioning due to an improperly tuned valve positioner on the control valve.

c. A flow control loop that is not functioning properly due to low resolution of the A/D and the D/A converters.

PART II

PROCESS DYNAMICS

Chapter 3

Dynamic Modeling

3.1 Introduction

Most chemical engineering courses are largely concerned with the steady-state aspects of chemical engineering systems. For example, thermodynamics is based solely upon a steady-state analysis and heat transfer, fluid flow, mass transfer and kinetics are primarily studied from a steady-state point of view. In addition, the study of process design and the laboratory study of unit operations are typically focused upon the steady-state aspects of these subjects. It is no wonder that most undergraduate students enter their process control course with little experience or feel for the dynamic behavior of chemical processes.

One of the most common responses from recent chemical engineering graduates after industrial experience is "There is no such thing as steady state". Due to an almost constant change in feed rates and composition of the feed to a process and due to other disturbances, such as steam pressure and cooling water temperature changes, most processes in the CPI are in a constant state of flux. The control systems of the units respond to these disturbances using changes in the manipulated variables to drive the controlled variables toward their setpoints. As a result, generally there are few periods if any that would resemble steady-state operation. Therefore, dynamics is an integral part of industrial operations including process control operations. Obviously, the understanding of process dynamics is an important part of understanding the behavior of process control.

The understanding of the dynamic behavior of chemical processes depends on understanding the steady-state behavior of these processes. For example, if a step change in an input to a process is made (e.g., a change in the manipulated variable), a steady-state analysis of the process using the new input level will indicate where the process will settle after a sufficient period of time. In addition, the dynamic characteristics of the process (e.g., the time constant and deadtime) determine how long it takes to approach the new steady-state and what path the process will take (see Figure 3.1). Understanding the dynamic behavior of a complex process made up of a number of separate unit operations (heat exchangers, reactors, holding tanks, etc.) requires combining the dynamic behavior of each unit operation in order to follow the

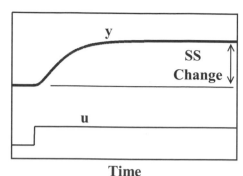

Figure 3.1 Dynamic response of a process to a step change in an input. SS-steady state.

transient behavior of the process as the effect of an input change propagates through the entire process.

3.2 Uses of Dynamic Models

Dynamic models are used for a variety of purposes in the CPI including:

Process Design. Dynamic models are used to design batch processing systems. For example, the volume of a batch reactor can be determined using a dynamic model of the reactor so that production rate and product quality specifications are met.

Analysis of Process Control Approaches. A range of potential process control configurations can be compared directly using dynamic models. That is, each control approach can be implemented on a dynamic model of the process and the resulting control performance can be calculated for a standard upset disturbance test. In this manner, a controlled comparison between different control approaches can be quantitatively assessed, i.e., each controller can be applied to exactly the same process with exactly the same disturbance. As processes become more highly integrated (i.e., using material recycle and heat recovery) in an effort to become more cost effective, the use of dynamic models for process control evaluation is becoming increasingly important to ensure that these highly integrated processes produce on-specification products with safe and reliable operation.

Operator Training. A dynamic simulation of a process can be interfaced with the same type of DCS that controls the actual process and the resulting system can be used to train operators. In this manner, the operator can be exposed to a wide range of major upsets and potentially dangerous operational scenarios without upsetting or endangering the process.

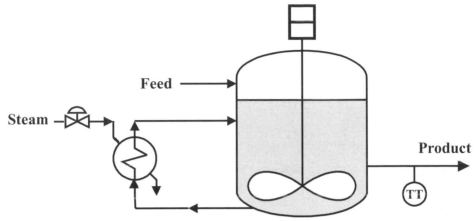

Figure 3.2 Schematic of a reactor.

Start-up/Shutdown Strategy Development.   Process startup and shutdown strategies that are safe and reliable can be identified using dynamic process simulators. This class of dynamic simulators must be able to model process behavior over a much wider range of operation than the dynamic simulators used for process control evaluation.

3.3 Classifications of Phenomenological Models

There are two general classifications of phenomenological process models (i.e., models based on conservation of mass and energy): **lumped parameter models** and **distributed parameter models**. A lumped parameter model assumes that the dependent variables of the process are not a function of spatial location within the process. Consider the schematic of a reactor shown in Figure 3.2. A lumped parameter model of this reactor would assume that the composition of the chemical species present in the reactor and the temperature in the reactor are uniform throughout the reactor volume. If the mixer on the reactor is properly designed, this assumption can be quite good. **Macroscopic balances** are used to model lumped parameter systems and consider what enters or leaves the process boundary and what is happening inside the process as a whole. For Figure 3.2, feed enters the reactor, product is removed, heat is added by the heat exchanger, and the same reaction rate occurs throughout the reactor volume.   A model developed from macroscopic balances is called a **macroscopic model**.

If the mixer on the reactor is not functioning properly, significant variation in the concentrations of the reactor species and reactor temperature can result. Models that consider the spatial variation in the dependent variables are referred to as distributed parameter models. **Microscopic balances**, i.e., balances based on differential elements, are typically used to model distributed parameter processes. These microscopic models are used to derive differential equations which are applied over the full spatial region in order to develop a model that describes the entire process. A model developed by applying microscopic balances is called a **microscopic model**.

3.4 Dynamic Balance Equations

In this section, balance equations for mass, moles, and thermal energy will be presented. These equations can be applied to develop either macroscopic or microscopic models depending upon whether the balances are applied around an overall process or to a differential element within the process, respectively.

Mass Balance Equation. Mass balance equations relate the rate of accumulation of mass in the system of interest to the rate of mass entering and leaving the process:

$$\begin{bmatrix} rate\ of\ accumulation \\ of\ mass\ in\ the \\ system \end{bmatrix} = \begin{bmatrix} rate\ of\ mass \\ entering\ the \\ system \end{bmatrix} - \begin{bmatrix} rate\ of\ mass \\ leaving\ the \\ system \end{bmatrix} \qquad \textbf{3.1}$$

This equation applies to the total mass of a system whether or not chemical reactions are occurring, but applies to the mass of any component only if no chemical reactions involving that component occur.

Mole Balance Equation. The following equation represents the conservation of the number of moles in a reacting system.

$$\begin{bmatrix} rate\ of\ accumulation \\ of\ moles\ in\ the \\ system \end{bmatrix} = \begin{bmatrix} rate\ of\ moles \\ entering\ the \\ system \end{bmatrix} - \begin{bmatrix} rate\ of\ moles \\ leaving\ the \\ system \end{bmatrix}$$
$$+ \begin{bmatrix} rate\ of\ generation \\ of\ moles\ by \\ reaction \end{bmatrix} - \begin{bmatrix} rate\ of \\ consumption\ of \\ moles\ by\ reaction \end{bmatrix} \qquad \textbf{3.2}$$

This equation applies to the total number of moles or the moles of a particular component in the system.

Thermal Energy Balance Equation. For processes such as reactors, heat exchangers, and distillation columns, potential energy changes, kinetic energy changes, mechanical work, and the heat generated by frictional losses are typically small compared with convective heat transfer (i.e., the heat carried with streams entering or leaving the process), heat exchange across the boundaries of the system, and the heat generated by reaction; therefore, the thermal energy balance equation used in these cases is given by

$$
\begin{bmatrix}
\textit{rate of} \\
\textit{accumulation of} \\
\textit{thermal energy}
\end{bmatrix}
=
\begin{bmatrix}
\textit{rate of convective} \\
\textit{heat transfer} \\
\textit{entering the system}
\end{bmatrix}
-
\begin{bmatrix}
\textit{rate of convective} \\
\textit{heat transfer} \\
\textit{leaving the system}
\end{bmatrix}
$$

$$
+
\begin{bmatrix}
\textit{net rate of heat} \\
\textit{generation by} \\
\textit{chemical reaction}
\end{bmatrix}
+
\begin{bmatrix}
\textit{net rate of heat transfer} \\
\textit{through the boundaries} \\
\textit{of the system}
\end{bmatrix}
\qquad 3.3
$$

It should be pointed out that for fluid flow through a piping system, kinetic energy, mechanical work, potential energy, and frictional losses are important and a mechanical energy balance, e.g., Bernoulli's equation[1], should be used to model these systems. Note that each of the previous dynamic equations (i.e., Equations 3.1 to 3.3) can be converted into a steady-state equation by simply setting its accumulation term equal to zero.

Constitutive Relationships. A number of physical relationships are required in order to implement the equations that result from the application of Equations 3.1 to 3.3. Examples of **constitutive relations** include:

- Gas law equations
- Vapor/liquid equilibrium relations
- Heat transfer correlation functions
- Expressions for reaction kinetics
- Correlation functions for pressure drop as a function of flow rate
- Enthalpy correlation functions

For example, to model the dynamic behavior of the temperature of a reactor, the reaction rate expressions for the major reactions are required. In order to model the dynamic behavior of a distillation column, one must use vapor/liquid equilibrium relationships.

Degrees of Freedom Analysis. Developing a dynamic model of a complex process can involve a large number of differential equations and constitutive relationships which are usually in the form of algebraic equations. A degrees of freedom analysis involves counting the total number of unknowns N_v, i.e., variables that are unknown and must be calculated, and the total number of equations N_e, both differential and algebraic. The degrees of freedom N_f of a model is given by

$$
N_f = N_v - N_e
$$

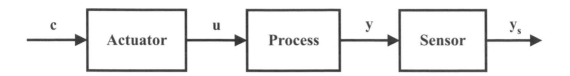

Figure 3.3 Schematic of a system made up of an actuator, a process, and a sensor.

When N_f is equal to zero, the model is referred to as **exactly determined** or **exactly specified**. For a model to be solvable, the number of degrees of freedom must be zero. When N_f is less than zero, the model is referred as **overdetermined** or **overspecified**. For this case, there are more equations than unknowns which usually results from including redundant equations or an improperly formulated model. When N_f is greater than zero, the model is referred to as **underdetermined** or **underspecified**. For this case, there are more unknowns than equations. In order to solve such a model, additional equations will have to be identified or unknown variables eliminated from the problem. The variables that need to be specified by the user are the **independent variables** while the variables computed from the solution of the equations are the **dependent variables**. Constants used in the model equations, such as densities, heat capacities, heat of reaction and gas constants, are called **process parameters**.

3.5 Modeling Examples

In this section, dynamic models and dynamic modeling results for several processes will be presented. The modeling examples considered here are simple and highly idealized. The dynamic modeling of industrial process is considerably more complex. Riggs[2] presents a systematic approach to process modeling which includes a detailed model validation procedure. Bequette[3] analyzes dynamic process behavior and presents the development of a number of dynamic models.

The representation of a process in a process control situation involves the combination of models of the actuator, process, and sensor as shown in Figure 3.3. That is, in order to affect a change in a process, the signal to the actuator must be changed which results in a change in a flow rate to the process which in turn causes the process to change. Finally, the resulting change in the process is measured by the sensor. The actuator, process, and sensor each has its own dynamic behavior. Here we will first develop dynamic models for an actuator system and for several common types of sensors. Then we will use these results to develop actuator/process/sensor

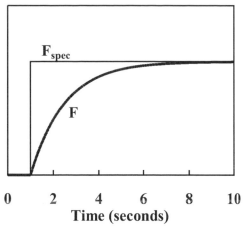

F_{spec}

F

0   2   4   6   8   10

Time (seconds)

Figure 3.4 The dynamic response of the flow through a flow control loop in response to a step change in the specified flow rate, F_{spec}.

models for a thermal mixing tank, a composition mixing tank, a level in a tank, an endothermic and exothermic CSTR, and a heat exchanger. Finally, a model for sensor noise is presented. It should be pointed out that the dynamic models for the actuators, the sensors, and the sensor noise are approximate models that only consider the general behavior of these systems and are not phenomenological models. That is, these approximate models are not based on the conservation of mass or energy while the models for the various chemical processes considered here are phenomenological models.

Actuator System Models. The actuator system (final control element) is made up of the I/P converter, the instrument air system, and the control valve. When a change in the analog signal is made to the I/P converter, the instrument air pressure to the valve changes. This causes the diaphragm in the control valve to expand or contract which in turn causes the valve stem position to change which affects the flow rate through the control valve. A properly designed instrument air system will typically respond much faster than the control valve will. After the valve stem position changes, the flow rate through the valve will change very quickly. On the other hand, the dynamic response of the valve stem position to changes in the instrument air pressure applied to the valve is considerably slower than either the response of the I/P system or the flow through the valve. Since the dynamic behavior of the control valve can be represented as a linear first order process, the flow rate, F, through a control valve can be represented by the following equation

$$\frac{dF}{dt} = \frac{1}{\tau_v}(F_{spec} - F)$$
                                                                                   3.4

where F_{spec} is the specified flow rate (input) and τ_v is the time constant of the valve. F is a dependent variable and F_{spec} is an independent variable. τ_v depends upon the size of the valve and typically ranges between 3 to 15 seconds for cases in which a valve positioner is not used or the valve is not applied in a flow control loop. When the actuator is part of a control loop, F_{spec} would be the output of a supervisory controller. The dynamic behavior of a flow control loop or a control valve with a positioner can also be effectively modeled using Equation 3.4 where the time constant, τ_v, typically ranges between 0.5 and 2 seconds. The larger the control valve, typically the larger the value of τ_v. Figure 3.4 shows the resulting dynamic behavior for a step change in F_{spec} for a flow control loop.

For certain systems it is convenient to lump a flow rate and a heat transfer process. For example, when an input variable to a process is the rate of heat transfer, the actuator system for such a process usually involves the flow rate of a heat transfer fluid (e.g., steam) and the transfer of heat through a contacting device (e.g., a heat exchanger). As a result, modeling the dynamic behavior of the actuator of such a process involves considering the dynamics of the flow control of the heat transfer fluid and the dynamics of the heat transfer process. For the flow control of the heat transfer fluid, a flow controller is typically used and the previous analysis is valid. Therefore, the time constant for the flow controller would be expected to have a time constant in the range of 0.5 to 2 seconds. The dynamics of the heat transfer process are affected by the dynamics of heating or cooling the metal that passes the heat from the hot to the cold source and the transport delay for the process fluid to flow through the tubes of the heat exchanger. That is, in order to increase the rate of heat transfer in a heat exchanger, the temperature of the metal tubes in the heat exchanger must be increased and the fluid must flow through the heat exchanger. The thermal lag associated with changing the temperature of the metal tubes provides the dynamic lag associated with heat transfer. The time constant for changing the temperature of the heat exchanger tubes is typically in the range of 1 to 6 seconds while the transport delay is in the range of 5 to 30 seconds. Modeling the combined dynamics of the actuator and the heat transfer system can be represented as a first order process given by

$$\frac{dQ}{dt} = \frac{1}{\tau_H}(Q_{spec} - Q) \qquad\qquad \textbf{3.5}$$

where Q_{spec} is the specified heat transfer rate and τ_H is the effective time constant for heat transfer (6 - 40 seconds). Q is a dependent variable and Q_{spec} is an independent variable.

Sensor Models. Dynamic models for level sensors, temperature sensors, and composition analyzers will be considered. The dynamic behavior of level sensors (e.g., a differential pressure sensor) and temperature sensors (e.g., a thermocouple or RTD) are well represented as linear first order models similar to Equation 3.4. For example, for a temperature sensor, the following equation can be used to model the measured temperature, T_s,

$$\frac{dT_s}{dt} = \frac{1}{\tau_{Ts}}(T - T_s) \qquad\qquad \textbf{3.6}$$

where T is the actual process temperature and τ_{Ts} is the time constant for the temperature sensor. τ_{Ts} typically ranges from 6 to 20 seconds depending on the mass of metal in the thermowell, thermal resistance between the temperature sensor and the inner wall of the thermowell, and the velocity of process fluid past the thermowell. That is, the separation between the temperature sensor and the surface of the thermowell, thickness of the thermowell walls, and the thickness of the heat transfer boundary layer outside the thermowell will affect the value of τ_{Ts}.

Similarly, the model for a level sensor is given by

$$\frac{dL_s}{dt} = \frac{1}{\tau_{Ls}}(L - L_s) \qquad\qquad \textbf{3.7}$$

where L_s is the measured level, L is the actual process level, and τ_{Ls} is the time constant for the level sensor. Since a differential pressure measurement is typically used to determine the level and the dynamics of differential pressure measurements are relatively fast, τ_{Ls} is typically less than one second. As a result, it is usually reasonable to neglect the dynamics of the level sensor and assume that the level sensor makes an instantaneous measurement. Differential pressure sensors are used to measure flow rates, levels, and system gauge pressure which can also usually be assumed to have fast sensor dynamics.

The most common composition analyzer in the CPI is the gas chromatograph (GC). Since a GC is a packed column, the analysis requires time for the sample to migrate by plug flow the length of the separation column. Therefore, the dynamic model of a GC is a pure time delay, i.e.,

$$C_s(t) = C(t - \theta_A) \qquad\qquad \textbf{3.8}$$

where $C_s(t)$ is the measured composition and $C(t - \theta_A)$ is the actual composition in the process θ_A time units before. θ_A is the cycle time for the analyzer or the time for the sample to flow through the packed column before it is subjected to the detector. Figure 3.5 shows a plot of $C_s(t)$ and $C(t)$. The arrows above the x-axis indicate when samples were injected into the GC. Note that the value $C_s(t)$ remains constant for θ_A time units since the GC requires θ_A time units to make a composition measurement.

CST Thermal Mixing Tank. Figure 3.6 shows a schematic for a **continuous stirred tank (CST)** thermal mixing tank. Assuming that the mixer volume is perfectly mixed, this process can be treated as a lumped parameter process suitably represented by a macroscopic model. Applying Equation 3.3 noting that there are no chemical reactions and no heat transfer yields:

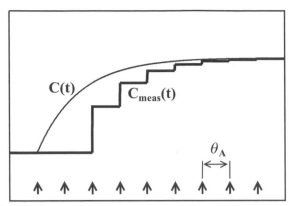

Figure 3.5 The dynamic response of the actual composition and the measured composition.

$$M\frac{dT}{dt} = F_1 T_1 + F_2 T_2 - (F_1 + F_2)\, T \qquad\qquad 3.9$$

assuming perfect level control (i.e., $F_T = F_1 + F_2$), that the heat capacity of all streams is the same and that the heat capacities at constant volume are equal to the heat capacities at constant pressure. The variables are defined as:

- M - mass of liquid in the mixer (100 kg)
- T - temperature of the mixed liquid (50°C)
- F_1 - mass flow rate of stream 1 (5 kg/s)
- T_1 - temperature of stream 1 (25°C)
- F_2 - mass flow rate of stream 2 (5 kg/s)
- T_2 - temperature of stream 2 (75°C)

These conditions represent the initial steady-state conditions. At time equal to 10 seconds, a step change in the specified flow rate for stream 1 is made from 5 kg/s to 4 kg/s. The flow control loop on stream 1 is assumed to have a τ_v equal to 2 seconds

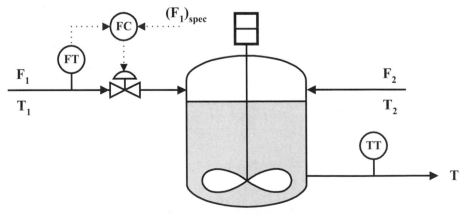

Figure 3.6 Schematic of the CST thermal mixing process.

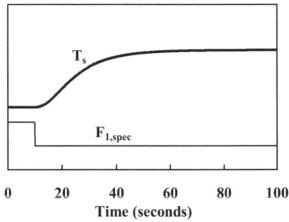

Figure 3.7 Dynamic response of the CST thermal mixer to a step change in $(F_1)_{spec}$.

while the temperature sensor has a time constant, τ_{Ts}, of 6 seconds. Figure 3.7 shows the resulting dynamic behavior of the measured temperature of the mixed liquid for this process. Note that after a change in the input, the process reaches a new steady-state condition; therefore, this process is referred to as a **self-regulating process**. These results were obtained by simultaneously integrating Equations 3.4, 3.6, and 3.9 which represent the combined effects of the flow controller, the thermal mixing process, and the temperature sensor. Therefore, the model equations that are used to represent the CST thermal mixer are given by

Actuator
$$\frac{dF_1}{dt} = \frac{1}{\tau_v}(F_{1,spec} - F_1)$$

Process
$$M\frac{dT}{dt} = F_1 T_1 + F_2 T_2 - (F_1 + F_2)T$$

Sensor
$$\frac{dT_s}{dt} = \frac{1}{\tau_{Ts}}(T - T_s)$$

Note that the process model is affected by changing $F_{1,spec}$ which changes F_1 resulting in a change in T which is measured by the sensor as T_s. F_1, T, and T_s are dependent variables and $F_{1,spec}$, F_2, T_1, and T_2 are independent variables. τ_v, M, and τ_{Ts} are process parameters. Figure 3.8 shows a comparison between the actuator/process/sensor model and a model of the mixer process by itself. Note that for the mixer model without the actuator and sensor included, the temperature of the product changes as soon as the specified value of F_1 changes while there is a noticeable time period before a significant change in the product temperature results for the actuator/process/sensor model. If the dynamics of the actuator and sensor are not included, the model has a very different dynamic response, particularly when the initial responses of the two models are compared; therefore, when dynamic models of a process are developed for

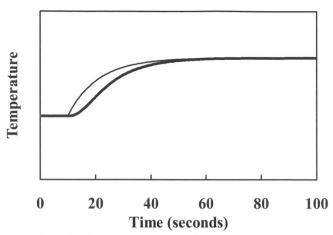

Figure 3.8 Comparison between the dynamic response of the model of the process by itself (thin line) and a model of the actuator/process/sensor (thick line).

process control purposes, the dynamics of the actuator and sensor should be considered.

CST Composition Mixing Tank. Figure 3.9 shows a schematic for a CST composition mixing tank. Assuming that the mixer volume is perfectly mixed, this process can be treated as a lumped parameter process and a macroscopic model can be applied. With no chemical reactions, uniform densities, and constant level (i.e., $F_T = F_1 + F_2$), Equation 3.2 becomes:

$$\rho V \frac{dC}{dt} = F_1 C_1 + F_2 C_2 - (F_1 + F_2) C \qquad\qquad \textbf{3.10}$$

where

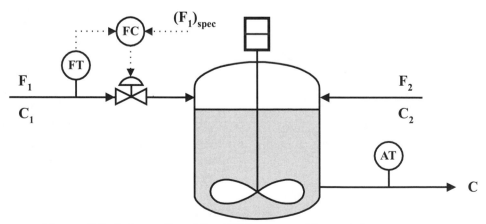

Figure 3.9 Schematic of the CST composition mixing process.

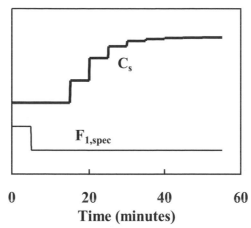

Figure 3.10 Dynamic response of the CST composition mixer for a step change in the specified value of F_1.

- V - the volume of the mixer (1000 liters)
- C - the concentration of the component in the mixed stream (0.75 gmoles/l)
- C_1 - the concentration of the component in stream 1 (0.5 gmoles/l)
- F_1 - the mass flow rate of stream 1 (500 kg/min)
- C_2 - the concentration of the component in stream 2 (1.0 gmoles/l)
- F_2 - the mass flow rate of stream 2 (500 kg/min)
- ρ - the density of the feed and product streams (1 kg/l)

These conditions represent the initial steady-state conditions. At time equal to 5 minutes, a step change in the specified feed rate for stream 1 is made from 500 kg/min to 400 kg/min. The flow control loop on stream 1 is assumed to have a τ_v equal to 2 seconds while the composition analyzer has an analyzer delay, θ_A, of 5 minutes. Figure 3.10 shows the measured mixer composition as a function of time. Note that this process is also self-regulating.

These results were obtained by simultaneously integrating Equations 3.4 and 3.10 while applying Equation 3.8 which represents the combined effects of the flow controller, mixer, and the composition analyzer. The equations that represent the CST composition mixer are given by:

Actuator
$$\frac{dF_1}{dt} = \frac{1}{\tau_v}(F_{1,spec} - F_1)$$

Process
$$\rho V \frac{dC}{dt} = F_1 C_1 + F_2 C_2 - (F_1 + F_2) C$$

Sensor
$$C_s(t) = C(t - \theta_A)$$

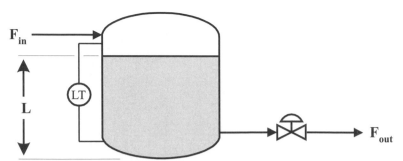

Figure 3.11 Schematic of a level in a tank process.

F_1, C, and C_s are dependent variables and $F_{1,spec}$, F_2, C_1, and C_2 are independent variables. τ_v, ρ, V, and θ_A are process parameters.

Level in a Tank. Figure 3.11 shows a schematic for the level in a tank. Assuming that the tank has a constant cross-sectional area, A_c,

$$\rho\, A_c \frac{dL}{dt} = F_{in} - F_{out} \qquad \textbf{3.11}$$

where L is the level of liquid in the tank (2 meters), ρ is the fluid density (1 kg/l), F_{in} is the mass flow rate of liquid into the tank (1.0 kg/s), and F_{out} is the mass flow rate of liquid leaving the tank (1.0 kg/s). These conditions represent the initial conditions. The control valve on the outlet stream from the tank has a τ_v of 5 seconds while the dynamics of the level sensor are assumed to be instantaneous. At time equal to 10 seconds, the specified value of F_{out} is changed from 1.0 to 0.9 kg/s. Figure 3.12 shows the level in the tank as a function of time.   Note that this process does not move to a new steady-state condition;   therefore,   this system   is   referred   to   as   a **non-self-regulating process**.   These results were obtained by simultaneously

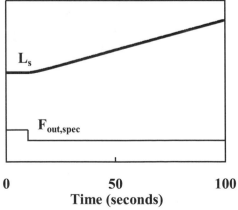

Figure 3.12 Dynamic response of a level in a tank to a step change in the flow rate leaving the tank.

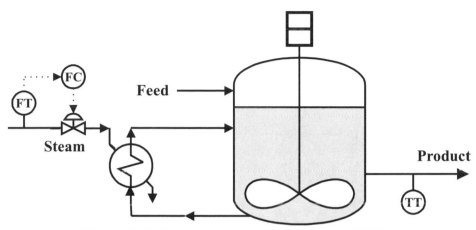

Figure 3.13 Schematic of an endothermic CSTR.

integrating Equations 3.4 and 3.11 which represents the combined effects of the flow controller and the level process.

Actuator
$$\frac{dF_{out}}{dt} = \frac{1}{\tau_v}\left(F_{out,spec} - F_{out}\right)$$

Process
$$\rho\, A_c\, \frac{dL}{dt} = F_{in} - F_{out}$$

Sensor
$$L_s = L$$

F_{out}, L, and L_s are dependent variables and $F_{out,spec}$ and F_{in} are independent variables. A_c and ρ are process parameters.

Endothermic CSTR. Figure 3.13 shows a schematic for an endothermic CSTR. Assuming that the CSTR is perfectly mixed, the process can be modeled as a lumped parameter process. Applying Equation 3.2 for a first order irreversible reaction and Arrhenius temperature dependence for the reaction rate constant results in

$$V_r\, \frac{dC_A}{dt} = \frac{F}{\rho}(C_{A0} - C_A) - V_r\, k_o\, C_A\, e^{-E/RT} \qquad \textbf{3.12}$$

which models the composition of the reactant assuming that the reactor volume is constant. In addition, Equation 3.3 is applied to model the reactor temperature

$$V_r\, \rho\, C_v\, \frac{dT}{dt} = F\, C_p(T_o - T) - V_r\, \Delta H\, C_A\, k_o\, e^{-E/RT} + Q \qquad \textbf{3.13}$$

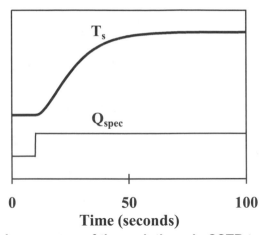

Figure 3.14 Dynamic response of the endothermic CSTR to a step increase in the heat addition rate to the reactor.

where

- V_r - reactor volume (100 l)
- F - mass feed rate (10 kg/s)
- C_{A0} - feed composition (1.0 gmoles/l)
- ρ - density of the reactor feed and product (1 kg/l)
- C_p - heat capacity of the reactor feed and product (1 cal/g - K)
- C_v - assumed equal to C_p
- ΔH - heat of reaction (160,000 cal/gmole)
- T_o - feed temperature (400 K)
- E/R - normalized activation energy (20,000 K)
- C_A - reactant concentration (0.25 gmoles/l)
- k_o - rate constant (1.97×10^{24} s^{-1})
- T - reactor temperature (350 K)
- Q - heat addition rate (700,000 cal/s)

These conditions represent the initial steady-state conditions. At time equal to 10 seconds, a step change in the specified heat addition rate (Q_{spec}) is made from 700,000 cal/s to 900,000 cal/s. Since heat addition by the heat exchanger involves a change in the flow rate of the steam as well as heat transfer in the heat exchanger, the dynamics of heat addition is modeled as a first order process with a time constant, τ_H, of 5 seconds. In addition, the temperature sensor is assumed to have a time constant, τ_T, of 6 seconds. Figure 3.14 shows the measured reactor temperature as a function of time for the step change in heat addition rate. These results were obtained by simultaneously integrating Equation 3.5, Equation 3.12, Equation 3.13, and Equation 3.6. Note that the reactant concentration must be modeled because C_A appears in Equation 3.13.

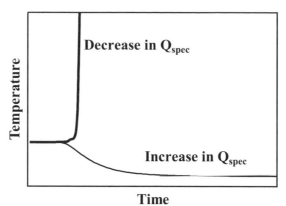

Figure 3.15 Open loop response of the exothermic CSTR to a 1% increase and decrease in the heat removal rate.

Lumped Actuator

$$\frac{dQ}{dt} = \frac{1}{\tau_H}(Q_{spec} - Q)$$

Process

$$V_r \frac{dC_A}{dt} = \frac{F(C_{A0} - C_A)}{\rho} - V_r k_0 C_A e^{-E/RT}$$

$$V_r \rho C_p \frac{dT}{dt} = F C_p (T_0 - T) - V_r \Delta H C_A k_0 e^{-E/RT} + Q$$

Sensor

$$\frac{dT_s}{dt} = \frac{1}{\tau_{Ts}}(T - T_s)$$

Q, C_A, T, and T_s are dependent variables and Q_{spec}, C_{A0}, F, and V_r are independent variables. τ_H, ρ, ΔH, k_0, E, R, and τ_{Ts} are process parameters.

Exothermic CSTR. The exothermic CSTR considered here is identical to the endothermic CSTR shown in Figure 3.13 except that an exothermic reaction occurs in the reactor and heat is removed in the heat exchanger by cooling water. The equations used to model this process are exactly the same as the equations used to model the endothermic CSTR. The process parameters are also the same except that Q_{spec} = -1,173,540 cal/s; C_A = 0.6415 gmoles/l; T = 340 K; and ΔH = -160,000 cal/gmole.

Figure 3.15 shows the open loop response of the exothermic CSTR to a 1% increase and a 1% decrease in the specified heat removal rate for the heat exchanger. This process is an example of an **open loop unstable process** since a decrease in the heat removed by the heat exchanger causes a temperature runaway and an increase causes the reaction to extinguish. It should be pointed out that not all exothermic reactors are open loop unstable processes. For the case in which the reaction is extinguished, the outlet temperature is determined almost exclusively by the inlet feed

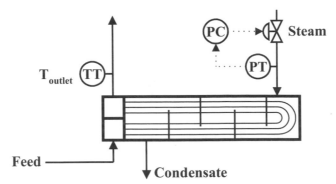

Figure 3.16 Schematic of a steam heated heat exchanger.

temperature and the heat removal rate since the reaction rate is essentially zero. This process is another example of a non-self-regulating process.

    Steam Heated Heat Exchanger. A schematic for a steam heated heat exchanger is shown in Figure 3.16. The feed enters the heat exchanger and flows through a number of parallel tubes that absorb heat from the condensing steam. The outlet temperature of the feed stream is measured by a temperature sensor/transmitter. Figure 3.17 shows a cross-section of one of the heat exchanger tubes. An energy balance for this cross-section indicates that the rate of accumulation of heat in the metal is equal to the rate of heat transfer from the condensing steam minus the rate of heat transfer from the metal tube to the tube-side liquid, i.e., after rearranging,

$$\frac{C_{vm}\,\rho_m}{4}(D_o^2 - D_i^2)\frac{dT_m}{dt} = D_o\,h_o\,(T_{stm} - T_m) - D_i\,h_i\,(T_m - T) \qquad \textbf{3.14}$$

where T_m is the temperature of the metal tube, T_{stm} is the temperature of the condensing steam, T is the temperature of the tube-side liquid, C_{vm} is the heat capacity of the metal tube (0.092 Btu/lb-°F), ρ_m is the density of the metal tube (556 lb/ft^3), D_o is the outside diameter of the metal tube (1.05 in), D_i is the inside diameter of the metal tube (0.824

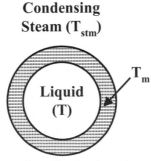

Figure 3.17 Cross-section of a tube in the steam heated heat exchanger.

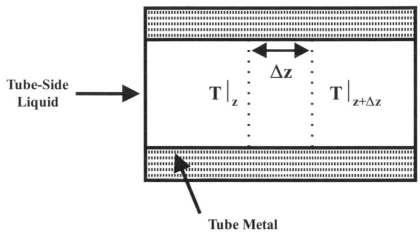

Tube Metal

**Figure 3.18 Cross-section of a tube from a steam heated heat exchanger.
Note that a differential volume is indicated inside the tube.**

in), h_o is the heat transfer coefficient between the steam and the tube metal (3000 Btu/ft^2-$^\circ$F), and h_i is the heat transfer coefficient between the tube-side liquid and the tube metal (1000 Btu/ft^2-$^\circ$F). Note that Equation 3.14 is valid for any point along the length of a heat exchanger tube and based upon neglecting heat conduction along the length of the metal tube.

Consider the cross-section of a tube containing a differential volume shown in Figure 3.18. Applying Equation 3.3 to the differential volume[4] noting that there are no reactions occurring results in

$$\rho C_v A \Delta z \frac{dT}{dt} = \rho C_p v A \, T(z) - \rho C_p v A \, T(z + \Delta z) + Q \pi D_i \Delta z$$

where A is the cross-sectional area of the tube and Q is the heat flux from the metal tube to the tube-side liquid. Rearranging this equation assuming that C_v is equal to C_p and using the expression for the cross-sectional area of the tube yields

$$\frac{dT}{dt} = v \frac{T(z) - T(z + \Delta z)}{\Delta z} + \frac{4Q}{\rho C_p D_i}$$

Substituting the equation for the heat flux [$Q = h_i (T_m - T)$] and taking the limit as Δz goes to zero results in the following partial differential equation

$$\frac{\partial T}{\partial t} + v \frac{\partial T}{\partial z} = \frac{4 h_i}{\rho_l C_{pl} D_i} (T_m - T) \qquad\qquad \textbf{3.15}$$

where T is the temperature of the tube-side fluid ($^\circ$F), T_m is the metal temperature ($^\circ$F), t is time (s), v is the average velocity of the tube-side fluid (7 ft/s), z is the axial position

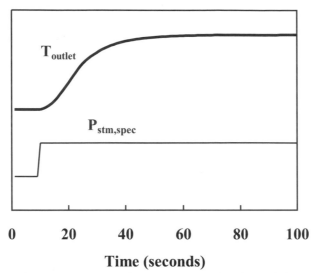

Figure 3.19 Open loop response of the measured value of the outlet temperature of the steam heated heat exchanger to a step increase in the specified value of the steam pressure applied to the heat exchanger.

(ft), ρ_l is the density of the tube-side fluid (62.4 lb/ft^2), and C_{pl} is the heat capacity of the tube-side liquid (1 Btu/lb-°F). The dependent variables are T and T_m at each node point along the length of the tube, T_{stm}, and T_{outlet} and the independent variable is $P_{stm,spec}$. Note that this model is a distributed parameter model since the temperature of the tube-side fluid and the metal tube varies over the length of the heat exchanger tube and are also functions of time. The inlet temperature of the feed is 80°F, the length of each tube is 80 ft, and initially the steam temperature is 250 °F. The temperature sensor dynamics were modeled using Equation 3.6 with time constant of 10 seconds while the dynamics of the pressure controller were neglected. At time equal to 10 seconds, the setpoint for the steam pressure controller was increased resulting in a 10°F increase in the steam temperature. Note that Equation 3.15 is a partial differential equation that constitutes an initial value problem.

In order to solve Equation 3.15, the method of lines[5] can be applied which results in an ordinary differential equation for each node point along the length of the heat exchanger tube. Equation 3.14 is also applied at each node point. In addition, the model for the temperature sensor on the outlet from the heat exchanger is applied. The resulting set of ordinary differential equations is stiff requiring an implicit integrator (LSODE[6]). The dynamic response of this process is shown in Figure 3.19.

Sensor Noise. All sensor readings have some degree of noise. Some sensor readings have very low levels of noise while others can be dominated by noise. A key characteristic of noise is the noise to signal ratio. The signal is the output of the sensor and the noise is the variation in the output from the sensor that does not correspond to changes in the process measurement. Noise can be caused by electrical interference, mechanical vibration, or process changes. As a result, the measured values of the process variables can show significant variations that are not real process changes

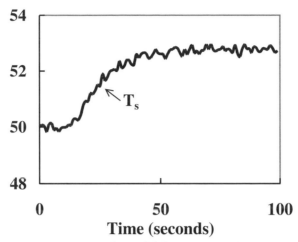

Figure 3.20 Dynamic response of the CST thermal mixer with noise modeled on the sensor reading.

when the noise to signal ratio is large. When a significant noise to signal ratio occurs for a controlled variable, the noise can be amplified by the feedback controller which is not desirable.

Modeling of sensor noise is important for the realistic modeling of industrial processes. Sensor noise can usually be modeled by assuming that it is **Gaussian distributed white noise**. In order to model Gaussian distributed white noise, one only has to choose the standard deviation of the noise, σ. Then the following equation[7] can be used to approximate a "bell-shaped" Gaussian distribution.

$$y_n = \frac{1.961\,\sigma\,(x_n - 0.5)}{[(x_n + 0.002432)(1.002432 - x_n)]^{0.203}} \qquad \textbf{3.16}$$

where y_n is the noise contribution to the measured value of the controlled variable and x_n is a random number between 0 and 1. Appendix A presents a simple algorithm for generating numbers that are very nearly random.

The procedure for modeling a sensor reading with noise is as follows.

1. Select the standard deviation of the noise. Remember that 4σ (i.e., $\pm2\sigma$) should contain 95% of the readings.
2. Identify the noise free sensor reading, y_{nf}. For example, Figure 3.14 shows the noise free sensor readings for a step change for the endothermic CSTR.
3. Generate a random number (0, 1), x_n.
4. Apply Equation 3.16 to calculate y_n.
5. Then the sensor reading is given by y_s.

$$y_s = y_{nf} + y_n$$

Each time a new sensor reading is called for, apply steps 2 to 5. The repeatability of the sensor reading of interest (Table 2.1) can be used to estimate the proper value of σ to use to model the sensor noise. For example, consider a level indicator. From Table 2.1, the repeatability is about $\pm 1\%$ corresponding to 4σ; therefore, σ is equal to 0.5%.

Figure 3.20 shows the results of adding sensor noise to the CST thermal mixer for a step change in the flow rate of stream 1. The noise on the temperature sensor reading is modeled using a σ of 0.1°C. The noise free temperature results are shown in Figure 3.7.

3.6 Numerical Integration of ODE's

The differential equation that represents a general dynamic system has the general form

$$\frac{dy}{dt} = f(t, y, u, d) \qquad\qquad \textbf{3.17}$$

with initial conditions   at $t = t_0$, $y = y_0$

which is referred to as an initial-valued ordinary differential equation (IV-ODE) where y is the dependent variable, t is time, u is the manipulated variable (independent variable), and d is a disturbance (independent variable). When $f(t,y,u,d)$ is a linear function, an analytical solution is available (e.g., Laplace transforms, Chapter 4). When $f(t,y,u,d)$ is nonlinear, a numerical solution procedure is generally required.

With regard to the numerical solution of IV-ODE's, there are two key issues: solution accuracy and stability of the numerical procedure. Accuracy is related to the error between the exact solution and the numerical approximation. As the step size, Δt, used by the integration method is reduced, the error between the exact solution and the numerical approximation, E_T, is also reduced. In general, E_T can be represented by

$$E_T = K \Delta t^n \qquad\qquad \textbf{3.18}$$

where n is the order of the numerical integration technique and K is a constant. This relationship indicates that the magnitude of Δt should be kept small in order to produce an accurate solution. n indicates the accuracy of an integration technique. For example, if n is equal to 1, E_T decreases linearly as Δt is reduced. For n equal to 2, E_T decreases with the square of Δt which means that E_T will decrease much faster than for n equal 1. Likewise, for a fourth order method (i.e., $n = 4$), the accuracy of the numerical solution will be much greater than for a first order or second order method with the same Δt. Therefore, **higher order integration methods provide greater accuracy than lower order integration methods.**

The numerical stability of an ODE integrator is determined by whether or not the round-off error damps out or grows with each step in time, Δt. If it damps out, the numerical integration is stable. If it does not, the round-off error will grow without bound and soon dominate the numerical solution. There are two general types of ODE integrators: explicit and implicit integrators. Explicit methods are susceptible to numerical instability as the magnitude of Δt is increased while implicit integration methods are not affected by stability regardless of the magnitude of Δt. Implicit methods must still keep Δt below a certain level in order to meet the accuracy requirements. More details concerning the issues of accuracy and stability for ODE integration can be found in Riggs[8].

The simplest ODE integrator is the explicit Euler method

$$y(t+\Delta t) = y(t) + \Delta t \, f \, [t, y(t), u(t), d(t)] \qquad \textbf{3.19}$$

The Euler method is a first order method (i.e., $n = 1$). It is referred to as explicit since the right hand side of Equation 3.19 is not a function of $y(t+\Delta t)$. The stability limit for explicit Euler integration can be derived analytically[8] and is given by

$$\Delta t < \frac{2}{|\lambda(t)|} \qquad \textbf{3.20}$$

where $\lambda(t)$ can be roughly approximated by

$$\lambda(t) = \frac{f(t, y, u)}{y(t)} \qquad \textbf{3.21}$$

Equation 3.20 indicates that the stability of an explicit integrator can be improved by reducing the time step size, Δt.

Another popular explicit integration method is the fourth order Runge-Kutta method. It uses evaluations of $f(t, y, u, d)$ at t, $t + \frac{1}{2}\Delta t$, and $t + \Delta t$ in order to more accurately approximate the effective slope for the time step, Δt. Since it is a fourth order method, it is much more accurate than the Euler method but has approximately the same stability dependence upon Δt.

A well known implicit integration method is the trapezoidal method.

$$y(t+\Delta t) = y(t) + \frac{\Delta t}{2} [f(t, y[t], u[t], d[t]) + f(t+\Delta t, y[t+\Delta t], u[t+\Delta t], d[t+\Delta t])]$$

$$\textbf{3.22}$$

This is referred to as an implicit method since $y(t+\Delta t)$ appears on the right hand side of Equation 3.22 and, in general, solving for $y(t+\Delta t)$ using Equation 3.22 requires the iterative solution of a nonlinear equation. **Implicit methods overcome stability limits on Δt but are usually much more difficult and computationally expensive to apply.** When is λ large, must accordingly Δt be reduced to retain stability for explicit methods; therefore, for these cases, implicit methods can offer significant advantages over explicit methods. Even so, most dynamic models used for process control analysis do not usually have λ's that are large enough to warrant the use of implicit integration techniques.

Consider the CST thermal mixer example. Applying Equation 3.21 to the actuator equation, process model equation, and sensor equation yields a largest value of λ of 0.33 $\sec^{-1}$ (i.e., $1/\tau_v$). As a result, this problem does not require an implicit integrator since the application of Equation 3.18 indicates that a maximum stable step size of 6 seconds can be used. In fact, the results shown in Figure 3.7 were obtained using an Euler integrator with $\Delta t = 0.1$ seconds.

3.7 Summary

Dynamic process models are useful for analyzing process control behavior. For example, quantitative comparisons of control alternatives can be developed using dynamic process models. Dynamic process models can be developed using conservation of mass, moles, or energy which consider accumulation, as well as the appropriate constitutive relations. When developing dynamic models for process control analysis, dynamic models of the actuator and sensors should be added to the dynamic model of the process. In addition, the modeling of most sensors should include measurement noise. The resulting dynamic equations for the actuator, process, and sensor can usually be integrated conveniently using an Euler integrator.

3.8 Additional Terminology

Constitutive relations - algebraic equations such as kinetic expressions or gas laws that are necessary to solve model equations.
CST - continuous stirred tank, i.e., a vessel in which the temperature and composition throughout the tank are uniform.
CSTR - continuous stirred tank reactor, i.e., a reactor in which the composition and temperature are uniform throughout the reactor volume.
Dependent variable - a process variable that is determined by the solution of the model equations.
Distributed parameter model - a process model that can be applied to a system for which the dependent variables vary with spatial location within the process.

Exactly determined - a system of equations with the same number of unknowns as equations.

Exactly specified - a system of equations with the same number of unknowns as equations.

Gaussian distributed white noise - noise that follows an equal probability-based Gaussian distribution.

Independent variable - a process variable that is selected by the user.

Lumped parameter model - a process model that assumes that the dependent variables are uniform throughout the spatial region of the process.

Marcoscopic balances - balances based on what enters or leave the process boundaries and treats the process in a lumped manner.

Macroscopic model - a model that is based upon macroscopic balances.

Microscopic balances - balances that consider that the dependent variables vary with spatial location within the process.

Microscopic model - a model that is based upon microscopic balances.

Non-self-regulating process - a process that does not move to a new steady-state condition after a change in a process input is made.

Open loop unstable process - a process that can go unstable (i.e., increase without bound) due to a small change in an input under open loop conditions.

Overdetermined - a system of equations with more equations than unknowns.

Overspecified - a system of equations with more equations than unknowns.

Process parameter - a constant appearing in a model equation, e.g., physical parameters, rate constants, gas constants, etc.

Self-regulating process - a process that moves to a new steady-state after a change in a process input is made.

Underdetermined - a system of equations with more unknowns than equations.

Underspecified - a system of equations with more unknowns than equations.

3.9 References

1. Bird, R.B., Stewart, W.E., and Lightfoot, E.N., *Transport Phenomena*, John Wiley and Sons, New York, p. 216 (1960).

2. Riggs, J.B., *An Introduction to Numerical Methods for Chemical Engineers*, Second Edition, Texas Tech University Press, Lubbock, Texas, pp. 387-420 (1994).

3. Bequette, B.W., *Modeling and Analysis of Dynamic Systems*, Prentice Hall, Englewood, New Jersey, (1998).

4. Stephanopoulos, G., *Chemical Process Control*, Prentice-Hall, Englewood, New Jersey, pp. 69-70 (1984).

5. Riggs, J.B., *An Introduction to Numerical Methods for Chemical Engineers,* Second Edition, Texas Tech University Press, Lubbock, Texas, pp. 220-228 (1994).

6. Ibid, pp. 200-207.

7. Unpublished work from R. Russel Rhinehart.

8. Riggs, J.B., *An Introduction to Numerical Methods for Chemical Engineers,* Second Edition, Texas Tech University Press, Lubbock, Texas, pp. 172-179 (1994).

3.10 Questions and Exercises

3.1 What are the differences between lumped parameter and distributed parameter models? Give an example of each.

3.2 Develop the model equations that can be used to represent the dynamic behavior of a stirred tank heater considering the combined models of the actuator, process, and sensor. Assume that the stirred tank heater is identical to the endothermic CSTR given in Section 3.5 except that no reactions take place.

3.3 Develop the set of dynamic equations that describe an isothermal CSTR in which series reactions occur using an acuator/process/sensor modeling approach. Assume that one feed steam enters the reactor and one product stream leaves the reactor.   The reaction scheme is given by

$$A \xrightarrow{\;r_1\;} B \xrightarrow{\;r_2\;} C$$

where $r_1 = k_1\, C_A$ and $r_2 = k_2\, C_B$.   Assume that the feed rate is the input variable and that the time constant for the flow controller for the feed rate has a value of 2 seconds and that the feed stream contains only component A at a concentration C_{A0}. The output variable is the concentration of B in the reactor product. Assume an analyzer delay of 3 minutes for the B analyzer on the product stream. Also assume perfect level control in the reactor (i.e., the flow rate out of the reactor equals the flow rate into the reactor). Identify all process variables and process parameters along with their dimensional units.

3.4 Develop the set of dynamic equations that describes a nonisothermal endothermic CSTR with the same series reactions given in Problem 3. Assume that the first order Arrhenius rate expressions are known along with the heats of reaction. Assume that the inputs are the feed rate and the heat addition rate with time constants of 2 and 6 seconds, respectively.   The output variables are the concentration of B and the temperature of the reaction mixture. Assume a 5 minute analyzer delay for the composition measurement and a time constant for the temperature measurement of 20 seconds. Also assume perfect level control in the reactor (i.e., the flow rate out of the reactor equals the flow rate into the reactor). Identify all process variables and process parameters along with their dimensional units.

3.5 Consider the level process shown in Figure 3.11 except that the inlet flow is the input and the outlet flow is given by

$$F_{out} = K\sqrt{L}$$

where K is a constant and L is the level in the tank. Develop an actuator/process/sensor model for this process. Assume that the flow controller on the feed stream has a time constant of 2 seconds. Identify all process variables and process parameters along with their dimensional units.

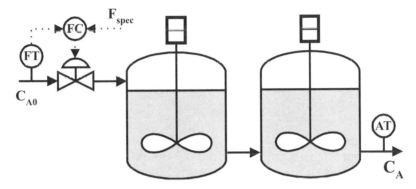

3.6 Develop the set of dynamic equations that describe two isothermal CSTR's in series (above) using an actuator/process/sensor modeling approach. Assume that a single irreversible reaction occurs in this system given by

$$A \xrightarrow{\ r\ } B$$

where $r = k\,C_A^2$. Assume that the feed rate to the first reactor is the input variable and that the flow controller on the feed has a time constant of 2 seconds. The inlet feed contains only component A at a concentration of C_{A0}. The output variable of this process is the concentration of B in the outlet product stream and the analyzer on this stream has an analyzer delay of 5 minutes. Also assume perfect level control in each reactor (i.e., the flow rate out of the reactor equals the flow rate into the reactor).

3.7 Develop a macroscopic model of a steam heated heat exchanger using an actuator/process/sensor modeling approach. The output variable is the outlet temperature of the process fluid and the input variable is the specified steam pressure. For a macroscopic model of a heat exchanger, the metal of the heat exchanger is assumed to be at one temperature and the temperature of the process stream used for heat transfer calculations is the average between the inlet temperature and the exit temperature for the heat exchanger, i.e., the heat transfer rate from the metal to the process fluid is given by

$$Q = U\,A(\overline{T_m} - \overline{T})$$

where U is the overall heat transfer coefficient, A is the surface area for heat transfer, $\overline{T}$ is the average temperature for the process fluid inside the heat exchanger, and $\overline{T}_m$ is the single temperature for the metal in the heat exchanger. Note that the result for the heat transfer rate can be used to calculate the outlet temperature of the process fluid. Assume that the pressure controller on the steam has a time constant of 2 seconds and the outlet temperature sensor for the process fluid has a time constant of 20 seconds. Identify all process variables and process parameters along with their dimensional units.

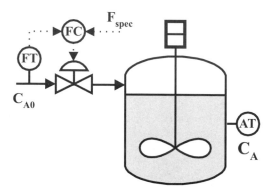

3.8 Develop the set of dynamic equations that describe an isothermal semibatch reactor (above) using an actuator/process/sensor modeling approach. Note that for a semibatch reactor feed is added to the reactor, but product is not removed. Assume the same reaction scheme and rate expression as used in Problem 3.6. Assume that the feed to the reactor is controlled by a flow controller with a time constant of 2 seconds and that the product composition is measured by an analyzer with a analyzer delay of 5 minutes. Identify all process variables and process parameters along with their dimensional units. (Hint: Remember to model the volume of the reactor as a function of time.)

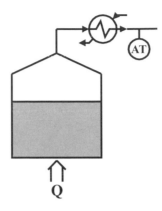

3.9 Consider the moonshine still shown above. This batch process consists of putting sour mash (i.e., largely water and ethyl alcohol) into the still and adding heat. The ethyl alcohol is lighter than water; therefore, the distillate from the still is rich in alcohol. Write a set of model equations for this process using the actuator/process/sensor approach assuming that the charge is already heated to the boiling point of the mixture. The heat input rate, Q, is the input variable and has a dynamic time constant of 20 seconds while the output variable is the concentration of ethyl alcohol in the product stream. Since the composition analysis is done by drawing a sample and measuring the density of the product, the analyzer delay is assumed to be 30 seconds. Assume that the mixture has a constant heat of vaporization and that the mass fraction of the alcohol in the vapor leaving the still, y, is related to the mass fraction of alcohol remaining in the still, x, by the following equation

$$y = \frac{\alpha x}{1+(\alpha - 1)x}$$

Identify all process variables and process parameters along with their dimensional units.

3.10 Consider a pressure vessel for which there is a fixed gas flow into the vessel and an exit line that has a control valve on it leaving the vessel. Assume that the input to this process is the signal to the control valve on the exit line and the output variable is the pressure of the gas in the vessel. Assume that τ_v is equal to 10 seconds. Develop a dynamic model for this process using the combined models of the actuator, process, and sensor. Identify all process variables and process parameters along with their dimensional units. (Hint: Use the ideal gas law to relate pressure to the number of moles of gas in the vessel.)

3.11 What type of numerical integrator would you used to integrate the equations in Problem 3.10? Use the stiffness of the equations to justify your answer.

Chapter 4

Laplace Transforms and Transfer Functions

4.1 Introduction

Laplace transforms represent a simple means to develop analytical solutions for linear dynamic equations. In addition, Laplace transforms can be used to develop transfer functions which conveniently and meaningfully represent the input/output behavior of a process. While Laplace transforms and transfer functions provide insight into the fundamental behavior of dynamic systems and will be used in Chapter 6 to analyze the behavior of feedback systems as well, they are not typically used industrially. Therefore, the material in this chapter is designed to provide insight and understanding of dynamic systems while introducing important terminology relevant to the process control field, but is generally not used industrially.

4.2 Laplace Transforms

The Laplace transform of a function, $f(t)$, is defined by

$$\mathcal{L}\{f(t)\} = \int_0^\infty f(t)e^{-st}dt = F(s) \qquad \textbf{4.1}$$

where $f(t)$ is a relatively general function of time, t, for $t > 0$, $\mathcal{L}$ is the Laplace operator, s is a complex variable, and $F(s)$ is the symbol for the Laplace transform of $f(t)$. Equation 4.1 can be rearranged to yield the expression for the inverse Laplace transform.

$$\mathcal{L}^{-1}\{F(s)\} = f(t) \qquad \textbf{4.2}$$

Laplace transforms are useful for solving **linear** dynamic equations. The time domain equations are transformed into the Laplace domain (Equation 4.1) where they are solved algebraically yielding an equation for the output variable in the Laplace domain. The output variable in the Laplace domain can then be transformed back to the time domain using inverse Laplace transforms (Equation 4.2).

A function, $f(t)$, is linear if

$$f(c_1\,t + c_2\,t) = c_1\,f(t) + c_2\,f(t) \qquad\qquad \textbf{4.3}$$

where c_1 and c_2 are real constants. As an example,

$$f(t) = at$$

is linear while

$$f(t) = at^2$$

and

$$f(t) = at^{1/2}$$

are nonlinear.

Table 4.1 lists the Laplace transforms of several commonly encountered functions. Table 4.1 can also be used to apply inverse Laplace transforms by going from the Laplace transform to the corresponding time function, $f(t)$.

There are two additional important properties of Laplace transform: the **final-value theorem** and the **initial-value theorem**. The final value theorem states that

$$\lim_{t \to \infty} \{f(t)\} \;=\; \lim_{s \to 0} \{s\,F(s)\} \qquad\qquad \textbf{4.4}$$

if the limit of $f(t)$ as $t \to \infty$ exists. The final-value theorem can be used to determine the steady-state conditions of a process if the Laplace transform of the function is known. The initial-value theorem is given by

$$\lim_{t \to 0} \{f(t)\} \;=\; \lim_{s \to \infty} \{s\,F(s)\} \qquad\qquad \textbf{4.5}$$

The initial -value theorem can be used to determine the initial conditions of a function if the Laplace transform of the function is known. Note that when time becomes large, s approaches zero and *vice-versa*.

Table 4.1	
Laplace Transforms of Common Functions	
f(t)	**Laplace transform of f(t)**
$f(t)$	$F(s)$
$K f(t)$	$K F(s)$
Unit impulse at $t = 0$	1
Unit step at $t = 0$	$1/s$
Unit ramp, t	$1/s^2$
t^2	$\dfrac{2}{s^3}$
t^n	$\dfrac{n!}{s^{n+1}}$
e^{-at}	$\dfrac{1}{s+a}$
$t^n e^{-at}$	$\dfrac{n!}{(s+a)^{n+1}}$
$\sin \omega t$	$\dfrac{\omega}{s^2 + \omega^2}$
$\cos \omega t$	$\dfrac{s}{s^2 + \omega^2}$
$e^{-at} \sin \omega t$	$\dfrac{\omega}{(s+a)^2 + \omega^2}$
$e^{-at} \cos \omega t$	$\dfrac{s+a}{(s+a)^2 + \omega^2}$
$\dfrac{d f(t)}{dt}$	$s F(s) - f(0)$
$\dfrac{d^2 f(t)}{dt^2}$	$s^2 F(s) - s f(0) - \left[\dfrac{df}{dt}\right]_{t=0}$
$\displaystyle\int_0^t f(t)\,dt$	$\dfrac{1}{s} F(s)$
$f(t - \theta)$	$F(s) e^{-\theta s}$

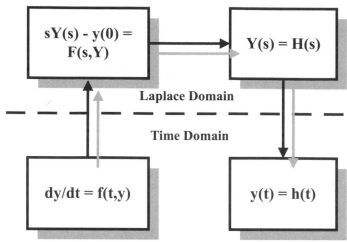

Figure 4.1 Schematic that shows how Laplace transforms can be used to solve linear differential equations.

4.3 Laplace Transform Solutions of Linear Dynamic Equations

　　　　Laplace transforms can be used to solve linear dynamic equations. A linear differential equation in the time domain is transformed into the Laplace domain by taking the Laplace transform of each term on both sides of the equation. Next, the transformed equation is algebraically rearranged to solve explicitly for the dependent variable in the Laplace domain, $Y(s)$. Finally, the time dependent behavior of the dependent variable, $y(t)$, is obtained by applying the inverse Laplace transform to $Y(s)$. This procedure is shown schematically in Figure 4.1.

Example 4.1　Solution of a General First Order Equation

Problem Statement　Consider the following first order differential equation

$$\frac{dy}{dt} = \frac{1}{\tau}(y_{ss} - y)$$

where $y(0) = 0$ and τ is a constant. y_{ss} undergoes a step change from zero to y_{ss} at time equal to zero. Determine $y(t)$ using Laplace transforms.

Solution.　The first step is to apply Laplace transforms to each term in the differential equation. Applying the Laplace transforms listed in Table 4.1 to each term of the differential equation yields

$$sY(s) - y(0) = \frac{y_{ss}}{\tau s} - \frac{Y(s)}{\tau}$$

Rearranging and solving for $Y(s)$ yields

$$Y(s) = \frac{y_{ss}}{s(\tau s + 1)} \qquad \text{(A)}$$

In order to apply the inverse Laplace transform, this equation must be converted into the following form

$$Y(s) = \frac{K_1}{s} + \frac{K_2}{\tau s + 1} \qquad \text{(B)}$$

where K_1 and K_2 are constants. Transforming Equation A into Equation B is referred to as a **partial fraction expansion.** Combining the two terms on the right hand side of Equation B yields

$$Y(s) = \frac{K_1 \tau s + K_1 + K_2 s}{s(\tau s + 1)} \qquad \text{(C)}$$

In order for Equations A and C to be equivalent, the coefficients of s in the numerator of both equations must be equal, i.e., equating the coefficients of s yields:

$$K_1 \tau = -K_2$$

Likewise, the constant terms in both numerators must be equal, i.e.,

$$K_1 = y_{ss}$$

Then

$$K_2 = -\tau y_{ss}$$

Thus

$$Y(s) = \frac{y_{ss}}{s} - \frac{\tau y_{ss}}{\tau s + 1} = \frac{y_{ss}}{s} - \frac{y_{ss}}{s + 1/\tau}$$

Now the inverse Laplace transforms of each term of this equation can be applied resulting in

$$y(t) = y_{ss}(1 - e^{-t/\tau})$$

Example 4.2   Solution of the CST Thermal Mixer Equation

Problem Statement The dynamic equation for a CST thermal mixing tank is given by Equation 3.9, i.e.,

$$M\frac{dT}{dt} = F_1 T_1 + F_2 T_2 - (F_1 + F_2)T$$

where T is the dependent variable of the process and F_1, F_2, T_1, and T_2 are inputs to the process. Determine the time behavior of T assuming that at time equal to zero, T is equal to T_0 and a step change in T_1 of magnitude ΔT_1 is implemented at time equal to zero while all other inputs remain constant.

Solution The first step is to take the Laplace transform of each term in the previous equation using Table 4.1.

$$M[sT(s) - T_0] = \frac{F_1[T_1 + \Delta T_1] + F_2 T_2}{s} - (F_1 + F_2)T(s)$$

Algebraically solving for $T(s)$ yields

$$T(s) = \frac{M T_0 + \dfrac{F_1 \Delta T_1 + F_1 T_1 + F_2 T_2}{s}}{M s + (F_1 + F_2)}$$

Rearranging yields

$$T(s) = \frac{T_0 s + F_1 \Delta T_1 / M + F_1 T_1 / M + F_2 T_2 / M}{s[s + (F_1 + F_2)/ M]} \qquad \textbf{(A)}$$

In order to apply the inverse Laplace transforms, we need to apply a partial fraction expansion, i.e.,

$$T(s) = \frac{C_1}{s} + \frac{C_2}{s + (F_1 + F_2)/ M}$$

By recombining the terms on the right hand side of this equation, the following results

$$T(s) = \frac{C_1 s + C_1 (F_1 + F_2)/ M + C_2 s}{s[s + (F_1 + F_2)/ M]} \qquad \textbf{(B)}$$

In order to solve for the value of C_1 and C_2, we equate the coefficients of the same powers of s in the numerators for Equation A and Equation B.

(s)

$$C_1 + C_2 = T_0$$

(Constant)

$$C_1(F_1 + F_2) = F_1 \Delta T_1 + F_1 T_1 + F_2 T_2$$

Thus

$$C_1 = \frac{F_1 \Delta T_1 + F_1 T_1 + F_2 T_2}{F_1 + F_2}$$

$$C_2 = T_0 - \frac{F_1 \Delta T_1 + F_1 T_1 + F_2 T_2}{F_1 + F_2}$$

Then

$$T(s) = \frac{F_1 \Delta T_1 + F_1 T_1 + F_2 T_2}{s(F_1 + F_2)} + \left[T_0 - \frac{F_1 \Delta T_1 + F_1 T_1 + F_2 T_2}{F_1 + F_2} \right] \frac{1}{s + (F_1 + F_2)/M}$$

Applying the inverse Laplace transform yields:

$$T(t) = \frac{F_1 \Delta T_1 + F_1 T_1 + F_2 T_2}{F_1 + F_2} + \left[T_0 - \frac{F_1 \Delta T_1 + F_1 T_1 + F_2 T_2}{F_1 + F_2} \right] e^{-t(F_1 + F_2)/M}$$

Note that at $t = 0$, $T = T_0$ and as $t \rightarrow \infty$

$$T \rightarrow \frac{F_1 \Delta T_1 + F_1 T_1 + F_2 T_2}{F_1 + F_2}$$

Example 4.3 Solution of Second Order Differential Equations

Problem Statement Consider a second order differential equation

$$a \frac{d^2 y}{dt^2} + b \frac{dy}{dt} + cy = f(t)$$

where

$$\left(\frac{dy}{dt} \right)_{t=0} = 0$$

$$y(0) = 0$$

and $f(t)$ is a step change from 0 to 1 at $t = 0$. Evaluate the possible solutions for this differential equation.

Solution Using Table 4.1 to apply Laplace transforms to each term in the differential equation results in

$$a\left[Y(s)\,s^2 - y(0)\,s - \left(\frac{dy}{dt}\right)_{t=o}\right] + b\left[Y(s)s - y(0)\right] + c\,Y(s) = 1/\,s$$

Simplifying and solving for $Y(s)$

$$Y(s) = \frac{1}{s(as^2 + bs + c)}$$

Before this equation can be converted back to the time domain by applying inverse Laplace transforms, the roots of the denominator must be calculated and a partial fraction expansion implemented. Applying the quadratic formula to factor the denominator into its roots yields

$$Y(s) = \frac{1}{as\left(s + \dfrac{b + \sqrt{b^2 - 4ac}}{2a}\right)\left(s + \dfrac{b - \sqrt{b^2 - 4ac}}{2a}\right)}$$

There are three cases that can result for this system:

Case 1 $b^2 - 4ac > 0$

Case 2 $b^2 - 4ac = 0$

Case 3 $b^2 - 4ac < 0$

Case 1 Consider the case in which $a = 1$, $b = 5$ and $c = 6$ (i.e., $b^2 - 4ac = 1$)

$$Y(s) = \frac{1}{s(s^2 + 5s + 6)} = \frac{1}{s(s+2)(s+3)}$$

Applying a standard partial fraction expansion

$$Y(s) = \frac{1}{s(s+2)(s+3)} = \frac{C_1}{s} + \frac{C_2}{s+2} + \frac{C_3}{s+3}$$

$$Y(s) = \frac{1}{6s} - \frac{1}{2(s+2)} + \frac{1}{3(s+3)}$$

Applying an inverse Laplace transform to each term yields

$$y(t) = \mathcal{L}^{-1}[Y(s)] = \mathcal{L}^{-1}\left(\frac{\frac{1}{6}}{s}\right) - \mathcal{L}^{-1}\left(\frac{\frac{1}{2}}{s+2}\right) + \mathcal{L}^{-1}\left(\frac{\frac{1}{3}}{s+3}\right)$$

$$y(t) = \frac{1}{6} - \frac{1}{2}e^{-2t} + \frac{1}{3}e^{-3t}$$

Case 2 Consider the case in which $a = 1$, $b = 6$ and $c = 9$ (i.e., $b^2 - 4ac = 0$)

$$Y(s) = \frac{1}{s(s^2 + 6s + 9)} = \frac{1}{s(s+3)(s+3)}$$

Applying a partial fraction expansion

$$Y(s) = \frac{1}{s(s+3)(s+3)} = \frac{C_1}{s} + \frac{C_2}{s+3} + \frac{C_3}{(s+3)^2}$$

Note that because of the repeated root (i.e., $s = -3$), a term with $(s + 3)^2$ must be used. Solving for C_1, C_2, and C_3 using special partial fraction expansion techniques[1] results in

$$Y(s) = \frac{1}{9s} - \frac{1}{9(s+3)} - \frac{1}{3(s+3)^2}$$

Applying an inverse Laplace transform to each term

$$y(t) = \frac{1}{9} - \frac{1}{9}e^{-3t} - \frac{1}{3}te^{-3t}$$

$$y(t) = \frac{1}{9}[1 - e^{-3t}(1 + 3t)]$$

This result corresponds to a critically damped response which will be discussed in Section 5.3.

Case 3 Consider the case in which $a = 1$, $b = 4$, and $c = 8$ (i.e., $b^2 - 4ac = -4$).

$$Y(s) = \frac{1}{s(s^2 + 4s + 8)} = \frac{1}{s(s+2-2i)(s+2+2i)}$$

Applying a partial fraction expansion

$$Y(s) = \frac{1}{s(s+2-2i)(s+2+2i)} = \frac{C_1}{s} + \frac{C_2}{s+2-2i} + \frac{C_3}{s+2+2i}$$

Solving for C_1, C_2, and C_3 yields

$$Y(s) = \frac{1}{8s} - \frac{(1-i)}{16(s+2-2i)} - \frac{i+1}{16(s+2+2i)}$$

Applying an inverse Laplace transform to each term yields the following after considerable algebra and the use of several identities from trigonometry[1].

$$y(t) = \frac{1}{8}[1 - \sqrt{2}\, e^{-2t} \sin(2t+\phi)]$$

where $\phi = 45°$. This result corresponds to damped sinusoidal behavior which will be described in more detail later in this chapter.

4.4 Transfer Functions

In the previous section, Laplace transforms were used to solve linear dynamic equations based on specified inputs. In this section, Laplace transforms will be used to develop transfer functions that relate the output (or dependent variable) to the input of the system. Transfer functions have the advantage that they can be combined with wide variety of inputs to determine the output of the process. Moreover, the general form of the transfer function indicates the fundamental dynamic characteristics of the corresponding process. In general, a transfer function can be expressed for each input/output pair when applied to MIMO processes (Chapter 12).

A transfer function is defined as

$$G(s) = \frac{Y(s)}{U(s)} \tag{4.6}$$

where $Y(s)$ is the Laplace transform of the output variable and $U(s)$ is the Laplace transform of the input variable both written in **deviation variable** form. Deviation variables (i.e., $y'(t)$ and $u'(t)$) represent changes in a variable from nominal or initial conditions. That is,

$$y'(t) = y(t) - y_0$$
$$u'(t) = u(t) - u_0 \tag{4.7}$$

where y_0 and u_0 are constants.

Example 4.4   Derivation of a Transfer Function

Problem Statement Convert the differential equation in Example 4.1 into deviation variable form and determine the transfer function for the process.

Solution The first order equation is given by

$$\frac{dy}{dt} = \frac{1}{\tau}(y_{ss} - y)$$

where y and y_{ss} are equal to y_0 at time equal to zero. First write each variable (y - output variable and y_{ss} - input variable) in deviation variable form

$$y' = y - y_o$$
$$y'_{ss} = y_{ss} - y_o$$

Rearranging yields

$$y = y' + y_o$$
$$y_{ss} = y'_{ss} + y_o$$

Substituting these equations into the differential equation results in

$$\frac{dy'}{dt} = \frac{1}{\tau}(y'_{ss} - y')$$

Taking the Laplace transform of this equation using the initial conditions $y' = y'_{ss} = 0$ at $t = 0$ yields

$$sY(s) = \frac{1}{\tau}[Y_{ss}(s) - Y(s)]$$

Solving for $Y(s)$ yields

$$Y(s) = \frac{Y_{ss}(s)}{\tau s + 1}$$

Then the transfer function of this system is given by

$$G(s) = \frac{Y(s)}{Y_{ss}(s)} = \frac{1}{\tau s + 1}$$

Then if a step change in $Y_{ss}(s)$ of magnitude A is made,

$$Y(s) = \frac{A}{s(\tau s + 1)}$$

and $y(t)$ can be calculated by expanding in partial fractions and taking the inverse Laplace transform.

That is,
$$Y(s) = \frac{C_1}{s} + \frac{C_2}{\tau s + 1}$$

And
$$y'(t) = C_1 + C_2 e^{-t/\tau}$$

If a ramp input is used, $Y_{ss}(s) = 1/s^2$

$$Y(s) = \frac{1}{s^2(\tau s + 1)}$$

Thus, the transfer function can be used with a wide variety of inputs to determine the output behavior.

Consider the general form of a transfer function

$$G(s) = \frac{Q(s)}{P(s)} \qquad\qquad \textbf{4.8}$$

The roots of $P(s) = 0$ [i.e., the values of s that render $P(s) = 0$] are called the **poles of the transfer function.** Assume that $P(s)$ can be factorized into a series of real poles, p_i.

$$G(s) = \frac{Q(s)}{a(s - p_1)(s - p_2)....(s - p_n)} = \frac{Y(s)}{U(s)} \qquad\qquad \textbf{4.9}$$

Assume that a unit step input $(U(s) = 1/s)$ is applied to the process in question.

$$Y(s) = \frac{Q(s)}{a s(s - p_1)(s - p_2).......(s - p_n)} \qquad\qquad \textbf{4.10}$$

By partial fraction expansion, this transfer function can be written as

$$Y(s) = \frac{C_0}{s} + \frac{C_1}{s - p_1} + \frac{C_2}{s - p_2} + ... + \frac{C_n}{s - p_n} \qquad\qquad \textbf{4.11}$$

Taking the inverse Laplace transform yields

$$y'(t) = C_0 + C_1 e^{p_1 t} + C_2 e^{p_2 t} + ... + C_n e^{p_n t} \qquad\qquad \textbf{4.12}$$

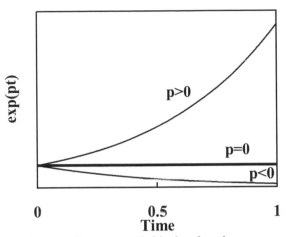

Figure 4.2 Different types of exponential behavior, i.e., exponential growth (p>0); constant value (p=0); and exponential decay (p<0).

Figure 4.2 shows the time behavior of $e^{p_i t}$ for positive and negative values of p_i. Note that positive values of p_i result in exponential growth with time and negative values of p_i result in exponential decay to zero.

Now assume that one of the factors of $P(s)$ is $(s^2 + p^2)$. After partial fraction expansion, a term with the following form results

$$\frac{C}{s^2 + p^2}$$

Note that the roots of this term are $s = i\,p$ and $s = -i\,p$. The inverse Laplace transform will yield

$$\frac{C}{p}\,\sin\,p\,t$$

which corresponds to sinusoidal behavior with an amplitude of C/p.

Now assume that one of the factors of $P(s)$ is $(s^2 + as + b)$. After partial fraction expansion, a term with the following form results

$$\frac{C}{s^2 + as + b}$$

Now factoring yields

$$\frac{C}{\left(s + \dfrac{a - \sqrt{a^2 - 4b}}{2}\right)\left(s + \dfrac{a + \sqrt{a^2 - 4b}}{2}\right)}$$

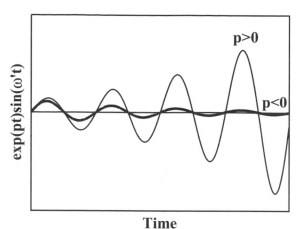

Figure 4.3 Exponentially growing ($p > 0$) and exponentially damped ($p < 0$) sinusoidal behavior.

If $a^2 - 4b > 0$, then real roots exist and the previous results for real roots apply.

If $a^2 - 4b = 0$, critically damped behavior (see Section 5.3) results and there are two real roots that are equal.

If $a^2 - 4b < 0$, the following results where $i\omega = \sqrt{a^2 - 4b}$

$$\frac{C}{\left(s + \dfrac{a - i\omega}{2}\right)\left(s + \dfrac{a + i\omega}{2}\right)}$$

This set of imaginary roots is called a complex conjugate pair. The inverse Laplace transform yields a term of the following form

$$C\, e^{pt} \sin \omega' t$$

Figure 4.3 shows the time behavior of this term for $p > 0$ and $p < 0$ which show exponentially growing sinusoidal behavior and damped sinusoidal behavior, respectively. Note that when $p < 0$, the larger the magnitude of p, the faster the sinusoidal response will damp out with time. Likewise, when $p > 0$, the larger the magnitude of p the faster the sinusoidal response will grow.

Figure 4.4 shows a plot of the poles in the complex plane which plots the real and imaginary components of each pole. Solid circles (●) represent exponential decay, solid triangles (▲) represent damped sinusoidal behavior, and solid squares (■) represent exponentially growing sinusoidal behavior. The poles represented by the solid circles correspond to real negative poles; therefore, these poles result in exponential decay (Figure 4.6a and Figure 4.6b). The poles represented by the solid

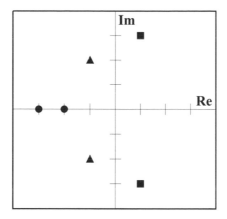

Figure 4.4 A complex plane with different types of poles: (●) exponential decay;   (▲) damped sinusoidal; and (■) unbounded sinusoidal growth. Im-Imaginary axis and Re- Real axis.

triangles have a negative real component with positive and negative imaginary components; therefore, these poles result in damped oscillatory behavior (Figure 4.6c and Figure 4.6d).   The poles represented by solid squares have a positive real component with positive and negative imaginary components; therefore, these poles result in oscillatory behavior that exponentially grows in amplitude (Figure 4.6e and Figure 4.6f). Note that poles in the right-half plane (i.e., the real component of the pole is positive) of this figure have exponential behavior that grows without bound as time increases which is referred to as **unstable behavior**. That is, a process is referred to as unstable when bounded input changes result in unbounded growth in the dependent variable. Also, poles corresponding to sinusoidal behavior appear as a pair of complex conjugate poles which are shown to be symmetric about the x-axis.   For complex conjugate poles, the larger the magnitude of the imaginary component (i.e., the further the pole is from the x-axis), the more oscillatory the dynamic response. These results show that **the poles of a transfer function [i.e., the roots of $P(s)$] indicate very specifically the type of dynamic behavior that the transfer function represents**. In other words, by simply determining the poles of a transfer function, one will automatically know the general dynamic behavior of the process that corresponds to that transfer function for a wide variety of inputs. Table 4.2 shows several different types of transfer functions and their corresponding dynamic behavior.   This table shows that the dynamic behavior of a process can be determined directly by examining the denominator of the transfer function of the process.

Consider the schematic of an actuator, process, and sensor in series shown in Figure 4.5 where $G_a(s)$ is the transfer function for the actuator, $G_p(s)$ is the transfer function for the process, and $G_s(s)$ is the transfer function for the sensor. By definition,

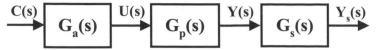

Figure 4.5 Schematic of a transfer function representation of an actuator/process/sensor system.

$$G_a(s) = \frac{U(s)}{C(s)}$$

$$G_p(s) = \frac{Y(s)}{U(s)}$$ **4.13**

$$G_s(s) = \frac{Y_s(s)}{Y(s)}$$

By substitution, the overall transfer function for the system, $G_{oa}(s)$, is given by

$$G_{oa}(s) = \frac{Y_s(s)}{C(s)} = G_a(s)\,G_p(s)\,G_s(s)$$ **4.14**

Table 4.2	
Different Types of Transfer Functions and their Corresponding Dynamic Behavior	
$G(s) = \dfrac{3}{s+1}$	Exponential decay of the form e^{-t}
$G(s) = \dfrac{3}{s-1}$	Unbounded exponential growth of the form e^t (i.e., unstable behavior)
$G(s) = \dfrac{3s+1}{(s+1)\,(s+3)}$	Exponential decay involving terms of the form e^{-t} and e^{-3t}
$G(s) = \dfrac{4}{(s+3i)\,(s-3i)}$	Sinusoidal behavior of the form $sin\ 3t$
$G(s) = \dfrac{2}{(s+1+2i)\,(s+1-2i)}$	Damped sinusoidal behavior of the form $e^{-t}\ sin\ 2t$
$G(s) = \dfrac{2}{(s-1+2i)\,(s-1-2i)}$	Exponentially growing sinusoidal behavior of the form $e^t\ sin\ 2t$ (i.e., unstable behavior)

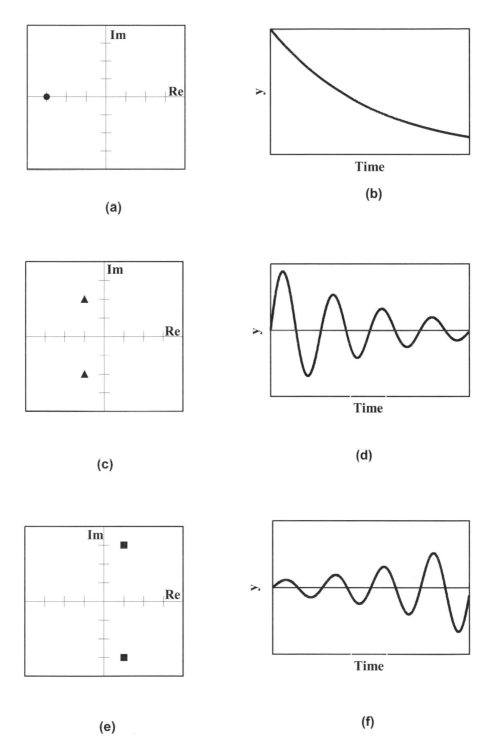

Figure 4.6 The correspondence between poles on a complex plane and dynamic behavior. (a) and (b) exponential decay; (c) and (d) damped sinusoidal behavior; (e) and (f) exponential growing sinusoidal behavior.

This indicates that the transfer function for a number of processes in series is simply the product of the transfer functions of each of the individual processes. This property of transfer functions in series is particularly useful when analyzing feedback systems.

Example 4.5 Transfer Function of an Actuator, Process, and Sensor System

Problem Statement. Determine the overall transfer function of an actuator, process and sensor for a first order process. Assume that the actuator and sensor also exhibit first order dynamics, i.e.,

$$G_a(s) = \frac{K_a}{\tau_a s + 1}$$

$$G_p(s) = \frac{K_p}{\tau_p s + 1}$$

$$G_s(s) = \frac{K_s}{\tau_s s + 1}$$

Solution. Substituting these transfer functions into Equation 4.14 yields

$$G_{oa}(s) = \frac{Y_s(s)}{C(s)} = \left(\frac{K_a}{\tau_a s + 1}\right)\left(\frac{K_p}{\tau_p s + 1}\right)\left(\frac{K_s}{\tau_s s + 1}\right) = \frac{K_a K_p K_s}{(\tau_a s + 1)(\tau_p s + 1)(\tau_s s + 1)}$$

Note that this result shows that the combined system of the actuator/process/sensor behaves as a third order process if the actuator, process, and the sensor each behave as a first order process (see Chapter 5).

4.5 Linearization of Nonlinear Differential Equations

The use of Laplace transforms to solve differential equations and to develop transfer functions is restricted to linear dynamic equations. But all real processes have some degree of nonlinearity. That is, changes in process gains and time constants represent examples of process nonlinearity. Moreover, a number of processes are inherently nonlinear: (a) temperature control of a reactor with reaction rates that are exponential functions of temperature, (b) composition control in a distillation column since there are upper and lower limits on product purity, and (c) neutralization of a acid with a base due to an s-shaped titration curve.

When the model equations of a process are nonlinear, the equations can be **linearized** about an operating point, thus converting the nonlinear equations into a form that allows the application of Laplace transforms. Consider a nonlinear dynamic equation,

$$\frac{dy}{dt} = f(y,u)$$

at $t = 0$, $y = y_0$ and $u = u_0$

where y is the output and u is the input variable. The linear approximation of $f(y,u)$ about (u_0,y_0) can be obtained by applying a Taylor series expansion[2] to this function truncating the second order and higher order terms.

$$\frac{dy}{dt} = f(y,u) \cong f(y_0,u_0) + (y-y_0)\frac{\partial f}{\partial y}\bigg|_{y_0,u_0} + (u-u_0)\frac{\partial f}{\partial u}\bigg|_{y_0,u_0} \qquad \textbf{4.15}$$

Converting to deviation variables results in

$$\frac{dy'}{dt} = y'\frac{\partial f}{\partial y}\bigg|_{y_0,u_0} + u'\frac{\partial f}{\partial u}\bigg|_{y_0,u_0} \qquad \textbf{4.16}$$

It should be pointed out that this approximation is accurate in the vicinity of (u_0,y_0). The more nonlinear the process, the smaller the region where Equation 4.16 is an accurate approximation. Conversely, the more linear the process, the larger the region where the linear approximation will be accurate. Taking the Laplace transform of each term in Equation 4.16 and rearranging yields the transfer function of the process at the operating point (u_0, y_0).

$$\frac{Y(s)}{U(s)} = \frac{\dfrac{\partial f}{\partial u}\bigg|_{y_0,u_0}}{s - \dfrac{\partial f}{\partial y}\bigg|_{y_0,u_0}} \qquad \textbf{4.17}$$

Example 4.6 Linearizing a CSTR Equation with Exponential Temperature Dependence

Problem Statement Develop a transfer function for the effect of Q on T for Equation 3.13 evaluated at $T=T_0$.

Solution In order to apply Equation 4.16, $\dfrac{\partial f}{\partial y}$ and $\dfrac{\partial f}{\partial u}$ must be calculated and evaluated at $T=T_0$.

$$\left.\frac{\partial f}{\partial T}\right|_{T=T_0} = \left[\frac{-F\,C_p + \dfrac{V_r\,\Delta H\,C_A\,k_0\,E}{R\,T_0^2}\exp\left(\dfrac{-E}{R\,T_0}\right)}{V_r\,\rho\,C_v}\right]$$

$$\frac{\partial f}{\partial Q} = \frac{1}{V_r\,\rho\,C_v}$$

Applying Equation 4.17 yields

$$G(s) = \frac{T(s)}{Q(s)} = \frac{\dfrac{1}{V_r\,\rho\,C_v}}{\left\{s - \left[\dfrac{-F\,C_p + \dfrac{V_r\,\Delta H\,C_A\,k_0\,E}{R\,T_0^2}\exp\left(\dfrac{-E}{R\,T_0}\right)}{V_r\,\rho\,C_v}\right]\right\}}$$

Note that this approximation shows that the pole of this transfer function is a strong function of T_0.

4.6 Summary

Laplace transforms are a convenient means for solving linear dynamic equations. The dynamic equation is transformed to the Laplace domain where the dependent variable can be solved for algebraically. Finally, the dependent variable in the Laplace domain is transformed back into the time domain yielding the time domain solution to the original dynamic equation.

Transfer functions are the ratio of the Laplace transform of the dependent variable to the Laplace transform of the input variable and can be derived from linear dynamic time domain equations by applying Laplace transforms once the dynamic equations have been expressed in deviation variable form. An advantage of transfer functions is that they can be combined with a wide variety of inputs to predict the dynamic behavior of the process. In addition, the roots of the denominator of a transfer function, i.e., the poles of the transfer function, directly indicate the dynamic behavior of the process.

4.7 Additional Terminology

Deviation variable - a variable that results from subtracting a nominal or constant value from the dependent variable.

Final-value theorem - An application of Laplace transforms that yields the long time behavior of a dependent variable.

Initial-value theorem - An application of Laplace transforms that yields the initial conditions of a dependent variable.

Linearization - developing a linear approximation of a nonlinear model.

Partial fractional expansion - expansion of a transfer function into a sum of terms each of which contains one of the factors of the denominator of the transfer function.

Poles of a transfer function - the roots of the equation $P(s) = 0$ where $P(s)$ is the denominator of the transfer function.

Unstable behavior - unlimited growth of a dependent variable for a bounded input.

4.8 References

1. Stephanopoulos, G., *Chemical Process Control*, McGraw-Hill, pp. 145-157 (1984)

2. Riggs, J.B., An Introduction to Numerical Methods for Chemical Engineers, Texas Tech University Press, p. 78 (1994).

4.9 Questions and Exercises

4.1 What is the definition of the Laplace transform of a function, $g(t)$?

4.2 Give an example of a nonlinear equation not given in the text.

4.3 Explain how Laplace transforms are used to analytically solve differential equations.

4.4 Determine $y(t)$ by applying partial fraction expansion for the following cases

a. $Y(s) = \dfrac{s+1}{(s+2)(s+3)}$ 　　　　　　b. $Y(s) = \dfrac{1}{(s+1)(s+2)}$

c. $Y(s) = \dfrac{s+3}{(s+1)^2}$ 　　　　　　　d. $Y(s) = \dfrac{s+2}{(s+1)(s+6)(s+7)}$

4.5 For each of the cases listed in Problem 4.4, indicate the value of $y(t)$ as $t \to \infty$ for a unit step input. Also, determine the initial conditions for the cases listed in Problem 4.4 and compare with the times solution results obtained for Problem 4.4.

4.6 Solve the following differential equation using Laplace transforms.

$$\frac{dy}{dt} = t^2 \qquad y(0) = 0$$

4.7 Determine $y(t)$ for each of the following differential equations assuming that

$$y(0) = \left(\frac{dy}{dt} \right)_{t=0} = 0$$

a. $\dfrac{d^2 y}{dt^2} + 5\dfrac{dy}{dt} + 6y = 2$ 　　　　　b. $\dfrac{d^2 y}{dt^2} + 3\dfrac{dy}{dt} = 5$

c. $\dfrac{d^2 y}{dt^2} + 4\dfrac{dy}{dt} - 5y = 4$ 　　　　　d. $\dfrac{d^2 y}{dt^2} + 4\dfrac{dy}{dt} + 4y = 1$

Also, indicate whether or not each of the solutions exhibits stable or unstable behavior.

4.8 For the following set of ODE's

$$\frac{dy_1}{dt} + 2y_1 + y_2 = 2 \qquad y_1(0) = 0$$

$$\frac{dy_2}{dt} + y_2 + y_1 = 0 \qquad y_2(0) = 0$$

a. Solve for Y_1(s) by eliminating Y_2(s). Then determine Y_2(s).

b. Solve for $y_1(t)$ and $y_2(t)$.

4.9 Describe what a transfer function is.

4.10 What are the poles of a transfer function and what are their significance?

4.11 Develop the transfer function for the effect of u on y for the following differential equation

$$\frac{d^2y}{dt^2}+5\frac{dy}{dt}+6y=u$$

4.12 Describe the dynamic behavior indicated by each of the following transfer functions.

a. $G(s)=\dfrac{2}{2s+1}$

b. $G(s)=\dfrac{3}{(s+1)(s+4)}$

c. $G(s)=\dfrac{1}{s^2+s+1}$

d. $G(s)=\dfrac{1}{s^2-s+1}$

4.13 For Problem 3.7, develop the transfer function for the effect of steam temperature changes on the actual temperature of the metal in the heat exchanger.

4.14 For Problem 3.5, develop the transfer function for the effect of inlet flow rate changes on the actual level in the tank. (Hint: Remember to linearize the equation before determining the transfer function.)

4.15 For Problem 3.10, develop the transfer function for the effect of the specified flow through the control valve on the measured pressure in the vessel.

4.16 For Problem 3.9, develop the transfer function for the effect of the specified heat duty to the still on the measured value of the ethyl alcohol in the product stream.

Chapter 5

Dynamic Behavior of Ideal Systems

5.1   Introduction

In the previous chapter, Laplace transform solutions and transfer functions were developed for several simple cases. In this chapter, the dynamic behavior of a variety of idealized systems is presented along with their corresponding transfer functions, e.g., a first order process, a second order process, an integrating process, etc. From this chapter, it should become clear that a full range of process behavior can be represented using these idealized representations. Moreover, even one type of idealized dynamic behavior can represent widely varying processes, e.g., a CST composition mixer, a CSTR with a first order reaction, flow through a control valve, temperature measurement from a thermocouple, and charge storage in a capacitor are all well represented with a simple first order dynamic model. Then for this example, the parameters of the first order dynamic model clearly indicate the dynamic behavior of the process, i.e., the speed of the response and the sensitivity of the process to changes in the input. In addition, it may also be necessary to combine two or more of these idealized elements in order to represent complex process dynamics, e.g., first order plus deadtime model or inverse acting behavior.

The material in this chapter is not directly applicable to the industrial practice of process control. The idealized models presented in this chapter are usually not used for process control applications (e.g., controller tuning). Even though an idealized model may accurately represent an industrial process, there are more direct means available for applying control loop analysis without developing process models. Idealized models are, however, critically important to the understanding of process dynamics and the terminology of the process control profession. For example, understanding second order dynamic behavior is important when tuning controllers. That is, underdamped or overdamped behavior, decay ratio, and settling time are important aspects of second order dynamic behavior as well as terms that are commonly used by process control engineers to describe controller performance.

5.2   Idealized Process Inputs

Process inputs include manipulated variables, measured disturbances, and unmeasured disturbances. Each of the input types considered here can be applied using a manipulated variable while only ramp and sinusoidal inputs are usually used to describe the effect of disturbances. By understanding how a process responds to one or more of these idealized inputs, one should be able to understand the general dynamic behavior of the process in question.

Impulse input. An impulse response has infinite height for an infinitesimal duration so that the area under the impulse is unity. An **impulse input** is shown graphically in Figure 5.1a. The Laplace transform of an impulse input at $t=0$ is (Table 4.1)

$$U(s) = 1 \qquad\qquad\qquad 5.1$$

Obviously, it is not possible to physically implement an impulse input. A rectangular pulse is a realistic means to approximate an impulse input.

Step input. One of the easiest input changes to implement is the **step change** which is a sudden and sustained change. A step change of magnitude A at $t=t_0$ can be represented as

$$\begin{aligned} u(t) &= 0 \qquad & t < t_0 \\ u(t) &= A \qquad & t \geq t_0 \end{aligned} \qquad 5.2$$

The Laplace transform for a step change of A when $t_0=0$ is given by (Table 4.1)

$$U(s) = \frac{A}{s} \qquad\qquad\qquad 5.3$$

An idealized step change is shown graphically in Figure 5.1b. In chemical process control, manipulated variables are normally flow rates; therefore, the actual flow rate will not change instantaneously due to valve dynamics and other factors. If the specified flow rate or the signal to the final control element is considered as the input to the process, virtually instantaneous step changes in inputs can be implemented on industrial processes.

Rectangular pulse. A **rectangular pulse** is similar to a step change except that the input is returned to its original value after a specified amount of time. Thus, a rectangular pulse can be considered to be a series of two step changes. A rectangular pulse is given by

$$\begin{aligned} u(t) &= 0 \qquad & t < t_0 \\ u(t) &= A \qquad & t_0 \leq t < t_0 + \Delta t \\ u(t) &= 0 \qquad & t \geq t_0 + \Delta t \end{aligned} \qquad 5.4$$

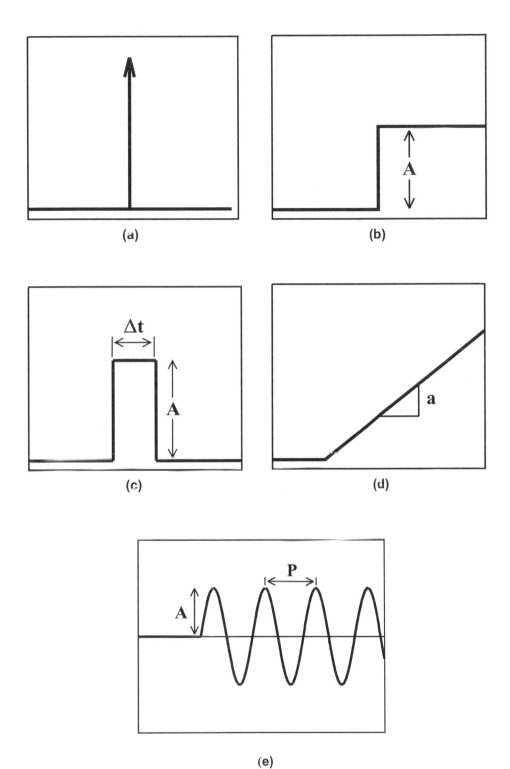

(e)

Figure 5.1 Idealized inputs (a) impulse (b) step (c) pulse (d) ramp (e) sinusoidal.

The rectangular pulse is said to have a strength of $A\Delta t$. Figure 5.1c graphically shows a rectangular pulse. The Laplace transform of a rectangular pulse is given by (Table 4.1)

$$U(s) = \frac{A}{s}[1 - e^{-\Delta t s}]$$ 5.5

when t_0 is equal to zero.

Ramp input. Certain types of disturbances can be reasonably represented as ramps. For example, air temperature or cooling water temperature can change steadily with a relatively constant slope during certain portions of the day. A **ramp input** is given by

$$u(t) = 0 \qquad t < t_0$$
$$u(t) = a t \qquad t \geq t_0$$ 5.6

and a ramp is illustrated in Figure 5.1d. The Laplace transform of a ramp input is given by (Table 4.1)

$$U(s) = \frac{a}{s^2}$$ 5.7

for t_0 equal to zero.

Sinusoidal inputs. The time scale over which inputs change can have an important effect on feedback control performance (see Chapter 8). For example, air temperature disturbances have a 24 hour period due to day-to-night variations. On the other hand, feed flow rate changes to a process can have a period of minutes or seconds. One way to evaluate the effect of different time scales for inputs is to use sinusoidal inputs with different frequencies since the frequency is directly related to the time scale of the input.

A **sinusoidal input** is given by

$$u(t) = 0 \qquad t < 0$$
$$u(t) = A \sin \omega t \qquad t \geq 0$$ 5.8

where ω is the frequency and A is the amplitude of the sinusoidal input. An example of a sinusoidal input is given in Figure 5.1e. Note that the period, P, is equal to $2\pi/\omega$. The Laplace transform for a sinusoidal input is (Table 4.1)

$$U(s) = \frac{A\omega}{s^2 + \omega^2}$$ 5.9

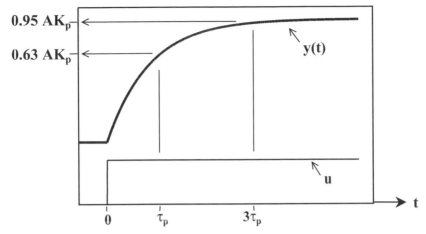

Figure 5.2 Dynamic response of a first order process to a step input change.

5.3   First Order Processes

A CST composition mixer, a CST thermal mixer, and an isothermal CSTR with a first order reaction are examples of **first order processes**. The differential equation for a first order process written in the standard form is given by

$$\tau_p \frac{dy(t)}{dt} + y(t) = K_p u(t) \qquad\qquad \textbf{5.10}$$

where y is the output variable, u is the input variable, K_p is the steady-state process gain, and τ_p is the process time constant. The process gain is the steady-state change in y divided by the corresponding change in u, i.e.,

$$K_p = \frac{\Delta y}{\Delta u}$$

The time constant for the CST thermal mixer and the CST composition mixer is the volume of liquid in the CST mixer divided by the total volumetric feed rate, i.e., the residence time of the CST mixer.

The transfer function for a first order process is given by

$$G_p(s) = \frac{K_p}{\tau_p s + 1} \qquad\qquad \textbf{5.11}$$

Note that the denominator of the transfer function contains s to the first power for a first order process. The thermal mixer can be seen to be a first order process since the differential equation [Equation 3.9] can be rearranged into the same form as Equation 5.10. Likewise, the transfer function of any first order process can be rearranged into

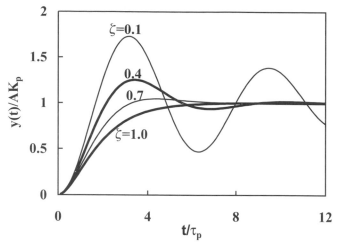

Figure 5.3 Dynamic response of an underdamped second order process (0.1<ζ<1.0).

the same form as Equation 5.11. In each case, the process gain and process time constant can be identified directly. Note that the standard form for a first order differential equation [Equation 5.10] requires that the coefficient of y be unity while the standard form for the transfer function of a first order process [Equation 5.11] requires that the constant term in the denominator be unity.

Figure 5.2 shows the response of a first order process (y) to a step change in u. The analytical solution of Equation 5.10 for a step change A in u is given by

$$y(t) = A K_p (1 - e^{-t/\tau_p}) \qquad\qquad\textbf{5.12}$$

The process gain, K_p, and the size of the step change, A, determine the new steady-state value of y. The time constant, τ_p, determines the dynamic path the process will take as it approaches the new steady-state, i.e., how long it will take to approach the new steady-state. Note that 63.2% of the final change occurs in one time constant after the input change. 95% of the change occurs in three time constants and 98% of the change occurs in four time constants.

5.4   Second Order Processes

Two first order processes in series or a first order process with a PI feedback controller behave as a **second order process**. The differential equation for a second order process written in the standard form is given by

$$\tau_p^2 \frac{d^2 y(t)}{dt^2} + 2\zeta\tau_p \frac{dy(t)}{dt} + y(t) = K_p u(t) \qquad\qquad\textbf{5.13}$$

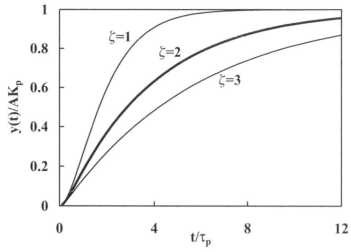

Figure 5.4 Dynamic response of an overdamped second order process ($\zeta > 1$).

where K_p is the steady-state process gain, τ_p is the time constant, and ζ is the **damping factor** which determines the general shape of the dynamic response. The transfer function for a second order process is given by

$$G_p(s) = \frac{K_p}{\tau_p^2 s^2 + 2\zeta\tau_p s + 1} \tag{5.14}$$

Note that the denominator of the transfer function of a second order process contains s^2 as the highest power of s. Similar to first order process, either the second order differential equation or the transfer function can be put into these standard forms in order to directly determine $K_p, \tau_p,$ and ζ. That is, in order to put the differential equation into the standard form corresponding to Equation 5.13, the coefficient of y is unity. Likewise, the standard form for the transfer function of a second order process requires that the constant term in the denominator be unity.

Figure 5.3 shows the response of a second order process to a step change in input, A, for several cases for which $\zeta < 1$ (**underdamped behavior**) as well as $\zeta = 1$ (**critically damped**). Figure 5.4 shows the step response for $\zeta = 1$ (critically damped) and $\zeta > 1$ (**overdamped behavior**). Note that the value of ζ determines the general shape of the dynamic behavior of a second order process, τ_p indicates the time scale of the response, and K_p determines the new steady-state value. In Chapter 4, it was shown that the poles of the transfer function determine the dynamic behavior of the process. In the case of a second order process, real distinct roots correspond to an overdamped system, two equal roots correspond to a critically damped system, and imaginary roots correspond to underdamped behavior. Figure 5.5 shows a typical underdamped response to a step input along with its key characteristics:

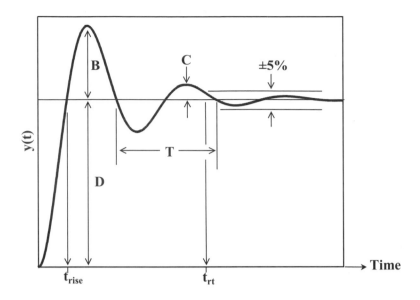

Figure 5.5 The key characteristics of an underdamped second order response.

   1. Rise time, t_{rise}, is the time required to first cross the new steady-state value and is given by the following analytical expression

$$t_{rise} = \tau_p \frac{\pi - \phi}{\sqrt{1 - \zeta^2}}$$

where

$$\phi = \tan^{-1}\left[\frac{\sqrt{1 - \zeta^2}}{\zeta}\right]$$

   2. Percentage overshoot is $B/D \times 100\%$. The analytical expression for percentage overshoot is

$$100 \exp\left\{\frac{-\pi \zeta}{\sqrt{1 - \zeta^2}}\right\} \qquad\qquad \textbf{5.15}$$

Therefore, one can estimate ζ by measuring the percentage overshoot and solving the previous equation for ζ.

   3. Decay ratio is C/B. The analytical expression for decay ratio is

$$\exp\left\{\frac{-2\pi \zeta}{\sqrt{1 - \zeta^2}}\right\} \qquad\qquad \textbf{5.16}$$

Likewise, one can estimate ζ by measuring the decay ratio and solving the previous equation for ζ.

    4. Period of oscillations, T, is the time for a complete cycle. The analytical expression for period of oscillation is

$$T = \frac{2\pi\tau_p}{\sqrt{1 - \zeta^2}}$$ **5.17**

    5. Response time, t_{rt}, (or **settling time**) is the time required for the response to remain within a $\pm 5\%$ band, based upon the steady-state change in y. That is, the $\pm 5\%$ band corresponds to $D \pm 0.05D$ for Figure 5.5. The above expressions are strictly valid only for second order processes.

    Decay ratio, percentage overshoot, settling time, and damping factor (ζ) can each be used as a basis for tuning. For example, a decay ratio of $\frac{1}{4}$ (i.e., quarter amplitude damping) is a common tuning criterion. Selecting a damping factor specifies the decay ratio and percentage overshoot for a second order process (Equations 5.15 and 5.16). Tuning based on minimum response time could also be used.

5.5   High Order Processes

    Staged separation devices, such as distillation and absorption columns, can be represented as a series of first order processes. For example, for a distillation column, each tray could be considered to be a first order process for contacting the vapor and the liquid. Since the overall transfer function for a process composed of a number of transfer functions in series is the product of each individual transfer function (Equation 4.14), the transfer function for a series of first order process with equal time constants is given by

$$G_p(s) = \frac{K_p}{\left(\tau_p s + 1\right)^n}$$ **5.18**

This represents an *n-th* order process since the largest power of s in the denominator is n. Figure 5.6 shows the response to a step input for an *n-th* order process for various values of n (i.e., $n = 3, 5, 15$). Note that as n becomes larger, the response becomes more **sluggish**, i.e., the slope of the response becomes smaller. For larger values of n, there is a period of time before a significant change in the output variable can be observed and this period of time (deadtime) increases as n increases. A first order plus deadtime (FOPDT) model can provide a good approximation of a high order system as will be shown later in this chapter. Also note that the response for $n=3$ is similar to the

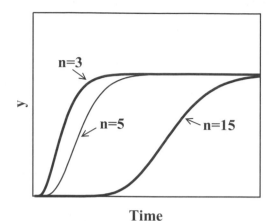

Figure 5.6 Dynamic response of three high order systems (n=3, 5, and 15).

open loop response of the CST thermal mixer which is also a third order linear process since the actuator, process, and sensor were each modeled as first order processes.

5.6 Integrating Processes

The most common type of **integrating process** is the level in a tank for which the outflow and inflow are set independently of the level. The differential equation describing the dynamic behavior of a level in a tank is given by

$$\rho A_c \frac{dL}{dt} = F_{in} - F_{out} \qquad \qquad \textbf{5.19}$$

where A_c is the cross-sectional area of the tank, L is the height of liquid level in the tank, ρ is the density of the feed and product, F_{in} is the mass flow rate into the tank, and F_{out}

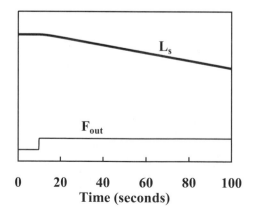

Figure 5.7 Dynamic response of an integrating process to a step input change.

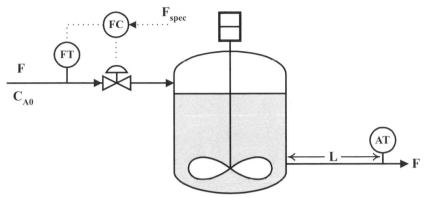

Figure 5.8 Schematic of a CSTR with transport delay.

is the flow rate out of the tank. Assuming the inflow, F_{in}, is constant, the transfer function for this process is

$$G_p(s) = \frac{L(s)}{F_{out}(s)} = \frac{-1}{\rho A_c s}$$ **5.20**

The s factor in the denominator of the transfer function indicates that this process is integrating in behavior. Using the final value theorem (Equation 4.4), one can easily determine that this process is non-self regulating. Figure 5.7 shows the response of an integrating process to a step change in F_{out}.

5.7 Deadtime

Deadtime or **transport delay** can result by plug flow transport through a pipe or by transport of solids by a conveyor belt. Figure 5.8 shows a CSTR that has a product line attached to it. It is assumed that the product flows by plug flow a length, L, at which point an on-line analyzer measures the product composition. The time, θ, that it takes the reaction mixture to flow by plug flow from the CSTR to the analyzer is

$$\theta = \frac{\rho L A_c}{F}$$ **5.21**

where A_c is the cross-sectional area of the product line, ρ is the density of the fluid, and F is the mass flow rate of the product through the product line. If the composition measurement is fast compared to θ, the measured composition, $C_s(t)$, will have been the reactor composition, $C(t)$, θ time units before, i.e.,

$$C_s(t) = C(t - \theta)$$ **5.22**

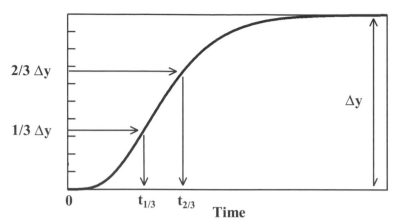

Figure 5.9 Graphical representation of an approach for determining the parameters of a FOPDT model.

where θ is the deadtime or transport delay for this process. The transfer function for deadtime is (Table 4.1)

$$G_p(s) = e^{-\theta s} \qquad\qquad \textbf{5.23}$$

Gas chromatographs (GC's) exhibit **analyzer deadtime** or **delay**. That is, the sample enters the GC and must flow through the separation column before the analysis is complete. The analyzer delay for a dedicated GC typically ranges between 3 to 10 minutes.

Process deadtime and/or analyzer deadtime can have a significant effect on feedback controller tuning and control performance when the deadtime is significant compared to the time constant of the process. For example, a five minute analyzer delay does not significantly affect feedback control performance for a large distillation column that has a time constant of three hours for composition dynamics. On the other hand, a five minute analyzer delay would dramatically affect a column with a time constant of five minutes for its composition dynamics.

Deadtime is usually combined with other models to take into account the effect of process and analyzer deadtime as well as the initial response of a highly overdamped process (e.g., a FOPDT model or an integrator plus deadtime).

5.8 First Order Plus Deadtime (FOPDT) Model

A **FOPDT** model is the combination of a first order model with deadtime:

$$G_p(s) = \frac{K_p\, e^{-\theta_p s}}{\tau_p s + 1} \qquad\qquad \textbf{5.24}$$

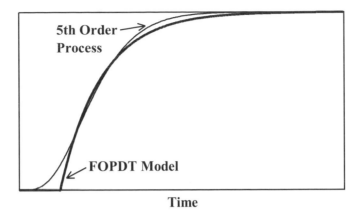

Figure 5.10 Comparison between a FOPDT model and an overdamped 5th order process.

A step test can be conveniently used to develop a FOPDT model. Figure 5.9 shows one such approach. First, identify the resulting change in y (i.e., Δy) and the step change in the input, Δu. Then from the step response, identify the time required for one-third of the total change in y to occur, $t_{1/3}$. Next, identify the time required for two-thirds of the total change in y to occur, $t_{2/3}$. Then the following estimates can be used.

$$\tau_p = \frac{t_{2/3} - t_{1/3}}{0.7}$$
$$\theta_p = t_{1/3} - 0.4\tau_p \qquad\qquad \textbf{5.25}$$
$$K_p = \frac{\Delta y}{\Delta u}$$

Note that $t_{1/3}$ and $t_{2/3}$ are based upon assuming that time is equal to zero when the step change in u is implemented. This modeling approach is particularly well suited for modeling high order processes. Figure 5.10 shows a fifth order process and a FOPDT model that was selected to match this high order process. There is slight mismatch initially between the FOPDT model and the high order process model, but overall the FOPDT model provides a good approximation for overdamped process behavior; therefore, the FOPDT model is one of the best idealized models to represent industrial processes.

5.9 Inverse Acting Processes

An **inverse acting process** can occur when opposing factors are acting within a process: one that is faster responding but with less steady-state gain than the other, i.e.,

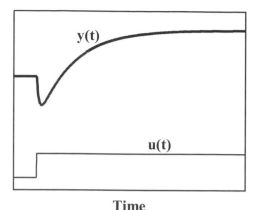

Figure 5.11 Dynamic response of an inverse acting process to step input change.

$$G_p(s) = \frac{K_p}{\tau_p s + 1} - \frac{K'_p}{\tau'_p s + 1} \qquad\qquad \textbf{5.26}$$

where $|K'_p| < |K_p|$ and $\tau'_p < \tau_p$. The response of an inverse acting process to a step change input is shown in Figure 5.11. For a short time the second term is controlling, but as time proceeds, the first term dominates the response.

Consider a mercury in glass thermometer initially at ambient temperature that is submersed in hot water. The glass can be viewed as a container for the mercury. The height of the mercury column is used to measure temperature. After the thermometer is put into the hot water, the temperature of the glass around the mercury column will increase before the temperature of the mercury. Since glass expands when heated, the inside diameter of glass container will increase slightly causing the height of the mercury column to decrease slightly. Soon after this decrease in the height of the mercury column, the temperature of the mercury will begin to rise causing the overall height of the mercury column to increase sharply. The effect of the expansion of the glass on the measured temperature is the low gain, small time constant effect while the expansion of the mercury column due to a temperature increase is the high gain, slower responding process which together result in inverse action.

Certain types of reboilers can exhibit inverse acting behavior for a step change in the steam flow rate to the reboiler[1]. An increase in steam flow to the reboiler causes the number and volume of bubbles produced on the shell side of the reboiler to immediately increase. This "swell" effect can cause the measured level to show an initial increase after a steam rate increase. Of course, since the reboiler duty is increased, the vapor boilup rate will increase which will eventually result in a decrease in the level in the reboiler. The swell is the low gain, quick responding behavior that yields inverse action while the increase in vapor rate from the reboiler is the high gain, slow responding behavior. When heat addition rate to the reboiler is used to control level in a reboiler that exhibits significant inverse action, a much more challenging

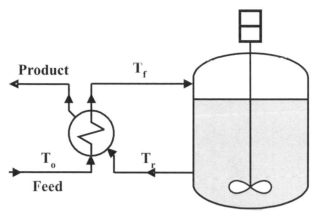

Figure 5.12 Schematic of an exothermic CSTR with heat integration.

control problem is encountered than is usually observed for conventional level control systems.

5.10 Recycle Processes

Recycle processes are used industrially to recover unreacted reactants and recycle them to the reactor as feed in order to increase overall conversion and to recycle heat within a process and thus reduce overall energy usage. Even though processes with recycle can have quite significant economic advantages compared to the corresponding process without recycle, the process control problems associated with recycle processes can be much more challenging. Recycling (also termed **process integration**) can have a dominant effect on the overall process dynamics and resulting control performance.

Figure 5.12 shows a schematic for an exothermic CSTR for which the product stream is used to preheat the feed to the reactor[2]. The temperature of the feed entering the reactor is T_f which is given by

$$T_f(s) = T_o(s) + \Delta T_f(s) \qquad\qquad 5.27$$

where $\Delta T_f(s)$ represents the temperature difference that the feed receives when passing through the heat exchanger. Note that each term in Equation 5.27 is written in deviation variable form since transfer functions are used. Heat transfer to the feed depends on the temperature of the reactor, T_r. Using a transfer function model of the heat exchanger yields

$$\Delta T_f(s) = T_r(s)\, G_H(s) \qquad\qquad 5.28$$

Likewise, the temperature of the reactor, T_r, is a function of the feed temperature to the reactor, T_f, which can be expressed using a transfer function, $G_R(s)$, as

$$T_r(s) = T_f(s) G_R(s) \qquad\qquad \textbf{5.29}$$

Substituting Equation 5.27 into Equation 5.29 and rearranging results in

$$T_r(s) = G_R(s) [T_o(s) + \Delta T_f(s)] \qquad\qquad \textbf{5.30}$$

Then Equation 5.28 is used to eliminate $\Delta T_f(s)$ from Equation 5.30.

$$T_r(s) = G_R(s) [T_o(s) + G_H(s) T_r(s)] \qquad\qquad \textbf{5.31}$$

The overall transfer function, $G_{oa}(s)$, for this process becomes

$$G_{oa}(s) = \frac{T_r(s)}{T_o(s)} = \frac{G_R(s)}{1 - G_R(s) G_H(s)} \qquad\qquad \textbf{5.32}$$

Assuming the following forms for $G_R(s)$ and $G_H(s)$

$$G_R(s) = \frac{K_R}{\tau_R s + 1}$$
$$G_H(s) = K_H$$

results in the following after rearranging into the standard form for a first order process

$$G_{oa}(s) = \frac{\dfrac{K_R}{1 - K_H K_R}}{\dfrac{\tau_R}{1 - K_H K_R} s + 1} \qquad\qquad \textbf{5.33}$$

Assuming the following numerical values

$$K_H = 0.5$$
$$K_R = 1.9$$
$$\tau_R = 1.0$$

yields

$$G_R(s) = \frac{1.9}{s + 1} \qquad \text{(without heat integration)} \qquad \textbf{5.34}$$

$$G_{oa}(s) = \frac{38}{20 s + 1} \qquad \text{(with heat integration)} \qquad \textbf{5.35}$$

Note that the gain and the time constant have both increased by a factor of 20 for the system with recycle. This is an extreme example, but one can easily see that material recycle and/or heat integration tends to increase the process gain while making the process slower responding.

5.11 Summary

The dynamic behavior of real processes can be described using idealized dynamic models. In this chapter, the dynamic behavior of first order processes, second order processes, high order processes, integrating processes, processes with deadtime, FOPDT processes, inverse acting processes, and recycle processes were considered.

5.12 Additional Terminology

Critically damped - $\zeta=1$ which corresponds to the transition point between overdamped and underdamped behavior.

Damping factor (ζ) - the characteristic of a second order process that determines the general shape of the dynamic response.

Deadtime - the time between when an input change is made and when the process output begins to change.

Decay ratio - the ratio of the successive peaks for a second order underdamped response.

First order process - a process with a transfer function that has the highest power of s in the denominator of unity.

FOPDT model - A first order plus deadtime model.

Impulse input - an input with an infinite height and with an infinitesimal duration.

Integrating process - a process that accumulates or depletes mass or energy.

Inverse acting process - a process that has two competing factors: one that is faster responding but with less steady-state gain than the other.

K_p - steady-state process gain ($\Delta y/\Delta u$).

Overdamped process - A second order or higher process which does not exhibit oscillatory behavior.

Percentage overshoot - the magnitude of the overshoot divided by the steady-state change times 100.

Period of oscillation - the time required for a complete cycle for a second order process.

Process integration - a term for using mass and energy recycle to make a process more economically efficient.

Ramp input - an input that increases or decreases at a constant rate.

Rectangular pulse - a step increase followed after a time by a step decrease that returns the input to its original value.

Recycle process - a process that recovers mass or energy from the process before they leave the process.

Response time - the time after a step change for the process to settle to within ± 5% of the steady-state change.

Rise time - the time after a step input change for an underdamped response to cross the ultimate steady-state condition for the first time.

Second order process - a process with a transfer function that has the highest power of *s* in the denominator equal to two.

Settling time - the time after a step change for the process to settle to within ±5% of the steady-state change.

Sinusoidal input - a process input that has a sine wave shape.

Sluggish - behavior of a process for which the output variable is slow to respond to input changes.

Step change - a sudden and sustained change.

Transport delay - the time for material to move one point in the process to another.

Underdamped process - a second order or higher order process which exhibits oscillatory behavior.

τ_p - process time constant, i.e., determines the speed of dynamic response.

θ_p - process deadtime.

5.13 References

1. Munsif, HP and Riggs, J.B. "An Analysis of Inverse Acting Column Levels", *Ind & Eng Chem Res,* Vol. 35, p. 2640 (1996).

2. Marlin, T.E., Process Control, McGraw-Hill, pp. 173-176 (1995).

5.14 Questions and Exercises

5.1 Why are rectangular pulse inputs more feasible to apply to industrial processes than impulse inputs?

5.2 What are the characteristics of a first order process subjected to a step input change?

5.3 Consider the following first order transfer function. What characteristics of the process can you identify from this transfer function?

$$G_p(s) = \frac{16}{456s + 100}$$

5.4 A one-dimensional model of a thermocouple yields the following differential equation

$$MC_p \frac{dT_s}{dt} = Ah(T_p - T_s)$$

where M is the mass of the thermocouple per length (1g/cm), C_p is the heat capacity of the thermocouple (0.1 cal/g-°C), T_s is the temperature of the thermocouple, A is the surface area per length (4 cm²/cm), h is the heat transfer coefficient between the thermocouple and the process fluid (25 cal/cm²-h-°C), and T_p is the temperature of the process fluid. Calculate the time constant in seconds for this thermocouple system based on this one-dimensional model.

5.5 Using the approach given in Problem 3.7, estimate the time constant for changing the temperature of the metal of a heat exchanger. Assume that the tubes are ½ inch schedule 40 copper tubes. Also, use "ballpark" values for the heat transfer coefficients for a liquid water/liquid water heat exchanger.

5.6 What is the difference between an underdamped response with ζ=0.1 and with ζ=0.5 ?

5.7 What is the difference between an overdamped response with ζ=2 and ζ=6 ?

5.8 Tuning controllers so that the resulting dynamic response has a decay ratio of 1/4 is a common tuning criterion. Assuming a second order response for the feedback system, what value of ζ corresponds to a decay ratio of 1/4 ?

5.9 Consider the following transfer function. Indicate as many characteristics of the process corresponding to this transfer function as possible

$$G_p(s) = \frac{323\, e^{-3s}}{4s^2 + 16s + 4}$$

5.10 Consider the following differential equation

$$\frac{d^2 y}{dt^2} + K \frac{dy}{dt} + 1 = u$$

Discuss the dynamic behavior of this system for $-5 \le K \le 5$.

5.11 Consider the CST thermal mixing process presented in Section 3.5. Assume that the effluent from the mixer goes to a mixing tank with the same volume as the first. Determine the dynamic behavior of the overall process.

5.12 What characteristic behavior does a high order process exhibit?

5.13 Consider four CSTR's in series. If there is a single irreversible first order reaction occurring in each reactor, what will be the dynamic response of the process?

5.14 What is the difference between analyzer delay and transport delay? How are they similar?

5.15 Consider the following set of input/output data

Time	Input	Output	Time	Input	Output
0	0	1.0	7	1	1.6
1	0	1.0	8	1	1.8
2	1	1.0	9	1	1.9
3	1	1.05	10	1	1.95
4	1	1.1	11	1	2.0
5	1	1.2	12	1	2.0
6	1	1.4			

Develop a FOPDT model for this input/output system and plot your approximation against the data.

5.16 In Section 1.3, it was stated "As a rule of thumb, one can assume that it takes approximately four time constants to observe the full effect of a step change of an input to a process under open loop conditions". Evaluate this statement using a FOPDT model.

5.17 What causes inverse action?

5.18 Consider the following set of input/output data. Develop a transfer function model based on this data.

Time	Input	Output	Time	Input	Output
0	0	1.0	7	1	1.2
1	0	1.0	8	1	1.3
2	1	1.0	9	1	1.4
3	1	1.0	10	1	1.5
4	1	1.0	11	1	1.6
5	1	1.0	12	1	1.7
6	1	1.1			

PART III

PID CONTROL

Chapter 6

PID Control

6.1 Introduction

Feedback control compares the measured value of the controlled variable with its setpoint and makes adjustments to the manipulated variable in an effort to drive the controlled variable to its setpoint. For the everyday examples of feedback control cited in Chapter 1 (i.e., the shower, bathtub, and driving a car) a human serves as the feedback controller. In the CPI, the **Proportional-Integral-Derivative (PID) controller** is the most common controller used and is used almost exclusively for flow control loops, pressure control loops, and level control loops, as well as many composition and temperature control loops. Operators also serve as controllers for certain loops, e.g., a composition loop based upon laboratory composition analysis once each eight hour shift. This chapter is concerned with the forms, characteristics, and types of PID controllers.

PID controllers came into use in CPI in the 1930's in the form of pneumatic controllers. Today PID controllers are implemented in DCS's while some older installations still use analog electrical controllers. The digital controllers in a DCS are less expensive per control loop than analog controllers for large installations with many control loops and they are much more reliable due to the redundancy and distributed nature of the DCS. In addition, many of the clever controller designs associated with analog devices became trivial in the digital world of a DCS.

PID controllers are simple to implement and are extremely flexible as evidenced by the fact that PID controllers have been applied to almost any conceivable process ranging from refineries to spacecraft to electronic devices to power plants. The PID algorithm is quite computationally efficient as you will see later in this chapter and much of the flexibility of a PID controller comes from the unique characteristics of proportional, integral, and derivative action.

6.2 Closed Loop Transfer Function

The transfer function for a feedback control loop will be derived in this section and it will be used later to determine the fundamental characteristics of proportional

145

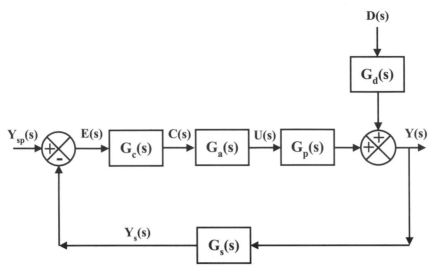

Figure 6.1 Block diagram of a general feedback control loop.

action, integral action, and derivative action as well as to examine the stability properties of a feedback loop. Consider the schematic for a feedback loop shown in Figure 6.1 where $G_c(s)$, $G_a(s)$, $G_p(s)$, $G_d(s)$, and $G_s(s)$ are the transfer functions for the controller, the actuator, the process as affected by the manipulated variable, the process as affected by the disturbance, and the sensor, respectively. Applying the properties of transfer functions and summation blocks ($\otimes$), the following relationships can be formulated:

(Process) $Y(s) = G_p(s)\, U(s) + G_d(s)\, D(s)$ **6.1**

(Actuator) $U(s) = G_a(s)\, C(s)$ **6.2**

(Controller) $C(s) = G_c(s)\, E(s)$ **6.3**

(Summation) $E(s) = Y_{sp}(s) - Y_s(s)$ **6.4**

(Sensor) $Y_s(s) = G_s(s)\, Y(s)$ **6.5**

First, substitute Equation 6.2 into Equation 6.1 to eliminate $U(s)$ resulting in

$$Y(s) = G_d(s)D(s) + G_p(s)G_a(s)C(s)$$

Next, substitute Equation 6.3 into this equation to eliminate $C(s)$ yielding

$$Y(s) = G_d(s)D(s) + G_p(s)\, G_a(s)G_c(s)E(s)$$

Then Equation 6.4 is substituted into this equation thus eliminating $E(s)$ resulting in the following expression

$$Y(s) = G_d(s)D(s) + G_p(s)\, G_a(s)G_c(s)[Y_{sp}(s) - Y_s(s)]$$

Finally, Equation 6.5 is substituted into the above equation and eliminating $Y_s(s)$

$$Y(s) = G_d(s)D(s) + G_p(s)\, G_a(s)G_c(s)[Y_{sp}(s) - G_s(s)Y(s)]$$

Collecting terms and solving for $Y(s)$ results in

$$Y(s) = \frac{G_d(s)D(s) + G_p(s)\, G_a(s)\, G_c(s)\, Y_{sp}(s)}{G_p(s)\, G_a(s)\, G_c(s)\, G_s(s) + 1} \qquad \textbf{6.6}$$

If $D(s)$ is zero (i.e., no change in the disturbance level is occurring), the closed loop transfer function for **setpoint tracking,** which is controlling for setpoint changes, is given by

$$\frac{Y(s)}{Y_{sp}(s)} = \frac{G_p(s)\, G_a(s)\, G_c(s)}{G_p(s)\, G_a(s)\, G_c(s)\, G_s(s) + 1} \qquad \textbf{6.7}$$

Setpoint tracking is also referred to as **servo control**.

If $Y_{sp}(s)$ is zero (i.e., a fixed setpoint is being applied), the closed loop transfer function for **disturbance rejection**, which is controlling to a fixed setpoint in the face of disturbance upsets, is given by

$$\frac{Y(s)}{D(s)} = \frac{G_d(s)}{G_p(s)\, G_a(s)\, G_c(s)\, G_s(s) + 1} \qquad \textbf{6.8}$$

Controlling for disturbance rejection is also called **regulatory control**.

Note that the denominator of the closed loop transfer function for setpoint tracking and disturbance rejection is the same. If the denominator of the closed loop transfer function is set equal to zero, the following equation results

$$G_p(s)\, G_a(s)\, G_c(s)\, G_s(s) + 1 = 0$$

which is called the **characteristic equation** of the feedback loop. The roots of the characteristic equation are the poles of the feedback process, and therefore, determine the dynamic behavior of the closed loop process. For example, if all the roots of the characteristic equation are real negative values, the closed loop dynamic behavior is overdamped. Further, if there are imaginary roots, oscillatory closed loop behavior will result. Finally, if any of the roots have positive real parts, the closed loop system will be unstable.

6.3 PID Algorithm

The ISA [Instrument Society of America] standard for the PID algorithm in the **position form** is given as

$$c(t) = c_0 + K_c \left[e(t) + \frac{1}{\tau_I} \int_0^t e(t)\,dt + \tau_D \frac{d\,e(t)}{dt} \right] \qquad \textbf{6.9}$$

where $K_c, \tau_I,$ and τ_D are the user selected tuning parameters, $c(t)$ is the output from the controller and $e(t)$ is $[y_{sp} - y_s(t)]$. **Note that c_0 is the value of the controller output when the controller is turned on**. Also, note that K_c is the controller gain and should not be confused with the process gain K_p. K_p has units of $\Delta y_s / \Delta c$ when the actuator, process, and sensor are lumped together while K_c has units corresponding to $\Delta c / \Delta y_s$. Equation 6.9 is written in a form corresponding to a direct acting controller. Equation 6.10 lists the position form for a reverse acting controller.

$$c(t) = c_0 - K_c \left[e(t) + \frac{1}{\tau_I} \int_0^t e(t)\,dt + \tau_D \frac{d\,e(t)}{dt} \right] \qquad \textbf{6.10}$$

The decision between using a direct acting controller (Equation 6.9) or a reverse acting controller (Equation 6.10) depends on the sign of the process gain and whether or not a direct or reverse acting final control element is used. Consider a heat exchanger in which the steam flow rate to the heat exchanger is manipulated in order to control the temperature of the process stream leaving the heat exchanger. Since an increase in steam flow to the heat exchanger results in an increase in the outlet temperature of the process stream, the process gain of this system is positive. Also, consider a direct acting final control element on the steam which causes an increase in steam flow rate when the signal to the final control element is increased. Further, consider the case in which the measured outlet temperature is below its setpoint [i.e., $e(t)$ is positive]. Since it is desired to move the controlled variable toward its setpoint, the steam flow rate to the heat exchanger should be increased; therefore, from an examination of Equations 6.9 and 6.10, it is clear that a direct acting controller (Equation 6.9) should be used. On the other hand, if the direct acting final control element were replaced with a reverse acting final control element, a decrease in the signal to the final control element would be required; therefore, a reverse acting controller (Equation 6.10) would be required. Remember that the choice between a reverse and direct acting final control element usually depends upon whether the final control element should fail open or closed when instrument air pressure is lost.

Now consider a heat exchanger in which the cooling water flow rate to the heat exchanger is manipulated to control the temperature of the process stream leaving the heat exchanger. Since an increase in cooling water flow rate to the heat exchanger results in a decrease in the controlled variable for this process, the process gain is negative. Also, consider a direct acting final control element. Similar to the previous example, consider the case in which the controlled variable is below its setpoint. Under these conditions, a decrease in cooling water flow rate would be required; therefore, a reverse acting controller should be used. Finally, if a reverse acting final control element was substituted for the direct acting final control element, a direct acting controller should be used. Table 6.1 summarizes these results. Obviously, these different combinations of positive and negative process gains and reverse and direct acting final control elements can each occur in the implementation of process control in industry. As a result, the process control engineer needs a way to conveniently choose a direct acting or a reverse acting controller. On a DCS, when a control loop is set up, there is typically a box to check in order to select a direct or reverse acting controller. For analog controllers, there is a switch on the back of the controller that allows the user to select the proper form for the controller, direct acting or reverse acting.

Table 6.1		
Guidelines for Selecting Direct and Reverse Acting Controllers		
Process Gain	**Direct Acting Actuator**	**Reverse Acting Actuator**
Positive	Direct Acting PID	Reverse Acting PID
Negative	Reverse Acting PID	Direct Acting PID

Another way to represent the controller gain is the **proportional band** (**PB**) which is an approach that was in more frequent use 10 to 15 years ago. PB can be expressed in terms of K_c when K_c is expressed in dimensionless form. For example, the controller output and the error from setpoint can be scaled 0-100% yielding a dimensionless K_c.

$$PB = \frac{100\%}{K_c}$$

As a result, the proportional band is small when the controller gain is large and PB is large when K_c is small. Also note that PB is expressed as a percentage.

When a setpoint change is made using the forms given by Equations 6.9 and 6.10, a spike in the calculated value of $de(t)/dt$ will occur causing a spike in $c(t)$. This behavior is called **derivative kick** and can be eliminated by replacing $de(t)/dt$ with $-dy_s(t)/dt$ yielding

$$c(t) = c_0 + K_c \left[e(t) + \frac{1}{\tau_I} \int_0^t e(t)\,dt - \tau_D \frac{d\,y_s(t)}{dt} \right] \qquad \textbf{6.11}$$

for a direct acting controller. The **derivative-on-measurement** form of the PID algorithm is recommended because it is not susceptible to derivative kick.

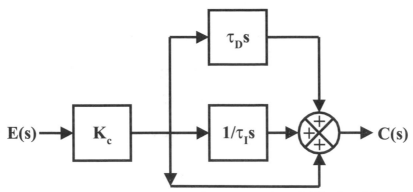

Figure 6.2 Block diagram of a conventional PID algorithm.

The transfer function for a PID controller is given by

$$G_c(s) = \frac{C(s)}{E(s)} = K_c\left[1 + \frac{1}{\tau_I s} + \tau_D s\right]$$ **6.12**

A block diagram for the PID algorithm is shown in Figure 6.2 which assumes that the derivative is taken on the error from setpoint. Note that proportional, integral, and derivative action act in parallel with each other.

Other commonly used forms of the PID algorithm are the proportional-integral (PI) and proportional-only (P-only) controllers. The PI controller results from setting τ_D equal to zero.

$$\text{PI-controller:} \quad c(t) = c_0 + K_c\left[e(t) + \frac{1}{\tau_I}\int_0^t e(t)\,dt\right]$$ **6.13**

The P-only controller has neither derivative nor integral action.

$$\text{P-only:} \qquad c(t) = c_0 + K_c\,e(t)$$ **6.14**

Equation 6.11 is applied within a DCS by implementing it in a digital form by using the following approximations

$$\int_0^t e(t)\,dt \approx \sum_{i=1}^n e(i\Delta t)\,\Delta t$$

where n is equal to $t / \Delta t$ and

$$\frac{d\,y_s(t)}{dt} \approx \frac{y_s(t) - y_s(t - \Delta t)}{\Delta t}$$

where Δt is the time interval between applications of the PID algorithm, i.e., the **control interval**. These approximations result in the digital version of the position form of the PID controller.

$$c(t) = c_0 + K_c \left[e(t) + \frac{\Delta t}{\tau_I} \sum_{i=1}^{n} e(i \cdot \Delta t) - \tau_D \left[\frac{y_s(t) - y_s(t - \Delta t)}{\Delta t} \right] \right] \qquad \textbf{6.15}$$

The PID algorithm can be also applied in the **velocity form**. Applying Equation 6.15 at $t - \Delta t$ results in the following equation

$$c(t - \Delta t) = c_0 + K_c \left[e(t - \Delta t) + \frac{\Delta t}{\tau_I} \sum_{i=1}^{n-1} e(i \cdot \Delta t) - \tau_D \left[\frac{y_s(t - \Delta t) - y_s(t - 2\Delta t)}{\Delta t} \right] \right]$$

$$\textbf{6.16}$$

Subtracting Equation 6.16 from Equation 6.15 results in the velocity form of the PID algorithm.

$$\Delta c(t) = K_c \left[e(t) - e(t - \Delta t) + \frac{\Delta t}{\tau_I} e(t) - \tau_D \left[\frac{y_s(t) - 2y_s(t - \Delta t) + y_s(t - 2\Delta t)}{\Delta t} \right] \right]$$

$$\textbf{6.17}$$

and then
$$c(t) = c(t - \Delta t) + \Delta c(t) \qquad \textbf{6.18}$$

Note that Equation 6.18 is written as a direct acting controller. A reverse acting controller would subtract $\Delta c(t)$ from $c(t-\Delta t)$. The velocity form for the derivative on the error from setpoint is given by

$$\Delta c(t) = K_c \left(e(t) - e(t - \Delta t) + \frac{\Delta t}{\tau_I} e(t) + \tau_D \left[\frac{e(t) - 2e(t - \Delta t) + e(t - 2\Delta t)}{\Delta t} \right] \right) \qquad \textbf{6.19}$$

Another popular version of the velocity form of the PID can be developed by eliminating proportional action for setpoint changes. Noticing that the proportional part of Equation 6.17 is simply the difference between $y(t)$ and $y(t-\Delta t)$ when the setpoint remains unchanged leads one to replace the difference between errors from setpoint with the difference between measured values of the controlled variable in the velocity form of the PID controller, i.e.,

$$\Delta c(t) = K_c \left[y_s(t - \Delta t) - y_s(t) + \frac{\Delta t}{\tau_I} e(t) - \tau_D \left[\frac{y_s(t) - 2y_s(t - \Delta t) + y_s(t - 2\Delta t)}{\Delta t} \right] \right]$$

$$\textbf{6.20}$$

The advantage of this form of the PID controller is that it will not act as abruptly to

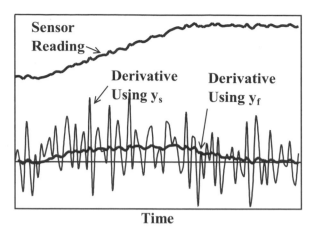

Figure 6.3 The instantaneous and filtered value for the derivative of a noisy sensor reading.

setpoint changes as Equation 6.17. In fact, from Equation 6.20 it can be seen that only the integral action will move the process toward a new setpoint. This reduction in aggressive setpoint tracking has an effect that is similar to bumpless transfer which is introduced in Chapter 11.

Note that the position form of the PID algorithm calculates the absolute value of the output of the controller while the velocity form calculates the change in the controller output which should be added to the current level of the controller output. The position and velocity modes are different forms of the same equation; therefore, they are generally equivalent while the velocity form is usually used industrially. In general, **DCS's offer the velocity form of the PID controller in three forms: the velocity form in which P, I, and D are based upon the error from setpoint (Equation 6.19), the velocity form in which P and I only are based upon the error from setpoint (Equation 6.17), and the velocity form in which only integral action is based upon the error from setpoint (Equation 6.20).**

When derivative action is applied to a process where there is significant noise on the sensor reading, erratic derivative action can result since the difference between successive sensor readings can be dominated by the noise. Figure 6.3 shows a sensor reading with noise and the corresponding derivative value. A **digital filter** can be used to "smooth-out" the noisy sensor reading:

$$y_f(t) = f\, y_s(t) + (1-f)\, y_f(t-\Delta t) \qquad\qquad \textbf{6.21}$$

where $y_f(t)$ is the sensor reading after a digital filter has been applied, $y_s(t)$ is the current sensor reading, and f is the filter constant which is normally between 0.01 and 0.5. A more complete coverage of signal filtering is presented in Appendix B. The digital filter provides a running average and tends to absorb the short term variations caused by the noise. In this manner, filtered values of the controlled variable can be used where the derivative is calculated in the PID control equation, i.e.,

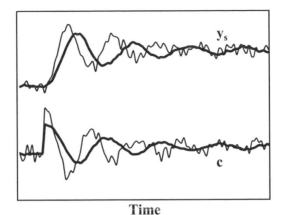

Time

Figure 6.4 Comparison of the results of a PI controller with and without filtering on the measured value of the controlled variable. Thick line - with filtering. Thin line - without filtering.

$$c(t) = c_0 + K_c \left(e(t) + \frac{1}{\tau_I} \sum_{i=1}^{n} e(i\Delta t)\Delta t - \tau_D \frac{y_f(t) - y_f(t-\Delta t)}{\Delta t} \right) \qquad \textbf{6.22}$$

Figure 6.3 also shows the value of the derivative calculated using filtered values of $y_s(t)$ with a filter factor of 0.08.

When the ratio of noise to measured value of the controlled variable is large, the measured value of the controlled variable used for proportional action may also require filtering (Equation 6.21). Figure 6.4 shows the results of a PI controller with and without filtering on the measurement of the controlled variable. Note that for the case without filtering, the noise on the measured value of the controlled variable is passed into the controller output by the proportional portion of the controller which in turn affects the level of the manipulated variable and thus the process. Figure 6.4 also shows the filtered value of the controlled variable and the corresponding controller output. Note that the filtering removes most of the noise on the controlled variable, and therefore, the controller output is considerably smoother than the case without filtering. It should be pointed out that the aggressiveness of the controller when filtering was applied had to be reduced in order to produce the same general dynamic response. That is, filtering of the controlled variable puts additional lag into the overall process; therefore, less aggressive tuning must be used. The detuning of the controller and the delay caused by the filtering process itself causes the filtered case to respond more slowly than in the case without filtering. It should be clear from this example that filtering is necessary in certain cases, but **a minimum level of filtering should be used in order to minimize the detrimental effect of filtering on control performance**.

An older version of the PID algorithm that was originally applied using analog devices is called an **interactive PID controller**. Figure 6.5 shows a block diagram of this controller that is also referred to as **"rate before reset"** since the derivative action is in series with and precedes the integral action. A PI or a P-only interactive controller is no different from the earlier form presented (i.e., non-interactive PID, Equation 6.9).

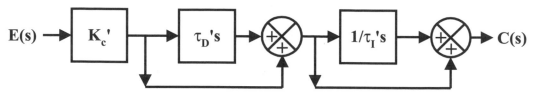

Figure 6.5 Block diagram for an interactive PID controller.

This can be seen by comparing Figures 6.2 and 6.5 with τ_D equal to zero. The only difference between an interactive and a non-interactive controller occurs for the PID controller. Both controllers apply the PID algorithm while there are differences in the tuning constants. That is, for the same amount of proportional, integral and derivative action, the interactive and non-interactive controllers would have different values of the tuning constants (i.e., K_c, τ_I, and τ_D). Following are formulas for converting from interactive tuning parameters (i.e., the tuning parameters with primes) to tuning parameters for the conventional non-interactive PID form

$$K_c = K_c' \left(1 + \tau_D' / \tau_I'\right)$$
$$\tau_I = \tau_I' \left(1 + \tau_D' / \tau_I'\right)$$
$$\tau_D = \tau_D' \left[\frac{1}{1 + \tau_D' / \tau_I'}\right]$$

Even though **interactive controllers** are an option on most DCS's, it is not recommended to use this form because it can cause confusion concerning the tuning parameters and it **offers no advantage over the non-interactive form of the PID controller**. As a result, only the formulas for converting the settings from the interactive form to the non-interactive form are presented here.

6.4 Analysis of P, I and D Action

In this section we will assume that the combination of the actuator, process and sensor is represented as a first order process, i.e.,

$$G_a(s)G_p(s)G_s(s) = \frac{K_p}{\tau_p s + 1}$$

Then the closed loop transfer function for a setpoint change (Equation 6.7) will be used to analyze the fundamental characteristics of proportional, integral, and derivative action.

The major objectives of feedback control are to:

- Minimize the response time of the closed loop process.
- Maintain reliable operation.
- Control to setpoints, i.e., reduce deviations from setpoint and eliminate offset.

Proportional, integral, and derivative action each affects feedback control performance with regard to these objectives. Moreover, controller tuning (i.e., selecting the individual levels of each of these feedback components) represents a compromise among these objectives. Chapter 7 will address controller tuning.

Proportional action. Feedback control based on **proportional action**,

$$c(t) = c_0 + K_c \, e(t)$$

takes action against the latest error from setpoint where K_c is the **controller gain**. In addition, the larger the error, the larger the control action. The transfer function for a proportional controller is

$$G_c(s) = K_c$$

Then the closed loop transfer function for a setpoint change (Equation 6.7) for the case of a first order actuator/process/sensor becomes

$$\frac{Y(s)}{Y_{sp}(s)} = \frac{\dfrac{K_c \, K_p}{\tau_p \, s + 1}}{\dfrac{K_c \, K_p}{\tau_p \, s + 1} + 1} = \frac{K_c \, K_p}{\tau_p \, s + 1 + K_c \, K_p}$$

Putting this result into the standard form for a first order process results in

$$\frac{Y(s)}{Y_{sp}(s)} = \frac{\dfrac{K_c \, K_p}{K_c \, K_p + 1}}{\dfrac{\tau_p}{K_c \, K_p + 1} \, s + 1}$$

This result can be used to determine several fundamental characteristics of proportional action:

1. The closed loop response of a first order process remains first order. In general, proportional action does not change the order of the process.

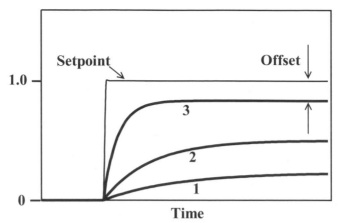

Figure 6.6 The effect of K_c on the response of a P-only controller for a first order process to a setpoint change. Note that K_c is increased from "1" to "3".

2. The closed loop time constant $[\tau_p / (K_c K_p + 1)]$ is smaller than the open loop time constant, τ_p. That is, proportional action makes the closed loop process respond faster than the open loop process.

3. The steady-state gain is not equal to unity. Figure 6.6 shows setpoint changes for three different values of $K_c K_p$. Note that the steady-state value differs from the setpoint value which indicates **offset**. Offset is the error between the new setpoint and the new steady state controlled variable value. Also note that as K_c increases, the offset is reduced. In fact, for this case the offset is given by

$$\text{Offset} = \frac{1}{1 + K_p K_c}$$

for a setpoint change of 1. Note that the same three conclusions can be reached if a disturbance were considered instead of a setpoint change.

Figure 6.7 shows the portion of the controller signal resulting from proportional action for a PI controller that is applying a setpoint change. Note that the proportional control action is positive when y is below y_{sp} and negative when y is above y_{sp} and that its magnitude is directly proportional to the error from setpoint. Initially, the setpoint change causes a spike in proportional action, but as y moves toward the setpoint, the proportional action is reduced and eventually goes to zero as y settles at the setpoint.

Integral action. Feedback control based on **integral action**, i.e.,

$$c(t) = c_0 + \frac{K_c}{\tau_I} \int_0^t e(t)\, dt$$

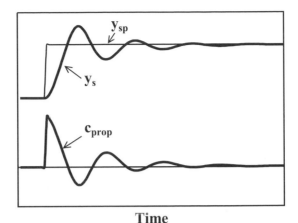

Time

Figure 6.7 The portion of the controller output resulting from proportional control (c_{prop}) for a setpoint change applied by a PI controller.

acts on the long term error from setpoint; therefore, it is easy to see that integral action is a much slower responding form of feedback control than proportional action. τ_I is the **reset time (integral time)** which is the tuning parameter for integral action. Consider Equation 6.9 after a setpoint change or a disturbance has affected the process. Further, assume that the process has reached steady-state conditions at the specified setpoint after the effects of the disturbances or the setpoint changes have been absorbed by the controller. Under these conditions, $e(t)$ and $dy(t)/dt$ are both zero which indicates that the proportional action and derivative action are also zero. But $c(t)$ must be significantly different from c_0 since a setpoint change or a disturbance change has occurred; therefore, the integral term is responsible for providing the incremental change at steady-state from c_0 necessary to maintain operation at the new operating condition. As a result, integral action is a critically important feature of PID feedback control. The transfer function for an integral-only controller is

$$G_c = \frac{K_c}{\tau_I\, s}$$

Then the closed loop transfer function for a setpoint change (Equation 6.7) for a first order process becomes

$$\frac{Y(s)}{Y_{sp}(s)} = \frac{\dfrac{K_c K_p}{\tau_I s(\tau_p s + 1)}}{\dfrac{K_c K_p}{\tau_I s(\tau_p s + 1)} + 1} = \frac{K_c K_p}{\tau_I \tau_p s^2 + \tau_I s + K_c K_p}$$

Putting this result into the standard form for a second order process (i.e., Equation 5.14) results in

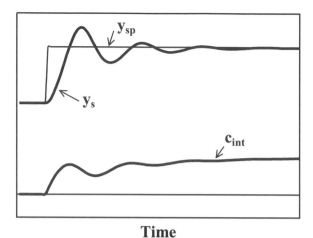

Time

Figure 6.8 The portion of the manipulated variable level resulting from integral action (c_{int}) for a setpoint change applied by a PI controller.

$$\frac{Y(s)}{Y_{sp}(s)} = \frac{1}{\dfrac{\tau_I \tau_p}{K_p K_c} s^2 + \dfrac{\tau_I}{K_p K_c} s + 1}$$

By comparing this equation with the standard second order form, the closed loop time constant τ'_p is given as

$$\tau'_p = \sqrt{\frac{\tau_I \tau_p}{K_p K_c}}$$

and solving for ζ yields

$$\zeta = \frac{1}{2}\sqrt{\frac{\tau_I}{\tau_p K_c K_p}}$$

and the closed loop gain is 1. These results along with the previous analysis provide several fundamental characteristics of integral action.

1. All the steady state corrections for disturbances or setpoint changes must come from integral action.
2. Since the gain of the closed loop transfer function is 1, there is no offset at steady state.
3. Integral action increases the order of the process dynamics by 1.
4. Based upon the equations for τ'_p and ζ, as τ_I is decreased, the process becomes faster but at the expense of larger overshoots and more sustained oscillations. For example, assume that $K_p K_c = 1$. If $\tau_I = \tau_p$, $\zeta = 0.5$ and $\tau'_p = \tau_p$. If $\tau_I = \frac{1}{4}\tau_p$, $\zeta = 0.25$ and $\tau'_p = 0.5\tau_p$. Therefore, increasing the

amount of integral action (decreasing τ_I) results in a faster responding feedback process, but increases the degree of oscillatory behavior.

Figure 6.8 shows the portion of the controller output resulting from integral action for a PI controller for the same process shown in Figure 6.7. Note that the peaks in c_{int} occur when y_s crosses y_{sp}. Also, note that as the process lines out at the setpoint, c_{int} lines out at a non-zero value.

Derivative Action. Feedback control based on **derivative action** is given by

$$c(t) = c_0 - K_c \tau_D \frac{d y_s(t)}{dt}$$

which indicates that derivative action acts to oppose the slope of the controlled variable in an effort to stabilize the feedback process. That is, as the slope of the controlled variable increases, derivative control action will also increase in an effort to reduce the slope in order to allow for more gradual changes in the controlled variable regardless of whether the controlled variable is moving away from or toward the setpoint. τ_D is the **derivative time** which is a tuning parameter for derivative action.

The transfer function for derivative action is

$$G_c(s) = K_c \tau_D s$$

Then the closed loop transfer function for a setpoint change (Equation 6.7) for a first order process becomes

$$\frac{Y(s)}{Y_{sp}(s)} = \frac{\dfrac{K_c K_p \tau_D s}{\tau_p s + 1}}{\dfrac{K_c K_p \tau_D s}{\tau_p s + 1} + 1} = \frac{K_c K_p \tau_D s}{(K_c K_p \tau_D + \tau_p)s + 1}$$

which indicates that derivative action does not change the order of the process but does increase the time constant for a first order process and does not eliminate offset.

It is also instructive to consider the effect of derivative action applied to a second order process. The closed loop transfer function for a setpoint change applied to this case yields

$$\frac{Y(s)}{Y_{sp}(s)} = \frac{\dfrac{K_p}{\tau_p^2 s^2 + 2\zeta \tau_p s + 1} K_c \tau_D s}{\dfrac{K_p}{\tau_p^2 s^2 + 2\zeta \tau_p s + 1} K_c \tau_D s + 1}$$

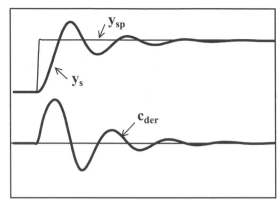

Time

Figure 6.9 The portion of the manipulated variable level resulting from derivative action (c_{der}) for a setpoint change applied using a PID controller.

Rearranging

$$\frac{Y(s)}{Y_{sp}(s)} = \frac{K_p K_c \tau_D s}{\tau_p^2 s^2 + (2\zeta\tau_p + K_p K_c \tau_D)s + 1}$$

For a second order process, τ_p remains unchanged while the closed loop damping factor is larger than the open loop damping factor. These results provide several fundamental characteristics of derivative action:

1. Derivative action does not change the order of the process.
2. Derivative action slows down the response of a first order process.
3. Derivative action does not eliminate offset.
4. Derivative action tends to reduce the oscillatory nature of feedback control.

Figure 6.9 shows the portion of the manipulated variable level resulting from derivative action (c_{der}) for a setpoint change using a PID controller. Note that c_{der} is zero at the peaks and valleys of y since it is directly related to the slope of y_s.

6.5 Controller Design Issues

When choosing between P-only, PI, or PID controllers, one should consider the dynamics of the combined actuator/process/sensor system. It has been estimated[1] for the conventional control loops in the CPI that approximately 93% of them use PI controllers, 2% use P-only controllers, and 5% use PID controllers. The following guidelines can be used to choose the proper controller mode based on process dynamics and control objectives.

P-only control. P-only control is used for processes that are not sluggish and for which some degree of offset is acceptable. A sluggish process is characterized by the fact that the process does not respond quickly to changes in the manipulated variable (i.e. not a first order like response). Typical applications: level control and pressure control. There are many control loops that should use P-only controllers, but instead use typical PI or PI with a relatively small amount of integral action since most operators do not want offset from setpoint.

PI control. PI controllers are used for processes that are not sluggish and for which it is necessary to have offset free operation. Typical applications are flow control, level control, pressure control, temperature control, and composition control.

PID control. PID controllers are useful for certain sluggish processes. Typical applications: temperature control and composition control. As a result, a sluggish process will exhibit a tendency to cycle under PI control due to the inertia that a sluggish process possesses; therefore, derivative action tends to reduce the tendency to cycling and allows more proportional action to be used both of which contribute to improved control performance. A key issue here is to determine whether or not a process is sluggish enough to warrant a PID controller. Assume that a FOPDT model has been fit to an open loop step test. If the resulting deadtime, θ_p, and time constant, τ_p, are such that

$$\frac{\theta_p}{\tau_p} < \frac{1}{2}$$

the process is not sufficiently sluggish to warrant a PID controller. **If**

$$\frac{\theta_p}{\tau_p} > 1$$

the process is sufficiently sluggish that PID controller should offer significant benefits over a PI controller. For

$$\frac{1}{2} < \frac{\theta_p}{\tau_p} < 1$$

either PI or PID control could be preferred. In the event that FOPDT models are not available, excessive oscillations of a PI controller or a sluggishly responding PI controller are indications that a PID controller may provide improved control performance. In addition, measurements of the controlled variable with significant noise levels can make the use of derivative action ineffective due to the sensitivity of the derivative to noise on the measurement. That is, since the measurements of the controlled variable have so much noise that if filtering is used, the lag added by the filter can negate any benefit produced by the derivative action.

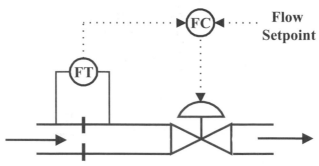

Figure 6.10 Schematic of a flow control loop.

6.6 Commonly Encountered Control Loops

In this section, five control loops commonly encountered in the CPI will be analyzed: a flow control loop, a level control loop, a pressure control loop, a temperature control loop, and a composition control loop. The relevant control characteristics of each loop are discussed from an actuator/process/sensor point of view and the problem of selecting a P-only, PI, or PID controller is addressed for each case.

Flow Control Loop. Flow control loops are the most common control loop used in the CPI. This is true because for almost every control loop in the CPI, other than a flow control loop itself, the manipulated variable is a setpoint to a flow rate control loop in a cascade control arrangement. A schematic of a flow control loop is shown in Figure 6.10. An orifice meter/differential pressure sensor is used to measure the flow rate and the actuator is a final control element (I/P converter, instrument air, and assembled control valve). The objective of this control loop is to maintain the flow rate at the setpoint for changes in the upstream and downstream pressures and for changes in the setpoint to the flow controller.

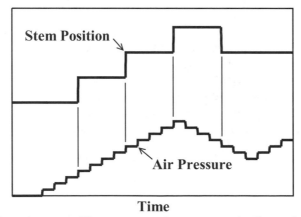

Figure 6.11 Valve stem position versus air pressure to the valve actuator for a valve with significant deadband.

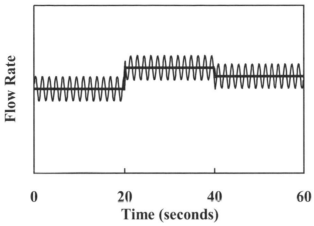

Figure 6.12 Measured flow rate and the specified average flow rate for a valve with a positioner. Thin line - measured flow rate. Thick line - flow rate setpoint.

The dynamics of the process (i.e., flow rate changes for changes in the valve stem position) and the sensor (i.e., changes in the measured pressure drop for changes in the flow rate) are quite fast compared with the dynamics of the control valve (i.e., changes in valve stem position for changes in signal to the final control element). Since the overall process is relatively fast and accurate control to setpoint is required, a PI controller is the proper choice for most flow control applications.

The most interesting aspect of flow control loops is that in spite of the fact that industrial control valves have a deadband of 10% to 25%, flow control loops are able to precisely meter deadband in the average flow typically to within 0.5% and down to 0.1% in certain cases. Figure 6.11 shows a plot of the actual valve position and the instrument air pressure delivered to the valve in an open loop case as a function of time. This behavior is due to deadband in the valve primarily caused by friction between the valve stem and the valve packing. As a result of the drag of the packing on the valve stem, a minimum force is necessary to cause the valve to move and when it does move it breaks loose and significant valve travel results.

In order to understand how a flow control loop can very accurately control the flow rate using such an imprecise actuator, consider the measured flow rate and specified flow rate shown in Figure 6.12. Note that the significant variation in the flow rate (i.e., sustained oscillations) is due to the deadband of the valve, but the average flow is precisely controlled due to the high frequency feedback control provided by the flow controller. Since the period of the flow variations is in the range of seconds and most chemical processes have time constants several minutes or larger, the process is sensitive only to the average flow and not to flow fluctuations; therefore, flow control loops can provide very precise metering of the **average flow rate** in spite of the fact that a very imprecise actuator is used. If a valve positioner is used, the valve positioner will provide the high frequency feedback necessary to counteract the detrimental effects of the control valve deadband on the metering precision of the average flow rate. That is, the high gain P-only controller applied by the valve positioner will open

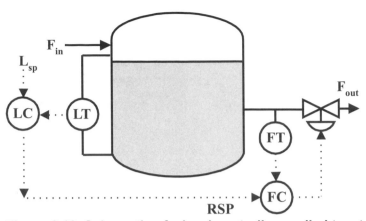

Figure 6.13 Schematic of a level controller applied to a tank.

and close the valve in a manner similar to the results shown in Figure 6.12. A flow control loop applied to a control valve with a positioner will eliminate the offset that the positioner does not account for and absorb unmeasured disturbances such as changes in upstream and downstream pressures.

Level Control Loop. Level control loops are used to control the liquid levels in the accumulator and reboiler of distillation columns, in steam boilers, in reactors, and in intermediate storage tanks. A schematic for a level control loop that is used to control the level in a tank is shown in Figure 6.13. A differential pressure sensor is used to measure the liquid level and the actuator is a flow control loop that controls the flow rate from the tank. The manipulated variable determined by the level controller is the setpoint for the flow controller on the line leaving the tank. This is an example of cascade control which is discussed in detail in Chapter 9. Some level controllers send their outputs directly to the valve on the line, but most level controllers in the CPI are implemented as shown in Figure 6.13 using flow control loops. The objective of this loop is to maintain the level within a certain range, for example, from 30 to 40% of full level for changes in this feed rate to the tank and changes in operating conditions. On the other hand, many operators want levels controlled to specified setpoints and are not satisfied if, for example, the level is 32% or 38% when the setpoint is 35%.

The dynamics of the sensor are quite fast and the dynamics of the actuator are usually fast compared with the dynamics of the process (i.e., percentage level changes for changes in flow leaving the tank). Since level systems are integrating processes, the rate of change of the level depends upon the change in flow rate and the cross-sectional area of the vessel. For a typical system under open loop conditions, a 5% level change can occur in about one minute for about a 10% change in feed rate to the tank. Thus, the response of the actuator/process/sensor system is typically controlled by the process dynamics. Since the overall process is not generally sluggish, a P-only controller is the proper choice when offset elimination is not required. When offset elimination is required (e.g., level control for a reactor), a PI controller should be used.

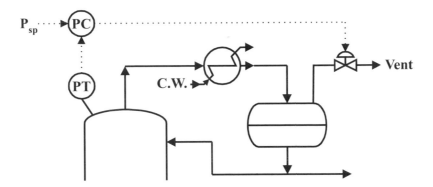

Figure 6.14 Schematic of a pressure controller for the overhead of a distillation column.

Pressure Control Loop. Pressure control loops are used to maintain system pressure for distillation columns, reactors, and other process units. A pressure control loop for maintaining overhead pressure in a column is shown in Figure 6.14. The actuator is a control valve on the vent line and the sensor is a pressure sensor mounted on the top of the column. Note that the output from the pressure controller goes directly to the control valve on the vent line. The objective of this loop is to maintain the column overhead pressure at or near setpoint for changes in condenser duty and changes in vapor flow rate up the column.

The pressure sensor is quite fast while the process (changes in pressure for changes in vent valve stem position) and the actuator are generally the slowest elements in the feedback system; therefore, this is also a relatively fast responding process. The P-only controller can be used if offset elimination is not important and a PI controller can be used when offset elimination is important.

Temperature Control Loop. Temperature control loops can be applied to control the temperature of a stream exiting a heat exchanger, the temperature of a tray in a distillation column, or the temperature of a CSTR. Figure 6.15 shows a schematic of a temperature controller applied to control the temperature of a process stream leaving a gas fired heater. The sensor is a RTD element placed in a thermowell located in the line leaving the heater and the actuator is a flow control loop on the gas line to the heater. The objective of the temperature control loop is to maintain the temperature of the exiting process stream on setpoint in the face of changes in the temperature of the process stream entering the heater and changes in the heating value of the gas.

The dynamics of the actuator are generally much faster than the dynamics of the process (i.e., change in outlet process temperature for a change in gas flow rate to the heater) and the sensor which typically has a dynamic time constant between 6 and 20 seconds for a properly installed RTD. The process fluid entering the gas fired heater flows by plug flow through the heat exchanger tubes that are exposed to high-temperature combusted gas. There is a thermal lag associated with changing the

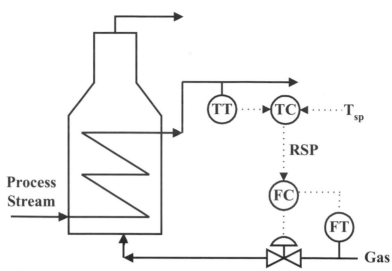

Figure 6.15 Schematic of a temperature controller for a gas-fired heater.

temperature of the metal of the heat exchanger tubes as well as transport delay caused by plug flow through the heater tubes. The transport delay and resulting overall process deadtime will increase as the feed rate of the process fluid is reduced. As a result, the process can be sluggish particularly for low feed rate operations. Since the heater is likely to behave as a sluggish process, a PID controller would be expected to be the controller mode of choice in this example. Excessive sensor noise can make the use of derivative action ineffective. If this process were less sluggish, a PI controller would be preferable. The guidelines presented in the previous section should be used to determine if the process is sufficiently sluggish to warrant the use of PID control.

Composition Control Loop. Composition control loops are used to keep products produced by distillation columns on specification, to maintain constant conversion in a reactor, and to maintain oxygen levels in the flue gas of a boiler to eliminate carbon monoxide emissions.   Figure 6.16 shows a schematic of a composition loop that controls the impurity level in the overhead product of a distillation column. The sensor is a gas chromatograph that samples the distillation product and the output of the controller for this loop is the setpoint for the reflux flow controller. The objective of the composition control loop is to keep the impurity level in the overhead product on setpoint during changes in the feed flow rate and feed composition.

The actuator dynamics are relatively fast while the sensor typically can have three to ten minutes of analyzer delay. The process (i.e., the change in impurity level in the overhead product for a change in the setpoint for the reflux flow controller) can be sluggish. If the process and analyzer delay result in a sluggish actuator/process/sensor system, a PID controller may be preferred. Once again, the guidelines presented in the previous section should be used to determine if the process is sluggish enough to warrant the use of PID control.

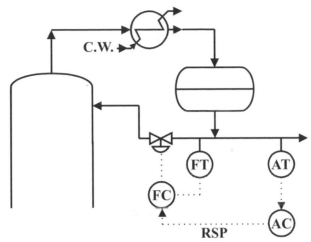

Figure 6.16 Schematic of a composition controller for the overhead of a distillation column.

6.7 Summary

The roots of the characteristic equation of the closed loop transfer function define the dynamic behavior of a feedback loop. PID controllers are extremely flexible and are the most commonly used controllers in the CPI. A PID controller has individual terms that separately apply proportional, integral, and derivative action. PID control is implemented using digital approximations of the integral of the error from setpoint and the derivative of the controlled variable value.

It is shown that (1) proportional action does not change the order of the process and makes the process respond faster, but does not eliminate offset, (2) integral action eliminates offset, but increases the order of the process and increases the oscillatory nature of the feedback response, and (3) derivative action does not change the order of the process and reduces the oscillatory nature of the closed loop response, but does not eliminate offset.

When deciding among P-only, PI, and PID control, one should consider the combined dynamic behavior of the actuator, process, and sensor. Processes with non-sluggish dynamic behavior should use P-only control when offset is not important and should use PI control when offset elimination is important. PID control should be used for sluggish processes, i.e., when the effective deadtime to time constant ratio is greater than unity.

6.8 Additional Terminology

c_0 - the value of the controller signal to the actuator when a PID controller is turned on.

Characteristic equation - the equation formed by setting the denominator of the closed loop transfer function equal to zero.

Control interval - the cycle time for applying control action.

Controller gain (K_c) - tuning parameter for a PID controller that determines the aggressiveness of the controller.

Derivative action - control action that is proportional to the derivative of the controlled variable.

Derivative kick - a spike in control action resulting from a setpoint change when the derivative is based on the error from setpoint.

Derivative-on-measurement - derivative action in a PID controller that is calculated based upon the slope of the measurement, i.e., does not suffer from derivative kick.

Derivative time (τ_D) - the tuning parameter for derivative action in a PID controller.

Digital filter - a numerical running average that is used to reduce the effect of noisy sensor readings.

Disturbance rejection - controlling to setpoint in the face of disturbance upsets.

Integral action - control action that is proportional to the integral of the error from setpoint.

Integral time (τ_I) - a tuning parameter for integral action in a PID controller.

Interactive PID controllers - an older form of PID control based upon the sequential application of derivative and integral action. Also known as rate before reset.

K_c - PID controller gain, tuning parameter for proportional action.

Offset - a persistent error from setpoint.

PB - proportional band.

PID controller - a linear controller that applies proportional, integral, and derivative action.

Position form - PID algorithm that calculates the total value of the controller output.

Proportional action - control action that is proportional to the latest error from setpoint.

Proportional band - a term that indicates the amount of proportional action used by a PID controller (inversely related to K_c).

Rate-before-reset - an older form of PID control based on the sequential application of derivative and integral action.

Regulatory control - controlling to setpoint in the face of disturbance upsets.

Reset time (τ_I) - a tuning parameter for integral action in a PID controller.

Servo control - controlling to setpoint in the face of setpoint changes.

Setpoint tracking - controlling to setpoint in the face of setpoint changes.

Velocity form of PID - PID algorithm that calculates the change in the controller output.

τ_D - PID derivative time, the tuning parameter for derivative action.

τ_I - PID reset time, the tuning parameter for integral action.

6.9 References

1. Private communication, Jim Downs, Tennessee Eastman Company (Nov 1998).

6.10 Questions and Exercises

6.1 What is the characteristic equation of a feedback loop and what is its significance?

6.2 What does the characteristic equation indicate about the dynamics of feedback systems for setpoint changes and disturbance rejection?

6.3 Write the ISA standard PID algorithm in the position form which has been modified to eliminate derivative kick for a direct acting final control element for a process with a negative gain.

6.4 Write the velocity form of the PID algorithm for a PI controller with a reverse acting final control element and a positive process gain.

6.5 Write the velocity form of a PID controller for a system with a positive process gain and a reverse acting final control element. Use the form that will provide a more gradual movement toward a new setpoint.

6.6 Write the digital version of the position form of a PID controller for a system that has a reverse acting final control element and a process gain that is negative. Use the form that is not susceptible to derivative kick.

6.7 Derive the velocity form of the PID algorithm starting with Equation 6.9.

6.8 What is the purpose of a digital filter? How do you decide how much filtering is appropriate?

6.9 Explain why one cannot simply add enough filtering to remove all the noise from a noisy measurement of the controlled variable before applying derivative action.

6.10 Compare and contrast the fundamental characteristics of proportional, integral, and derivative action.

6.11 Apply a P-only controller to the following process simulators provided with this text and tune for reasonable performance.

      a. CST thermal mixer.   b. CST composition mixer.

      c. Level process.   d. Endothermic CSTR.

      e. Heat exchanger.

6.12 Apply an integral-only controller to the following process simulators provided with this text and tune for reasonable performance.

      a. CST thermal mixer.   b. CST composition mixer.

      c . Level process.   d. Endothermic CSTR.

      e. Heat exchanger.

6.13 How do you decide between a PID and a PI controller?

6.14 How can a control valve with a deadband of 10% be used to control the flow rate to a deadband of less than 0.5% ?

6.15 When is the dynamics of the actuator system important to the overall dynamic behavior of the feedback loop? Give an example.

6.16 When is the dynamics of the sensor system important to the overall dynamic behavior of the feedback loop? Give an example.

6.17 Give an example in which the dynamics of the process is insignificant compared to the actuator.

6.18 Under what conditions would the dynamics of an actuator of a level control process be significant compared with the dynamics of the process? Be specific.

Chapter 7

PID Controller Tuning

7.1 Introduction

Tuning PID loops is one of the major responsibilities of a process control engineer and the resulting controller settings have a dominant effect on the performance of a PID control loop. Tuning a PID controller requires selecting values for K_c, τ_I, and τ_D that meet the operational objectives of the control loop which usually requires making a proper compromise between performance (minimizing deviations from setpoint) and reliability (the controller's ability to remain in service while handling major disturbances). This chapter will present tuning criteria and performance assessment approaches, analyze the effect of controller tuning parameters on feedback control performance, consider controller reliability, describe several well known tuning approaches, and finally present two controller tuning methods that are recommended for tuning industrial PID controllers.

7.2 Tuning Criteria and Performance Assessment

Tuning Criteria. In order to guide the tuning process, the following tuning objectives should be considered.

- Deviations from setpoint should be minimized.
- Good setpoint tracking performance should be attained.
- Excessive variation of the manipulated variable levels should be avoided.
- The controlled process should remain stable for major disturbance upsets.
- Offset elimination may or may not be important.

It is not possible to simultaneously satisfy each of these objectives; therefore, tuning is a compromise among these objectives. For example, tuning for minimum deviation from setpoint for normal disturbances is contrary to tuning the controller to remain stable for major disturbances. That is, if the controller is tuned for normal disturbances, the closed loop system may go unstable when a major disturbance enters the process. On the other hand, if the controller is tuned for the largest possible disturbance, control performance is likely to be excessively sluggish for normal disturbance levels.

Performance Assessment. There are a number of performance statistics that can be used to evaluate **control performance**:

Integral Absolute Error (*IAE*)

$$IAE = \int_0^\infty \left| y_{sp}(t) - y_s(t) \right| dt$$

Integral Time Absolute Error (*ITAE*)

$$ITAE = \int_0^\infty t \left| y_{sp}(t) - y_s(t) \right| dt$$

Integral Square Error (*ISE*)

$$ISE = \int_0^\infty \left[y_{sp}(t) - y_s(t) \right]^2 dt$$

Integral Time Square Error (*ITSE*)

$$ITSE = \int_0^\infty t \left[y_{sp}(t) - y_s(t) \right]^2 dt$$

Each one of these measures values the error from setpoint differently. *ITAE* and *ITSE* penalize deviations at long time more severely than *IAE* and *ISE*. *ISE* and *ITSE* penalize larger deviations more severely than *IAE* and *ITAE*.

Figure 7.1 shows the setpoint response of a process tuned for sluggish performance (Figure 7.1a), for a decay ratio of 1/10 (Figure 7.1b), for a decay ratio of 1/4 (**quarter amplitude damping, QAD**, Figure 7.1c), and for a decay ratio of 1/1.5 (Figure 7.1d). The 1/1.5 decay ratio results in excessive cycling which is called **ringing**. It is easy to see from visual inspection that QAD provides better control performance than the other three results. It should be noted that the aggressiveness of the controller is increased going from Figure 7.1a to Figure 7.1d. Table 7.1 lists the IAE, ITAE, ISE, and ITSE for a range of decay ratios for this process. Note that QAD tuning results in the best overall performance without regard to **reliability**. Also note that each of these statistics goes through a minimum as the decay ratio is increased. It should be pointed out that these statistics are used in academic research to compare the control performance for different controllers using dynamic process simulations, but are not usually used in industry.

Industrial **control performance** is many times assessed by the variability in the final products produced. The deviation from setpoint (σ) can be used as a measure of variability in industrial products and thus a measure of control performance.

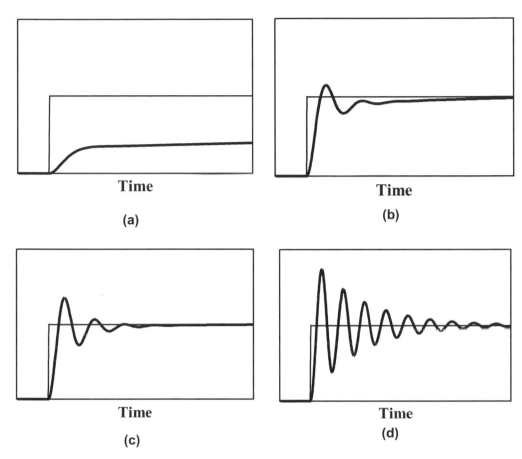

Figure 7.1   Control response for a setpoint change. (a) Controller tuned for sluggish response. (b) Controller tuned for 1/10 decay ratio. (c) Controller tuned for QAD. (d) Controller tuned for ringing response.

Table 7.1				
Several Performance Statistics as a Function of Decay Ratio				
Decay Ratio	IAE	ITAE	ISE	ITSE
1/1.5	39.6	1244	31.1	470
1/2.0	28.3	628	22.8	231
1/3.0	20.9	347	17.8	117
1/4.0	19.8	387	16.8	92.8
1/5.0	20.7	503	16.8	91.2
1/6.0	22.0	635	17.1	97.4
1/8.0	24.9	903	17.9	119
1/10.0	27.4	1141	18.8	145

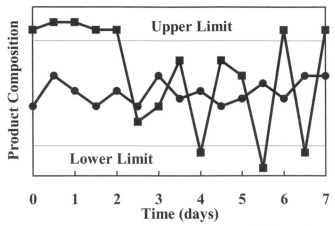

Figure 7.2 SPC chart based upon a seven day period of data for two different controllers on the same process.

$$\sigma = \sqrt{\dfrac{\sum\limits_{i=1}^{N}[y_s(t_i) - y_{sp}]^2}{N}}$$

where $y_s(t_i)$ is the sampled controlled variable value at time equal to t_i and N is the number of samples. Note that the smaller the deviation from setpoint, the better the control performance. Remember that the standard deviation is based on the error from the average value of a set of data while this statistic is based on the error from setpoint.

Most companies keep statistical process control (SPC) charts that track the laboratory analysis of final products which are typically sampled one to three times daily. Figure 7.2 is an example of an industrial SPC chart. Note the upper and lower limits on product purity. This chart shows control results for two different controllers for two different seven day periods. It is easy to see which controller performed better.

7.3 Effect of Tuning Parameters Upon Dynamic Behavior

When tuning a loop, it is important to understand how each tuning parameter affects the dynamic behavior of the closed loop system. In this section, the effect of tuning parameters on P-only, PI, and PID control behavior is studied.

P-only control. Consider the effect of controller gain, K_c , for a P-only controller applied to a FOPDT process. The transfer function for a FOPDT process is

$$G_p(s) = \frac{K_p e^{-\theta_p s}}{\tau_p s + 1} \qquad \text{7.1}$$

Using the first order Pade' approximation[1] for the deadtime term, $e^{-\theta_p s}$,

$$e^{-\theta_p s} \approx \frac{1 - \frac{1}{2}\theta_p s}{1 + \frac{1}{2}\theta_p s}$$

Equation 7.1 results in

$$G_p(s) = \frac{K_p(1 - \frac{1}{2}\theta_p s)}{(\tau_p s + 1)(1 + \frac{1}{2}\theta_p s)} \qquad \text{7.2}$$

Then using the closed loop transfer function for a setpoint change (Equation 6.7) for P-only control assuming $G_a(s) = G_s(s) = 1$ yields

$$\frac{Y(s)}{Y_{sp}(s)} = \frac{\dfrac{K_c K_p \,(1 - \frac{1}{2}\theta_p s)}{(\tau_p s + 1)(1 + \frac{1}{2}\theta_p s)}}{\dfrac{K_c K_p \,(1 - \frac{1}{2}\theta_p s)}{(\tau_p s + 1)(1 + \frac{1}{2}\theta_p s)} + 1} \qquad \text{7.3}$$

Rearranging results in

$$\frac{Y(s)}{Y_{sp}(s)} = \frac{K_c K_p \,(1 - \frac{1}{2}\theta_p s)}{\frac{1}{2}\tau_p \theta_p \, s^2 + [\tau_p + \frac{1}{2}\theta_p(1 - K_c K_p)]s + 1 + K_c K_p} \qquad \text{7.4}$$

Since the poles of the closed loop transfer function are the roots of the denominator and determine the dynamic behavior of the process, the poles of this transfer function are evaluated analytically.

$$p_1 = \frac{-(\tau_p + \frac{1}{2}\theta_p[1 - K_c K_p]) + \sqrt{(\tau_p + \frac{1}{2}\theta_p[1 - K_c K_p])^2 - 2\tau_p \theta_p (1 + K_c K_p)}}{\tau_p \theta_p}$$

$$\text{7.5}$$

and

$$p_2 = \frac{-(\tau_p + \frac{1}{2}\theta_p[1 - K_c K_p]) - \sqrt{(\tau_p + \frac{1}{2}\theta_p[1 - K_c K_p])^2 - 2\tau_p \theta_p (1 + K_c K_p)}}{\tau_p \theta_p}$$

$$\text{7.6}$$

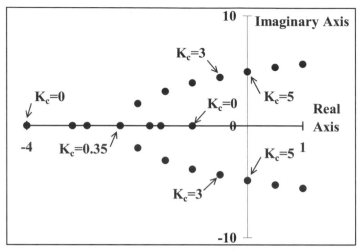

Figure 7.3 Root locus diagram for the results in Table 7.2.

by applying the quadratic formula. Table 7.2 lists values of the two poles, p_1 and p_2, at different values of K_c assuming that $K_p = 1$, $\tau_p = 1$, and $\theta_p = 0.5$. Figure 7.3 shows these results plotted on the complex plane. This plot is called a **root locus diagram** and graphically shows the effect of K_c on the dynamic characteristics of the feedback system.   Note that for $0 < K_c < 0.35$, the poles are real and negative indicating

Table 7.2		
Effect of K_c on the Poles of the Closed Loop Transfer Function for P-only Control on a FOPDT Process ($K_p = 1$, $\tau_p = 1$, and $\theta_p = 0.5$).		
K_c	p_1	p_2
0	-1.0	-4.0
0.25	-1.58	-3.18
0.30	-1.78	-2.92
0.35	-2.32	-2.32
0.5	$-2.25 + 0.97\,i$	$-2.25 - 0.97\,i$
1.0	$-2.0 + 2.0\,i$	$-2.0 - 2.0\,i$
2.0	$-1.5 + 3.1\,i$	$-1.5 - 3.1\,i$
3.0	$-1.0 + 3.9\,i$	$-1.0 - 3.9\,i$
4.0	$-0.5 + 4.4\,i$	$-0.5 - 4.4\,i$
5.0	$4.9\,i$	$-4.9\,i$
6.0	$0.5 + 5.3\,i$	$0.5 - 5.3\,i$
7.0	$1.0 + 5.6\,i$	$1.0 - 5.6\,i$

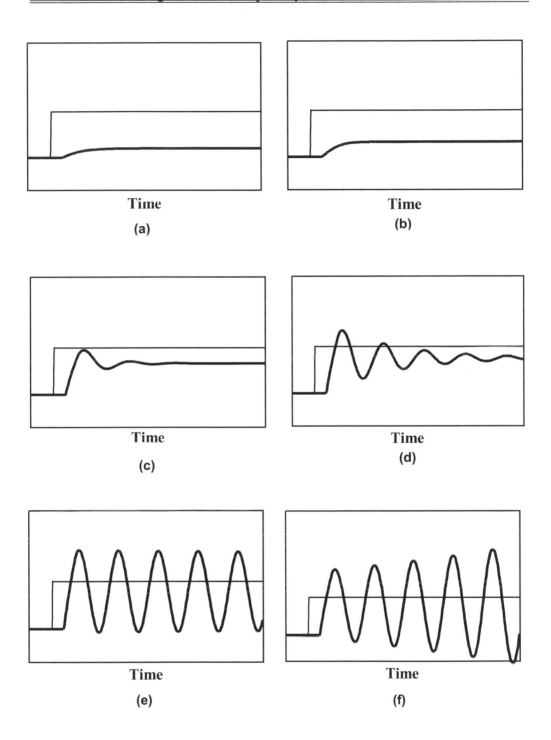

Figure 7.4 The response of a FOPDT process with a P-only controller to a setpoint change. (a) K_c=0.25; (b) K_c=0.35; (c) K_c=1.0; (d) K_c=3.0; (e) K_c=5.0; (f) K_c=5.2.

overdamped dynamic behavior. Remember that real negative poles yield time domain solutions that involve exponential decay with time (e^{-at}). At $K_c = 0.35$, the closed loop system is critically damped since both poles are -2.32 and any increase in K_c results in oscillatory behavior. For $0.35 < K_c < 5.0$, the system is underdamped. The poles in this region are complex conjugates ($p_1 = a + i\omega$ and $p_2 = a - i\omega$) which in the time domain result in terms of the form $e^{-at} \sin bt$. Since the real part of these complex conjugate poles are negative, damped oscillatory behavior is indicated. Moreover, the magnitude of the real portion (a) is decreasing as K_c is increased from 0.35 to 5 which indicates that the degree of damping of the oscillations is also decreasing. At $K_c = 5$, sustained oscillations result. This marks the boundary between stable operation ($K_c < 5$) and unstable operation ($K_c > 5$). For $K_c > 5$, the real components of the complex conjugate poles are positive, indicating exponentially growing oscillations which corresponds to unstable operation. Note that for $K_c > 5$, the magnitude of the positive real portion of the complex conjugate poles is also increasing indicating an increase in the exponential growth rates with an increase in K_c. Figure 7.4 shows the time domain response for several values of K_c (0.25, 0.35, 1.0, 3.0, 5.0, 5.2) for a setpoint change in y which corresponds to (a) sluggish behavior, (b) critically damped, (c) oscillatory performance, (d) ringing, (e) sustained oscillations, and (f) unstable behavior, respectively. Note that as K_c increases, the system response becomes faster. Although this was a simple case, industrial control loops show the same general behavior; that is, **as the controller gain is increased, an open loop overdamped process will move from overdamped behavior to critically damped to underdamped to ringing to sustained oscillations to unstable oscillations.**

PI Control. Consider the effect of K_c and τ_I on PI control applied to a FOPDT process model. Using the transfer function of the process (Equation 7.2) and the transfer function of the controller (Equation 6.12 with $\tau_D = 0$) in the closed loop transfer function assuming $G_a(s) = G_s(s) = 1$ results in

$$\frac{Y(s)}{Y_{sp}(s)} = \frac{\dfrac{K_c\left(1+\dfrac{1}{\tau_I s}\right)K_p\,(1-\frac{1}{2}\theta_p s)}{(\tau_p s+1)(1+\frac{1}{2}\theta_p s)}}{\dfrac{K_c\left(1+\dfrac{1}{\tau_I s}\right)K_p\,(1-\frac{1}{2}\theta_p s)}{(\tau_p s+1)(1+\frac{1}{2}\theta_p s)}+1} \qquad\qquad 7.7$$

Table 7.3 shows the poles of this transfer function for a range of K_c's for $\tau_I = 1.0$, $K_p = 1.0$, $\tau_p = 1.0$, and $\theta_p = 0.5$. Since the rearrangement of Equation 7.7 results in a cubic equation in s in the denominator, there are three poles for this closed loop system. Note that as K_c is increased, the dynamic behavior goes from overdamped to critically damped to underdamped to sustained oscillations to

Table 7.3

The Effect of K_c on the Poles of the Closed Loop Transfer Function for PI Control Applied to a FOPDT Model ($K_p = 1$, $\tau_p = 1$, $\theta_p = 0.5$ and $\tau_I = 1.0$).

K_c	Poles		
	p_1	p_2	p_3
0.2	-1.0	-0.224	-3.58
0.4	-1.0	-0.519	-3.08
0.6	-1.0	-1.04	-2.35
0.8	-1.0	-1.60 + 0.800 i	-1.60 - 0.800 i
1.0	-1.0	-1.50 + 1.32 i	-1.50 - 1.32 i
1.5	-1.0	-1.25 + 2.11 i	-1.25 - 2.11 i
2.0	-1.0	-1.0 + 2.65 i	-1.0 - 2.65 i
4.0	-1.0	0 + 4.0 i	0 - 4.0 i
6.0	-1.0	1.0 + 4.80 i	1.0 - 4.80 i

Table 7.4

The Effect of τ_I on the Poles of the Closed Loop Transfer Function for PI Control Applied to a FOPDT model ($K_p = 1$, $\tau_p = 1$, $\theta_p = 0.5$, and $K_c = 0.3$).

τ_I	Poles		
	p_1	p_2	p_3
0.02	-7.21	1.26 + 2.60 i	1.26 - 2.60 i
0.05	-5.61	0.453 + 2.02 i	0.453 - 2.02 i
0.1	-4.77	0.0333 + 1.59 i	0.0333 - 1.59 i
0.2	-4.16	-0.271 + 1.17 i	-0.271 - 1.17 i
0.4	-3.72	-0.410 + 0.753 i	-0.410 - 0.753 i
0.6	-3.53	-0.586 + 0.473 i	-0.586 - 0.473 i
0.8	-3.41	-0.642 + 0.164 i	-0.642 - 0.164 i
1.0	-3.34	-0.359	-1.0
2.0	-3.16	-0.135	-1.40
4	-3.05	-0.0620	-1.58

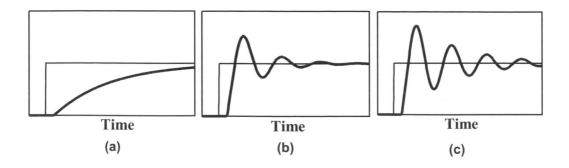

Figure 7.5 PI controller responses for a FOPDT process with varying amounts of proportional action. (a) K$_c$ too low. (b) K$_c$ tuned for QAD. (c) K$_c$ too large.

unstable oscillations as in the results for P-only control. In comparing the results of Tables 7.2 and 7.3, one can see that the addition of integral action caused the onset of unstable behavior to occur at lower values of K_c compared with the P-only results.

Table 7.4 shows the poles for the closed loop transfer function for a range of values of τ_I for $K_c = 0.3$, $K_p = 1.0$, $\tau_p = 1.0$, and $\theta_p = 0.5$. In this case as τ_I is decreased, the dynamic behavior goes from overdamped to critically damped to underdamped to unstable oscillations. Note that as the amount of integral action is increased (i.e., as τ_I is decreased), the dynamic behavior goes through this same sequence of phases as an increase in proportional action produced.

Figure 7.5 shows the dynamic behavior of the same FOPDT process that was considered in Table 7.3 with a PI controller for a setpoint change with different amounts of proportional action. Figure 7.5b shows the results for a PI controller tuned for QAD. In addition, the QAD tuning was modified by increasing K_c (Figure 7.5c) while keeping τ_I constant and by decreasing K_c (Figure 7.5a) while keeping τ_I constant. Note that the increase in K_c resulted in ringing while the decrease in K_c resulted in sluggish behavior. In addition, note that larger controller gains result in

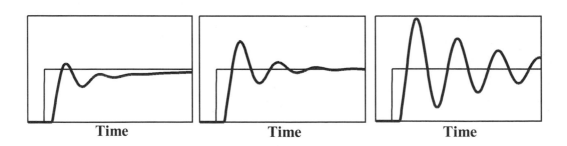

(a)   (b)   (c)

Figure 7.6 PI controller response for a FOPDT process with varying levels of integral action. (a) τ_I too large. (b) τ_I tuned for QAD. (c) τ_I too small.

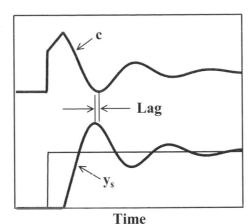

Time

Figure 7.7 The lag between the controller output and controlled variable for a QAD tuned PI controller.

longer settling times. Figure 7.6 shows similar results for the effect of variations in τ_I. Figure 7.6b shows the results for QAD tuning and is the same result as shown in Figure 7.5b. A decrease in τ_I from QAD settings results in ringing (Figure 7.6c) and an increase results in a slow removal of offset (Figure 7.6a). By comparing Figures 7.5a and 7.6a, it can be seen that when K_c is too low, long rise times and sluggish behavior results and when integral action is too low (i.e., τ_I is too large), offset results. Also, note that ringing from too much proportional action (Figure 7.5c) and ringing from too much integral action (Figure 7.6c) are quite similar; therefore, when controller ringing results, it is difficult to tell whether there is excessive proportional action or excessive integral action or both.

Figure 7.7 shows the manipulated and controlled variables for a QAD tuned controller. Note that the controller output "lags" behind the controlled variable for this case. The lag between the controlled variable and the controller output is discussed in more detail in Chapter 8. Figure 7.8 shows the same system except that the K_c is

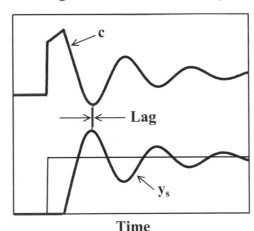

Time

Figure 7.8 The lag between the controller output and controlled variables for a controller with too much proportional action.

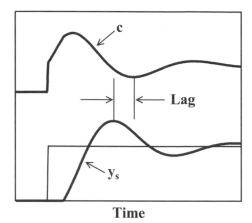

Time

Figure 7.9 The lag between the controller output and controlled variable for a controller with too much integral action.

increased by 25% and τ_I is increased by a factor of 2 (i.e., the ringing is caused by too much proportional action). Note that the lag between the controlled variable and the controller output is significantly reduced; therefore, excessive gain reduces the lag between the controlled variable and the controller output. Figure 7.9 shows the case in which K_c and τ_I are reduced by a factor of 2 compared with the QAD settings. In this case, the lag increases significantly; therefore, excessive integral action results in an increase in the lag of the system. **Therefore, the lag between the controller output and the controlled variable can be used to determine if a controlled process is ringing from too much proportional action or too much integral action.** This analysis can also be used to compare the ringing results shown in Figure 7.5 and 7.6. These results also show that the lag between the controlled variable and the controller output is larger when there is excessive integral action, but the differences are less distinct than those shown in Figures 7.8 and 7.9. With pure proportional action, the maximum c occurs at the maximum deviation from setpoint which corresponds to zero lag (i.e., **in-phase**). For pure integral action, the maximum c occurs when the error from setpoint changes sign which corresponds to a large lag.

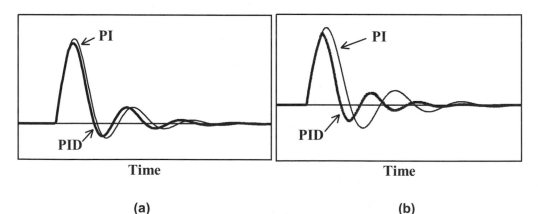

(a)　　　　　　　　　　　　　　　　　　(b)

Figure 7.10 Comparison between PI and PID controller for a process with (a) low deadtime and (b) larger deadtime.

Table 7.5

Effect of τ_D on the Poles of the Closed Loop Transfer Function for PID Control Applied to a FOPDT Model ($K_p = 1$, $\tau_p = 1$, $\theta_p = 1$, $K_c = 1$, and $\tau_I = 1$).

τ_D	Poles	
	p_1	p_2, p_3
0	-1.0	$-0.50 \pm 1.33\,i$
0.1	-1.21	$-0.618 \pm 1.21\,i$
0.2	-1.64	$-0.678 \pm 1.03\,i$
0.3	-2.44	$-0.639 \pm 0.87\,i$
0.4	-3.51	$-0.577 \pm 0.79\,i$
0.5	-4.95	$-0.524 \pm 0.73\,i$
0.6	-7.03	$-0.483 \pm 0.69\,i$

PID Control. The effect of proportional and integral action on the feedback behavior of a PID controller is similar to that observed for the PI controller test case that was just studied. Table 7.5 lists the closed loop poles for a PID controller applied to a FOPDT model for a range of values of τ_D. The results are based on K_c, τ_I, K_p, τ_p, and θ_p all equal to unity. Note that the magnitude of the real root increases as τ_D increases indicating that faster damping is provided by derivative action. Also, the frequency of the oscillations, which is indicated by the coefficient of the imaginary component, decreases as τ_D increases, indicating that derivative action reduces the oscillatory nature of the feedback system. Figure 7.10a shows PID and PI control on a FOPDT process: ($K_p = 1$, $\tau_p = 1$, $\theta_p = 0.1$). Figure 7.10b shows PID control and PI on the another FOPDT process with more deadtime: ($K_p = 1$, $\tau_p = 1$, $\theta_p = 2$). These results support the conclusion that derivative action is useful for processes that have significant deadtime to time constant ratio. Figure 7.11 shows a case which has too much derivative action in the PID controller. Note that the feedback response shows a "stairstep" behavior which indicates that too much derivative action is being used. The stairstep behavior is caused because as the process moves toward the setpoint excessive derivative action causes the process to stall or level out. When the process stalls, the proportional and integral action act on the process to move the controlled variable toward the setpoint. When this occurs, the derivative of the controlled variable will build up and the derivative action will act against it causing the stairstep effect.

Control Interval. The PID control results presented so far have been based on a continuous application of the controller. The digital application of feedback

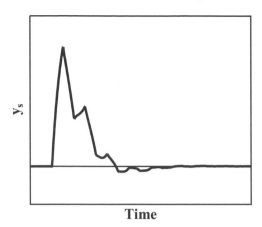

Time

Figure 7.11 The control performance of a PID controller with too much derivative action.

control is applied at discrete points in time. DCS's use sequential microprocessors that perform control calculations for a large number of control loops. Typical control loops are executed every 0.5 to 1.0 seconds for regulatory loops and 30 to 120 seconds for supervisory loops. The time between control applications is the control interval (Δt). PID control is applied industrially on DCS's using digital formulas which are applied at discrete control intervals (Equations 6.17 to 6.19).

Consider the QAD tuned continuous PI controller that was applied to the FOPDT process ($K_p = 1$, $\tau_p = 1$, $\theta_p = 0.5$). If these settings are applied using a control interval of 0.5, the control behavior is unstable. The PI controller was retuned using a control interval of 0.5 and the results are compared with continuous control for a setpoint change in Figure 7.12. The controller gain for discrete control ($\Delta t = 0.5$) was reduced by 60% compared to the continuous controller. Because of the detuning and the delayed response, the discrete controller resulted in a longer settling time.

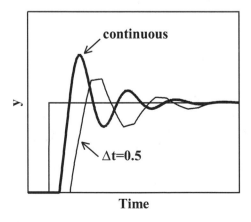

Time

Figure 7.12 Comparison between a continuous PI controller and a PI controller applied each 0.5 time units.

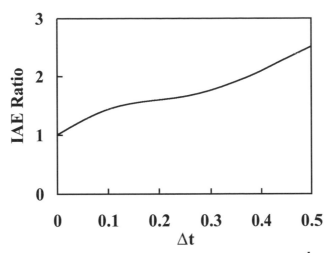

Figure 7.13 The effect of control interval on relative control performance.

Figure 7.13 shows the ratio of the IAE for discrete control to the IAE for continuous control versus control interval for the same FOPDT process ($K_p = 1$, $\tau_p = 1$, $\theta_p = 0.5$) for a step disturbance test ($K_d = 1$, $\tau_d = 1$, $\theta_d = 0$). Note that for each control interval considered, the digital PI controller was retuned. As a general rule[2], **the control interval should be selected such that**

$$\Delta t \ \leq \ 0.05 \, (\theta_p + \tau_p)$$

in order to obtain control performance approaching that of continuous control. For feedback control using an on-line GC, the control interval is set by the cycle time for the analyzer updates (typically 3 10 minutes). No advantage is gained by applying control action more frequently than the GC updates since new information on the process response is available only when the GC updates. For sensors that provide continuous readings (e.g., temperature sensor), the maximum recommended control interval is typically equal to one sensor time constant. For level, pressure, and flow loops, sensor dynamics do not usually present a significant constraint for the choice of the control interval.

7.4 Controller Reliability

Controller reliability is concerned with whether or not a controller will remain stable during severe upsets. Consider the closed loop transfer function for disturbance rejection (Equation 6.8):

$$\frac{Y(s)}{D(s)} = \frac{G_d(s)}{G_c(s) \, G_a(s) \, G_p(s) \, G_s(s) + 1}$$

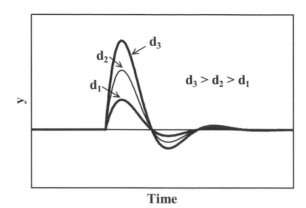

Figure 7.14 The effect of disturbance magnitude on the dynamic response of a linear process.

For a particular set of controller tuning parameters and fixed process models [i.e., $G_a(s)$, $G_p(s)$, and $G_s(s)$ remain unchanged], this equation indicates that the dynamic behavior of the process, i.e., the roots of the characteristic equation, are fixed and remain unchanged regardless of the size or the character of the disturbance. Figure 7.14 shows the dynamic behavior of a linear process subjected to several different levels of a disturbance. Note that the larger disturbance levels produce larger deviations but the dynamic behavior (decay ratio and time constant) remains unchanged. The previous section showed that the dynamic behavior of a closed loop process varies directly with the aggressiveness of the controller tuning for a linear process, but this analysis indicates that the dynamic characteristics of the feedback behavior of a linear process remain unchanged with the type and magnitude of a disturbance.

It is well known from industrial experience that controlled processes which are stable under normal conditions can become unstable when subjected to severe upsets thus indicating that the dynamic characteristics of feedback processes are **not** always constant. Let's examine this apparent discrepancy.

Up until this point we have assumed that the process model, sensor model, and actuator model are all constant as the operating conditions change. In fact, these models can change with operating conditions. For example, all real processes exhibit some degree of nonlinearity. Figure 7.15 shows the process gain, K_p, as a function of the controlled variable, y, for a linear process (a), a moderately nonlinear process (b), and a severely nonlinear process (c). Note that for a very narrow region near y_0, even the severely nonlinear process behaves relatively linearly (i.e., exhibits a relatively constant process gain). Also, note that the farther removed from y_0, the larger the resulting gain change.

In addition, feed flow rate changes can cause process time constant and deadtime changes which represent another type of process nonlinearity. For example, for the CST thermal mixer (Section 3.5), the process time constant, τ_p, is given by

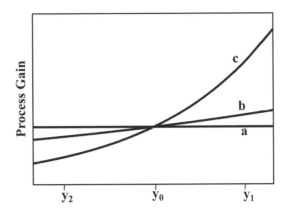

Figure 7.15 Process gain as a function of the controlled variable for (a) a linear process, (b) a moderately nonlinear process, and (c) a severely nonlinear process.

$$\tau_p = \frac{\rho V_r}{F_1 + F_2}$$

This equation shows that the process time constant varies inversely with the total feed rate to the process. In addition, Section 5.7 showed that transport deadtime varies inversely with flow rate.

In order to demonstrate the effect of process nonlinearity combined with disturbances, consider the application of a PI controller to the endothermic CSTR presented in Chapter 3. This process exhibits changes in both process gain and time constant. A PI controller was tuned for a setpoint change using the QAD tuning criterion. Table 7.6 shows the results of this system for different levels of feed composition upsets, ΔC_{A_o}.

Table 7.6	
Effect of Disturbance Magnitude on Closed Loop Dynamic Behavior	
$\Delta C_{A_0} \, (gmole \, / \, l)$	**Decay Ratio**
-0.1	1/2.50
-0.2	1/2.35
-0.3	1/2.18
-0.4	1/1.94
-0.5	1/1.64
-0.6	1/1.34
-0.7	1/0.91 (unstable)

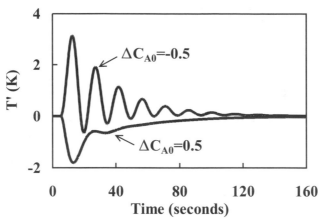

Figure 7.16 The effect of the disturbance direction on the dynamic behavior of the endothermic CSTR.

Note that the decay ratio decreases sharply with an increase in the disturbance magnitude which leads to ringing. For the largest feed composition upset, unstable feedback behavior results. Therefore, for this nonlinear process as the disturbance magnitude increases, the dynamic behavior of the process goes through the same sequence of phases that was observed for the controller tuning in the previous section.

Figure 7.16 shows the closed loop results for the original endothermic case for a positive and negative 0.5 gmole/l feed composition upset. Note that the negative feed composition change results in ringing while the positive change results in sluggish behavior. The effect of process nonlinearity and disturbance magnitude on dynamic behavior can be understood by recognizing that a disturbance moves the controlled variable from its normal operating range which results in process gain and time constant changes. These process changes cause changes in the dynamic behavior of the closed loop process. For example, consider the severely nonlinear process gain depicted in Figure 7.15. A disturbance enters this process and results in an increase in y from y_0 to y_1 where the process gain at y_1 is over twice the gain at y_0. Likewise, if a different disturbance moves the process to y_2, the process gain would be less than half the original process gain at y_0. As a result, a nonlinear process can exhibit severe ringing or instability and at other times behave in a very sluggish manner depending upon the type, magnitude, and direction of the disturbance.

Table 7.7 shows the effect of disturbance magnitude on the dynamic behavior of the endothermic CSTR with a reaction rate expression with a lower activation energy (E/R = 2000 K). The lower activation energy results in a more linear process than the original endothermic CSTR. For the case with a reduced activation energy, the decay ratio also depends on the magnitude of the disturbance but is a much weaker function of the disturbance magnitude. In fact, the PI controller remains stable for the full range of changes in the magnitude of the disturbance. As one would expect, this case with a less nonlinear process is shown to be less sensitive to disturbances than the more nonlinear process.

Table 7.7

Effect of Disturbance Magnitude on Closed Loop Dynamic Behavior (E/R = 2000 K)

ΔC_{A_0} (gmole / l)	Decay Ratio
-0.1	1/3.05
-0.2	1/2.88
-0.3	1/2.65
-0.4	1/2.48
-0.5	1/2.28
-0.6	1/2.12
-0.7	

7.5 Classical Tuning Methods

There is a wide range of PID tuning methods that have been proposed. This section considers two of the earliest methods developed (the Cohen and Coon method[3] and the Ziegler-Nichols method[4]). In addition, a more recent technique (the Cianione and Marlin method[5]) is also considered.

Each of these methods is based upon a preset compromise between performance and reliability. As a result, even when they are used industrially, they are usually used as initial controller settings. Then control engineers use their knowledge of the nonlinearity and the severity of disturbances for the particular control loop in question to adjust the controller tuning to meet the proper compromise between reliability and performance for that particular loop. These methods are presented here for historical perspective as well as for insight into the relative tuning of P-only, PI, and PID.   The next section will present the methods that are recommended for tuning industrial control loops.

Cohen and Coon Method. The Cohen and Coon approach[3] assumes that a FOPDT model of the process is available. The Cohen and Coon parameters for a P-only, PI, and PID controller are listed in Table 7.8. These results are based on QAD tuning for a FOPDT process. A QAD response for a second order process corresponds to a damping factor (ζ) of 0.22 with a 50% overshoot.

Table 7.8

Cohen and Coon PID Settings Based on a FOPDT Model

Controller	K_c	τ_I	τ_D
P-only	$\dfrac{1}{K_p}\dfrac{\tau_p}{\theta_p}\left(1+\dfrac{\theta_p}{3\tau_p}\right)$		
PI	$\dfrac{1}{K_p}\dfrac{\tau_p}{\theta_p}\left[0.9+\dfrac{\theta_p}{12\tau_p}\right]$	$\dfrac{\theta_p\left[30+\dfrac{3\theta_p}{\tau_p}\right]}{9+20\left[\dfrac{\theta_p}{\tau_p}\right]}$	
PID	$\dfrac{1}{K_p}\dfrac{\tau_p}{\theta_p}\left(\dfrac{16+3\dfrac{\theta_p}{\tau_p}}{12}\right)$	$\dfrac{\theta_p\left[32+\dfrac{6\theta_p}{\tau_p}\right]}{13+8\left[\dfrac{\theta_p}{\tau_p}\right]}$	$\dfrac{4\theta_p}{11+2\left[\dfrac{\theta_p}{\tau_p}\right]}$

Ziegler-Nichols Tuning. Ziegler-Nichols (**ZN**) tuning[4] uses experimental measurements of the **ultimate gain**, K_u, and the **ultimate period**, P_u to calculate the controller settings   The ultimate parameters are obtained by operating a P-only controller under sustained oscillations and then measuring the period of the oscillations and noting the gain of the P-only controller. The procedure is as follows

1. Turn off integral and derivative action to give a P-only controller.
2. Increase K_c until oscillations are sustained for a relatively small setpoint change (Figure 7.17).
3. K_u is the P-only controller gain that results in the sustained oscillations.
4. P_u is the period of the sustained oscillations (Figure 7.17).
5. Calculate the controller settings using Table 7.9.

¼ Decay Ratio

Table 7.9

Ziegler-Nichols PID Settings

Controller	K_c	τ_I	τ_D
P	$0.5 K_u$	---	---
PI	$0.45 K_u$	$P_u/1.2$	---
PID	$0.6 K_u$	$P_u/2$	$P_u/8$

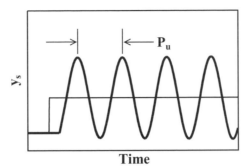

Figure 7.17 The controlled variable for an ZN ultimate test, i.e., operation at sustained oscillations with a P-only controller.

The Ziegler-Nichols settings are based on a QAD tuned response. Note that according to these settings, PID uses a 33% larger K_c than a corresponding PI controller and that a P-only controller uses a K_c that is 10% larger than a corresponding PI controller.

Cianione and Marlin Tuning. The Cianione and Marlin controller tuning approach[5] uses FOPDT parameters along with dimensionless tuning parameter plots to determine the controller settings. This approach was derived using the closed loop transfer function to develop dimensionless relationships that can be used to select tuning parameters. Consider a FOPDT model of the process

$$G_a(s)G_p(s)G_s(s) = G'_p(s) \cong \frac{K_p e^{-\theta_p s}}{\tau_p s + 1} \qquad \textbf{7.8}$$

Then the closed loop transfer function for disturbance rejection is given by

$$\frac{Y(s)}{D(s)} = \frac{G_d(s)}{G_c(s)G'_p(s)+1} = \frac{G_d(s)}{K_c\left(1+\dfrac{1}{\tau_I s}+\tau_D s\right)\left(\dfrac{K_p e^{-\theta_p s}}{\tau_p s+1}\right)+1} \qquad \textbf{7.9}$$

The following relationships can be used to non-dimensionalize this equation

$$\bar{s} = s(\theta_p + \tau_p) \qquad \textbf{7.10}$$

Eliminating s from the closed loop transfer function for disturbance rejection yields

$$\frac{Y(\bar{s})}{D(\bar{s})} = \frac{G_d(\bar{s})}{1+K_c K_p\left(1+\dfrac{1}{\tau_I \bar{s}/(\theta_p+\tau_p)}+\dfrac{\tau_D \bar{s}}{\theta_p+\tau_p}\right)\left(\dfrac{e^{-\theta_p \bar{s}/(\theta_p+\tau_p)}}{1+\dfrac{\tau_p \bar{s}}{\theta_p+\tau_p}}\right)} \qquad \textbf{7.11}$$

Note that

$$\frac{\tau_p}{(\theta_p + \tau_p)} = 1 - \frac{\theta_p}{\theta_p + \tau_p} \qquad \textbf{7.12}$$

and $[\theta_p / (\theta_p + \tau_p)]$ is referred to as the **fractional deadtime**[5]. Therefore, the process model is converted from six parameters $(K_c, \tau_I, \tau_D, K_p, \tau_p, \theta_p)$ into four parameters $[K_p K_c, \theta_p / (\theta_p + \tau_p), \tau_I / (\theta_p + \tau_p), \tau_D / (\theta_p + \tau_p)]$. Using this approach, dimensionless forms of the tuning parameters are obtained, i.e.,

$$\text{Dimensionless Gain} = K_c K_p$$

$$\text{Dimensionless Reset Time} = \frac{\tau_I}{\theta_p + \tau_p}$$

$$\text{Dimensionless Derivative Time} = \frac{\tau_D}{\theta_p + \tau_p}$$

Cianione and Marlin[6] developed correlation functions for the dimensionless gain, reset time and derivative time as a function of the fractional deadtime as shown in Figure 7.18. These correlation functions are based on tuning for minimum IAE performance considering ±25% error in the model parameters (i.e., variations in K_p, τ_p, and θ_p). These results show some of the differences between tuning for setpoint changes and disturbance rejection. Note that the correlation functions for disturbances and setpoint changes are similar, but the dimensionless reset time for disturbances is quite different at low values of fraction deadtime [i.e., $\theta_p / (\theta_p + \tau_p) < 0.3$]. Note that more integral action is used for disturbances than for setpoint changes. Also there is some difference between the dimensionless derivative time at low fractional deadtime for setpoint tracking and disturbance rejection.

While the FOPDT model is flexible enough to reasonably model a wide range of real processes, developing accurate FOPDT models for industrial processes can be a difficult and time consuming process. In addition, the assumption of ±25% parameter uncertainty is arbitrary. For example, relatively linear processes with low disturbance levels can be expected to result in FOPDT parameters that are much more uniform than ±25%. On the other hand, highly nonlinear processes would be expected to result in FOPDT parameter variations well in excess of ±25% for major disturbance upsets. Therefore, while this approach is certainly interesting and provides insight into the PID tuning process, it should also be viewed as providing only initial estimates of tuning parameters.

Overview. The Cohen and Coon method and the Cianione and Marlin method require a FOPDT process model and, as was pointed out, FOPDT process models are difficult and time consuming to develop. Also, the settings for these tuning methods

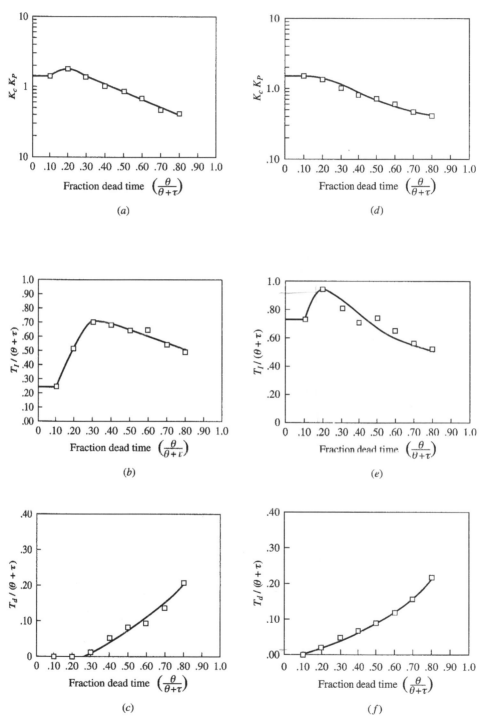

Figure 7.18 Cianione and Marlin's correlation functions for dimensionless tuning constants. For disturbance rejection (a) K_c (b) τ_I (c) τ_D . For setpoint changes (d) K_c (e) τ_I (f) τ_D . Note that T_d and T_I in this figure correspond to τ_D and τ_I. This figure is reprinted with permission from McGraw-Hill Publishing Co.

are based on a preset compromise between performance and reliability that may not be consistent with the characteristics of the control loop under consideration.

The Ziegler-Nichols method requires an ultimate test that can unnecessarily upset the process. It does have the advantage that it is a direct measurement on the process. But once again, it is also based on QAD and nonlinear processes using these settings can lead to ringing or unstable behavior. A very large number of tuning methods have been proposed. Each of these methods suffers from one or more of the same limitations as the three tuning methods presented here.

7.6 Recommended Tuning Approaches

This section presents tuning approaches recommended for tuning industrial control loops: fast responding loops or slow responding loops. In addition, a method is presented for calculating the initial settings for level control loops. The first step that a control engineer should perform when tuning a control loop is to select the controller tuning criteria based on the process nonlinearity, the disturbance severity, and the process objectives and constraints. For a fast acting process that is relatively linear with moderate disturbances, tuning approaching QAD can be appropriate in certain cases. Even though Table 7.1 shows that QAD provides the best overall performance in terms of errors from setpoint, many companies are reluctant to have their control engineers tune even well behaved control loops for QAD because of the 50% overshoot associated with QAD and because QAD is too close to the onset of instability. In addition, since QAD causes significant variation in the manipulated variable levels, QAD can result in unduly upsetting other parts of the process. For these reasons, it is probably better to tune well behaved loops for decay ratios of 1/6 to 1/8. For a process that is more nonlinear with more severe disturbances 1/10 amplitude damping would be more appropriate. Finally, if the process is highly nonlinear with severe disturbances or if there are operational constraints preventing overshoot, critically damped tuning criterion could be used. The point here is that **no single tuning criterion will work effectively for all control loops because the process nonlinearity, disturbance type and magnitude, and operational objectives must all be considered when choosing the proper tuning criterion.** For the results shown in Table 7.1, $K_c = 0.5$ corresponds to critically damped behavior and $K_c = 2.0$ corresponds to a decay ratio of 1/6; therefore, this range of tuning criterion represents a wide range of controller K_c values. In this manner, as the control loop becomes more challenging, a more conservative tuning criterion can be selected which means that larger process changes in K_p, τ_p, and θ_p are required to render the control loop unstable; therefore, using this approach, a challenging process control loop is more likely to remain in closed loop operation than if it were tuned more aggressively. Of course, more conservative tuning will penalize the control performance.

After selecting the tuning criterion, the next step should be to filter the measurement of the controlled variable (see Section 6.3 and Appendix B). All process measurements have some degree of noise and this noise will be passed to the manipulated variable and sometimes amplified if filtering of the sensor readings is not used. One commonly used filter is a linear first order filter given in Equation 6.20. Tuning this filter involves selecting the value of f. If the value of f is too large (i.e., not enough filtering is used), the noise on the sensor reading will still affect the performance of the feedback loop. On the other hand, if f is too small (i.e., too much filtering used), extra lag will be added to the feedback system and the control performance will suffer. Therefore, when tuning a filter, select a value of f that is only as small as necessary to remove the appropriate amount of the noise.

Fast-Response Loops. For fast-response loops such as flow control and pressure control loops, the simplest and quickest tuning method available for PI controllers is field tuning which is based upon a trial-and-error selection of tuning parameters. In addition, some level and temperature loops also behave as fast responding control loops. Since these processes respond quickly, trial-and-error tuning is effective. That is, it is usually easier to field tune a fast responding loop rather than identify FOPDT parameters, use initial tuning parameters from a chosen tuning method, and adjust the tuning in order to meet the selected tuning criterion. The recommended procedure for field tuning follows.

1. Based on the nonlinearity of the process, the type and severity of disturbances, and the operational objectives of the control loop in regard to the overall process select a tuning criterion (e.g., somewhere between a 1/6 decay ratio and critically damped behavior).

2. Filter the process measurement.

3. Turn off the derivative action ($\tau_D = 0$) and the integral action ($\tau_I \to \infty$).

4. Make an initial estimate of K_c , i.e., $K_c = \dfrac{1}{2 K_p}$. Estimate K_p from process knowledge.

5. Using setpoint changes, increase K_c in small increments until the response meets the tuning criterion. (See Figure 7.19 which is based upon a 1/6 decay ratio).

6. Decrease K_c by 10%.

7. Make an initial estimate for τ_I, i.e., $\tau_I \cong 5\tau_p$. Estimate τ_p from process knowledge.

8. Using setpoint changes, decrease τ_I until offset is eliminated and the tuning criterion is met. (See Figure 7.20 which is also based upon a 1/6 decay ratio).

9. Check to ensure that adequate levels of proportional and integral action are being used.

Note that PID controllers are not usually required for fast responding processes. Table 7.10 lists ranges of PID tuning parameters for flow controllers, gas pressure controllers, liquid pressure controllers, level controllers, temperature controllers, and composition controllers. Note that the gain is expressed in proportional band (Section 6.3) and the larger the PB the lower the K_c. Flow control loops are actually a special case for tuning. Because of the sustained oscillations that results about the setpoint

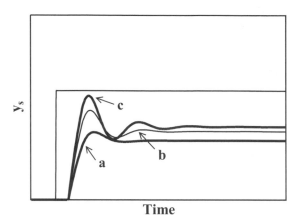

Figure 7.19 Selection of K_c during field tuning (a) Results for initial value of K_c (b) Results for an increase in K_c (c) Results for final value of K_c (1/6 decay

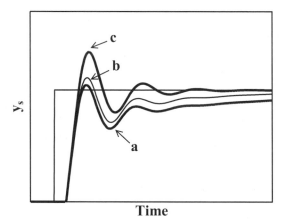

Figure 7.20 Selection of τ_I during field tuning (a) Results for initial value of τ_I (b) Results for a decrease in τ_I (c) Results for the final value of τ_I (1/6 decay ratio).

(Figure 6.12), flow control loops are usually tuned with more integral action than proportional action compared with other control loops which is consistent with Table 7.10.

Slow-Response Processes. For slow response loops (e.g., certain temperature and composition control loops), field tuning can be a time consuming procedure that leads to less than satisfactory results. Step test results can be used to generate FOPDT models and tuning parameters can be calculated from a variety of techniques. This approach suffers from the fact that it takes approximately the open loop response time of the process to implement a step test and during that time, measured and unmeasured disturbances can affect the process thus corrupting the results from the step test. In addition, it is unlikely that the tuning approach selected will result in the proper balance between reliability and performance.   Because of model mismatch and the likely selection of an inappropriate tuning criterion, significant adjustments to the tuning is still required.

Table 7.10 Typical Tuning Parameters for Common Loops in the CPI			
Loop Type	PB	$\tau_I(s)$	$\tau_D(s)$
Flow Controller	100 - 500%	0.2 - 2.0	0
Gas Pressure Controller	1 - 15%	5-100	0
Liquid Pressure controller	100 - 500%	0.2 - 2.0	0
Level Controller	5 - 50%	5 - 60	0
Temperature Controller	10 - 50%	40 - 4000	30 - 2000*
Composition Controller	100 - 1000%	100 - 5000	30 - 4000*

*τ_D should always be smaller than τ_I.

The **ATV**[7] (autotune variation) method determines the ultimate gain and period in a manner similar to the ultimate method, but ATV tests can be implemented without unduly upsetting the process. Controller settings can be calculated, and the controller can then be tuned on-line to meet the selected dynamic performance.

Figure 7.21 graphically demonstrates the ATV method. The user must select *h*, the relay height used or the change in the manipulated variable that is to be applied. *h* should be small enough that the process is not unnecessarily upset, yet large enough that the resulting amplitude, *a*, can be accurately measured.

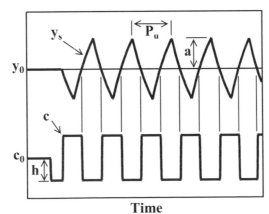

Time

Figure 7.21 Graphical representation of an ATV test.

In order to initiate an ATV test, the process should be at steady-state or near steady-state conditions, c_0 and y_0. Next, the controller output is set to $c_0 + h$ (or $c_0 - h$) until y deviates significantly from y_0. At that point, the controller output is set to $c_0 - h$ (or $c_0 + h$) which will turn the process back toward y_0. Then each time y crosses y_0, the controller output is switched from $c_0 + h$ to $c_0 - h$ or from $c_0 - h$ to $c_0 + h$. The process is also referred to as a relay feedback experiment. A standing wave is established after 3 to 4 cycles; therefore, the values of a and the ultimate period, P_u, can be measured directly and the ATV test is concluded. The ultimate gain, K_u, is calculated by

$$K_u = \frac{4h}{\pi a} \qquad\qquad 7.13$$

K_u and P_u can be used in one of several tuning schemes. One tuning approach is the Ziegler-Nichols (ZN) ultimate settings (Table 7.9). Consider the ZN settings for a PI controller:

$$K_c^{ZN} = 0.45 K_u$$
$$\tau_I^{ZN} = P_u / 1.2$$

ZN settings tend to be fairly aggressive and can lead to ringing behavior for nonlinear processes due to the relatively small value of τ_I (i.e., large integral action).

Another tuning approach that was developed for processes that behave like an integrator plus deadtime system is the Tyreus and Luyben (TL) settings[8]:

$$K_c^{TL} = 0.31 K_u$$
$$\tau_I^{TL} = P_u / 0.45$$

The TL settings are less aggressive with considerably less integral action than the ZN settings. The TL settings are recommended for more sluggish processes that are well represented as integrator plus deadtime for a good portion of its step test (e.g., a sluggish distillation column). After the ZN or TL settings are calculated, they may require on-line tuning, particularly for the ZN settings in order to meet the desired dynamic performance (e.g., 1/6 decay ratio or critically damped). For example, the ZN settings would be tuned on-line as follows:

$$K_c = K_u^{ZN} / F_T$$
$$\tau_I = \tau_I^{ZN} \times F_T \qquad\qquad 7.14$$

by adjusting F_T on-line. Note that as F_T is increased, K_c decreases while τ_I increases by the same proportion (detuning). The tuning factor, F_T, can be adjusted to meet the performance requirements for each individual application. Therefore, on-line tuning has been reduced to a one-dimensional search for the proper level of controller

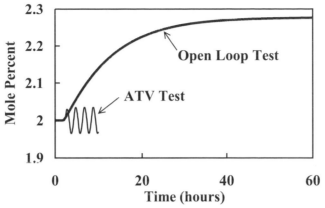

Figure 7.22 Comparison of an ATV and an open loop test.

aggressiveness for a PI controller. If the controller is too aggressive, F_T is increased. If the controller is too sluggish, decrease F_T.

Note that the procedure based on ATV identification with on-line tuning is applicable for tuning PI controllers. It should be pointed out that for certain cases after this procedure has been applied it will be evident that the proper balance between proportional and integral action has not been used, e.g., if offset elimination is slow. In these cases, adjustments in the relative amount of proportional or integral action may be required. For example, if the TL settings were used and not enough integral action resulted, the 0.45 factor in the TL settings for integral action (i.e., $P_u /0.45$) could be increased in order to speed up offset elimination. Figures 7.5 and 7.6 can be helpful in determining if not enough proportional action or if not enough integral action is being used.

As an example of an ATV test, consider its application to a dynamic simulator of a C_3 (propylene/propane) splitter. Figure 7.22 shows an ATV test and an open loop test on the same time scale for the bottom product composition control loop. Note that the four cycles of the ATV test required 6-8 hours while the open loop test required in excess of 60 hours. The ATV results were used with TL settings and the results for three different tuning factors are shown in Figure 7.23.

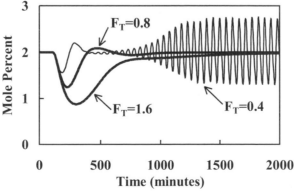

Figure 7.23 Effect of F_T on dynamic response.

Summarizing, identifying the ultimate gain and ultimate period of a slow-response loop using the ATV method has been shown to be relatively fast providing a "snap shot" of the process without unduly upsetting the system.   In addition, the on-line tuning procedure provides a systematic method of selecting the proper degree of controller aggressiveness.   Therefore, the ATV test with on-line tuning represents an industrially relevant means of attaining high quality controller tuning for loops with large response times.

Example 7.1   Example of ATV Identification and On-line Tuning

Problem Statement   Apply ATV identification with on-line tuning to tune a PI controller applied to the CST composition mixer process developed in Chapter 3. Tune for a 1/6 decay ratio. Note that the combined actuator/process/sensor system should be considered.

Solution Figure 7.24 shows an ATV test using a value of h equal to 0.5 kg/s applied to the specified value of F_1. The values of a and P_u are

$$a = 0.107 \text{ gmoles/l}$$

$$P_u = 30 \text{ min}$$

Note that since y_s is not symmetric about y_0, an average value of a is computed. Then using Equation 7.13 results in

$$K_u = 5.96 \ (\text{kg/s}) / (\text{gmole/l})$$

Then the ZN settings are

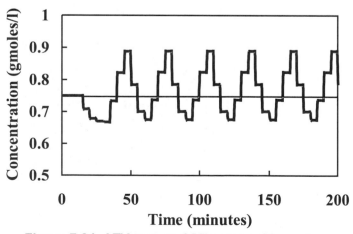

Figure 7.24 ATV test on CST composition mixer.

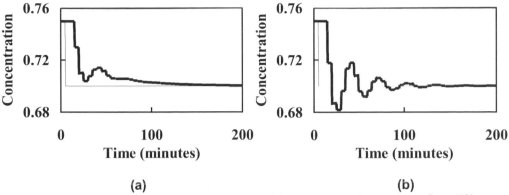

(a)   (b)

Figure 7.25   Dynamic response for the CST composition mixer for different tuning factors. (a) F_T=0.75 (b) F_T=0.5.

$$K_c^{ZN} = 2.68 \text{ (kg/s)} / \text{(gmole/l)}$$

$$\tau_I^{ZN} = 25 \text{ min}$$

Figures 7.25 shows the closed loop results for a setpoint change in the product composition for F_T equal to 0.75 and 0.5, respectively. For F_T equal to 0.75 (Figure 7.25a), the decay ratio is 1/12 and for F_T equal to 0.5 (Figure 7.25b) the decay ratio is 1/2.6; therefore, the tuning factor for a decay ratio of 1/6 is between 0.5 and 0.75. Note that in this case since the oscillations are not always symmetric about the setpoint, the decay ratio can be determined based upon adjacent peak to valley heights. In fact, F_T was determined to be 0.61 for a decay ratio of 1/6. Figure 7.26 shows the control performance for the tuned controller for a step change in feed composition for stream 1 from 0.5 to 0.55 gmole/ l. Note that the results shown in Figure 7.26 indicate that not enough integral action was applied since the oscillations are not symmetric about the setpoint and the offset is slow to be removed.

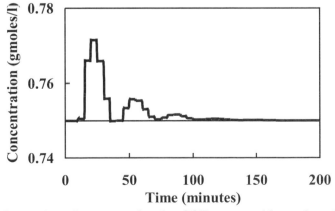

Figure 7.26 Control performance for the CST composition mixer for a feed composition upset.

PID tuning. PID tuning of slow response processes is less systematic than tuning PI controllers since the on-line tuning procedure (Equation 7.14) is not generally effective for PID controllers. That is, applying a tuning factor, F_T, to the derivative time and tuning a PID controller by adjusting only F_T does not, in general, lead to a well tuned PID controller. The recommended procedure for tuning PID controllers is as follows

1. Tune a PI Controller using ATV identification with on-line tuning. Make sure that the proper balance between proportional and integral action is used. It may be necessary to reduce τ_I in order to produce symmetric oscillations about the new setpoint.

2. Add derivative action and tune τ_D for minimum response time. Initially set τ_D equal to $P_u/8$ where P_u comes from the ATV test.

3. Increase K_c and τ_D by the same factor until the desired dynamic response is obtained.

4. Check the response to ensure that the proper level of integral action is being used.

Example 7.2 PID Tuning Example

Problem Statement.   Apply the proposed PID tuning procedure to tune a PID controller applied to a FOPDT process ($K_p = 1$, $\tau_p = 1$, $\theta_p = 2$) for QAD.

Solution. An ATV test was applied to a simulation of this FOPDT process and the amplitude of the resulting standing wave was 0.0859 with an ultimate period of 5.2 for a relay height (h) of 0.1. The TL settings were applied because of the deadtime to time constant ratio and the online tuning factor was adjusted until QAD performance was obtained for a setpoint change from 0.0 to 1.0 resulting in a value of F_T of 0.58 . It was observed that inadequate integral action was being applied since the oscillations in y_s were not symmetric about the setpoint and were below the setpoint. The value of τ_I was reduced by 60% which resulted in proper integral action. Next, derivative action was added and τ_D was set equal to $P_u /8$. The resulting controller provided a decay ratio of 1/6 . Then K_c and τ_D were both increased by 10% yielding QAD performance. When the PID controller performance was compared with the PI controller, the PID controller provided 50% less overshoot and a 40% shorter settling time than the corresponding PI controller tuned for QAD.

Level Controller Tuning. If a level control process is fast responding, then field tuning is effective. If the level control process is relatively slow responding, it can be helpful to use the following approach to select the initial settings for the level controller. Marlin[9] developed closed-form solutions for the dynamic behavior of PI and P-only control of level in a constant cross-section tank. He used these expressions to derive analytical expressions for the tuning parameters that result in a **critically damped response** for the closed loop level control process:

$$K_c = \left.\frac{-F'_{MAX}}{L'_{max}}\right\} \quad P-only \; control \qquad\qquad \textbf{7.15}$$

$$\left.\begin{aligned} K_c &= \frac{-0.736\, F'_{MAX}}{L'_{MAX}} \\[2mm] \tau_I &= \frac{4A_c\,\rho}{-K_c} \end{aligned}\right\} \quad PI \; control \qquad\qquad \textbf{7.16}$$

where A_c is the cross-sectional area of the tank, ρ is the density of the liquid, F'_{MAX} is the maximum expected step change in the feed rate to the tank, and L'_{MAX} is the desired level change that F'_{MAX} should cause under feedback conditions.

These tuning relations can be used for both tight level control and loose level control depending upon the selection of L'_{MAX}. If L'_{MAX} were selected to correspond to about a 2% level change, it would represent tight level control and K_c would have a correspondingly high value. On the other hand, if L'_{MAX} were selected to correspond to a 40% level change, it would represent quite loose level control and K_c would be correspondingly lower.

This analysis is based on an idealized model of the level of a tank and does not consider sensor or actuator dynamics and does not consider that horizontal tanks do not have a constant cross-section. For these reasons, it is recommended that Equation 7.15 and 7.16 be used as initial estimates of the tuning parameters and that an on-line tuning factor, F_T, be used to tune for the desired level control performance:

$$\begin{aligned} K'_c &= K_c/F_T \\ \tau'_I &= \tau_I \times F_T \end{aligned}$$

Example 7.3   Calculation of Initial Tuning Parameters for a Level Controller

Problem Statement. Consider level control in a horizontal cylinder tank that is 6 feet in diameter and 20 feet long. Normally, the feed rate to the tank is 10,000 pounds per hour of a dilute aqueous solution. Feed rate step changes are normally within the range of ± 10% of the normal feed rate. The setpoint for the level is usually set at 20%. The pressure taps for the level indicator are located at the top and bottom of the tank. Determine the tuning parameters for a PI controller that will keep the level within ±5% of setpoint based upon Equation 7.16 for ±10% feed rate changes.

Solution. By geometric analysis, the width of the liquid level in the tank at 20% full is 4.8 feet; therefore, the cross-sectional area is 96 ft². Using the density of pure water,

$$F'_{MAX} = (0.1)(10,000 \ lbs \ / \ h)\left(\frac{h}{60\min}\right) = 16.67 \ lbs \ / \min$$

$$K_c = \frac{-0.736(1000 \ lbs \ / \ h)}{5\%} = -147.4 \ \frac{lbs \ / \ h}{\%}$$

$$\tau_I = \frac{(4)(96 \ ft^2)(62.4 \ lbs \ / \ ft^3)(6 \ ft \ / \ 100\%)}{147.4 \dfrac{lbs \ / \ h}{\%}} = 585\min$$

7.7 Summary

One of the major responsibilities of a process control engineer is PID control loop tuning which is generally a compromise between controller performance and controller reliability with consideration given to the operational objectives of the process. Control performance is measured by the error from setpoint while reliability is determined by the severity of the disturbances that a controller is able to reliably handle. The control engineer should consider the combined effect of process nonlinearity, the severity of disturbances, and the operational objectives of the process when selecting the tuning criterion (e.g. 1/6 decay ratio or critically damped in the extremes) for a particular control loop.

It was shown that as the amount of proportional action or integral action is increased, the dynamic behavior of a feedback system can change from overdamped to critically damped to oscillatory to ringing to sustained oscillations to instability. As the amount of derivative action is increased, the damping rate increases and the rate of oscillations decreases.

Classical tuning methods are based on one preset tuning criterion, e.g., QAD or minimum IAE; therefore, they can result in control loops that are excessively aggressive or excessively sluggish, depending on the combined effect of process nonlinearity and disturbance severity for a particular process.

The recommended tuning procedure is first to determine the tuning criterion based upon an analysis of the process nonlinearity, disturbance severity, and process objectives. Next, apply the proper degree of filtering to the measured value of the controlled variable. Then if the process is fast acting (e.g., flow or pressure control loops), use a field tuning procedure to match the closed loop performance to the selected tuning criterion. If the process is slow responding, use ATV identification of the ultimate gain and period followed by on-line tuning in order to attain closed loop performance which is consistent with the selected tuning criterion.

7.8 Additional Terminology

ATV - autotune variation; a relay feedback experiment designed to measure the ultimate gain and ultimate period of a control loop.

Cohen and Coon tuning - control settings for P-only, PI, and PID controllers based on a minimum IAE tuning criterion using FOPDT process models.

Controller performance - a measure of the error from setpoint.

Controller reliability - a measure of how well a controller stays in service. It can be quantified by the maximum severity of a disturbance that a control loop can handle and remain in service.

F_T - the on-line tuning factor for PI controller tuning.

Fractional deadtime - $\theta_p / (\theta_p + \tau_p)$

IAE - integral absolute error.

ISE - integral squared error.

ITAE - integral time absolute error.

ITSE - integral time squared error.

In-phase - y_s is in-phase with c when the peaks for y_s and c both occur at the same point in time.

K_u - the ultimate gain of a loop, i.e., the controller gain for a P-only controller that causes sustained oscillations.

P_u - the period of sustained oscillations using a P-only control.

Quarter amplitude damping (QAD) - the amplitude damping ratio of ¼.

Reliability - the ability of a controlled process to remain stable when subjected to severe disturbances.

Ringing - oscillatory behavior with low amplitude damping (e.g., a decay ratio of 1/1.5).

Root locus diagram - a plot of the real and imaginary components of the poles of a closed loop transfer function as a function of the controller gain, K_c.

Ziegler-Nichols (ZN) tuning - controller settings for P-only, PI, or PID controllers using K_u and P_u which is based upon a QAD tuning criterion.

7.9 References

1. Stephanopoulos, G., *Chemical Process Control*, Prentice-Hall, Inc., p. 215 (1984).

2. Marlin, T.E., Process Control, McGraw-Hill, p. 393 (1995).

3. Cohen, G.H. and G.A. Coon, "Theoretical Considerations of Retarded Control", *Trans ASME*, Vol. 75, p. 827 (1953).

4. Ziegler, J.G. and N.B. Nichols, "Optimum Settings for Automatic Controllers", *Trans ASME*, Vol. 64, p. 759 (1942).

5. Marlin, T.E., *Process Control*, McGraw-Hill, p. 300 (1995).

6. Cianione, R. and T.E. Marlin, "Tune Controllers to Meet Plant Objectives", *Control*, Vol. 5, p. 50 (1992).

7. Astrom, K.J. and T. Hagglund, *Automatic Tuning of PID Controllers,* Instrument Society of America, p. 233 (1998).

8. Tyreus, B.D. and W.L. Luyben, "Tuning PI Controllers for Integrator/Deadtime Processes", *Ind. Eng. Chem. Res.*, Vol. 31, p. 2625 (1992).

9. Marlin, T.E., *Process Control*, McGraw-Hill, pp 588-590 (1995).

7.10 Questions and Exercises

7.1 List several commonly used tuning objectives and explain why they cannot be simultaneously meet.

7.2 Explain what a statistical process control chart is and how it can be used to assess control performance.

7.3 Define a root locus plot and explain what it shows.

7.4 For open loop overdamped processes, explain what sequence of phases the process behavior goes through as the controller aggressiveness is increased.

7.5 Consider a PI controller. How can you tell if there is too little proportional action? How can you tell if there is too little integral action?

7.6 Consider a PI controller that results in ringing. How can you tell if there is too much proportional action or too much integral action?

7.7. What determines whether or not one should use field tuning or ATV-based tuning?

7.8 Consider a FOPDT process (i.e., $K_p=1$, $\tau_p=2$, $\theta_p=0.5$). What is the maximum size of the control interval that should be used for this case without deteriorating the control performance? What would happen if a larger or a smaller control interval were used?

7.9 Why should one not tune all controllers for one tuning criterion?

7.10 Explain how the Cohen and Coon, the ZN, and the Cianione and Marlin methods are used to tune a control loop.

7.11 Why are the methods listed in 7.10 not recommended for tuning industrial control loops?

7.12 What two things should be done before tuning a controller?

7.13 For each of the following process simulators provided with the text, apply filtering to the measured value of the controlled variable. Compare the filtered value with the unfiltered data for lined out periods and periods when the controlled variable is changing. Next, double the standard deviation of the noise and repeat the filter tuning procedure. Then, take the original noise level and divide it by a factor of two and repeat the filter tuning procedure. Compare the results of this exercise.

    a. CST thermal mixer   b. CST composition mixer

    c. Level control process   d. Endothermic CSTR

    e. Heat exchanger

7.14 For each of the following process simulators provided with the text, tune the filter on the measured value of the controlled variable. Applying field tuning techniques, tune a PI controller for the process for a 1/6 decay ratio*. Next, apply a filter factor of 0.5 and retune the controller. Finally, apply a filter factor of 0.01 and retune the controller. What can you conclude from this exercise?

    a. CST thermal mixer   b. CST composition mixer

    c. Level control process   d. Endothermic CSTR

    e. Heat exchanger

7.15 For each of the following process simulators provided with the text, apply an ATV test to determine the ultimate gain and ultimate period. Apply ZN settings and tune a PI controller for a 1/8 decay ratio* using the on-line tuning factor. Apply TL settings and tune a PI controller for a 1/8 decay ratio* using the on-line tuning factor. Remember that fine tuning adjustments may be required to ensure that the proper amount of proportional and integral action are being used.

    a. CST thermal mixer   b. CST composition mixer

    c. Level control process   d. Endothermic CSTR

    e. Heat exchanger

7.16 For each of the following process simulators provided with the text, apply an ATV test to determine the ultimate gain and ultimate period. Using ZN settings and an on-line tuning factor, tune the process for a dynamic response corresponding to critically damped behavior, a 1/10 decay ratio, and a 1/6 decay ratio for a setpoint change. Test each controller with a step change in the disturbance level and plot all the disturbance result tests on the same figure.

   a. CST thermal mixer   b. CST composition mixer

   c. Level control process   d. Endothermic CSTR

   e. Heat exchanger

7.17 For each of the following process simulators provided with the text, apply the field tuning procedure. Tune the process for a dynamic response corresponding to critically damped behavior, a 1/10 decay ratio*, and a 1/6 decay ratio* for a setpoint change. Test each controller with a step change in the disturbance level and plot all the disturbance result tests on the same figure.

   a. CST thermal mixer   b. CST composition mixer

   c. Level control process   d. Endothermic CSTR

   e. Heat exchanger

7.18 For the heat exchanger process simulator provided with the text, tune a PI and a PID controller for a decay ratio of 1/8 using small amplitude setpoint changes. Then test both controller for a step disturbance upset and compare the results.

7.19 Apply a PI and a PID controller to each of the following FOPDT processes for which K_p and τ_p are equal to unity. Tune both controllers for setpoint changes and test them for step disturbances.

   a. $\theta_p = 0.3$ b. $\theta_p = 0.6$

   c. $\theta_p = 1.2$ d. $\theta_p = 2.4$

7.20 Calculate the initial PI controller settings for a level controller with a critically damped response for a 10 ft diameter tank (i.e., a cylinder placed on its end) and a measured height of 10 ft that normally handles a feed rate of 1000 lb/h. Assume that it is desired to have a maximum level change of 5% for a 20% feed rate change and that the liquid has a density corresponding to water.

* When measuring the decay ratio of a response, it is generally easier and more accurate to take the ratio of the difference from the peak to the valley height for first two oscillations.

Chapter 8

Frequency Response Analysis

8.1 Introduction

To this point, dynamic process behavior, both open loop and closed loop, has primarily been studied for step changes in manipulated variables, setpoints, and disturbances. In this chapter, we will study the effect of sinusoidal inputs over a range of frequencies, ω's, where

$$u(t) = a \sin \omega t$$

This procedure is called **frequency response analysis**.

The frequency of an input can have a very significant effect upon the resulting behavior of the process. For example, consider a mixing tank with a time constant of 10 minutes for its composition dynamics. If sinusoidal variations in one of the inlet concentrations are applied at a frequency of 10 cycles per second, no measurable sinusoidal variation in the outlet concentration will result. Since the time constant of the process is 10 minutes, the peaks and the valleys of the sinusoidal variation of the input will average out because the input changes are occurring faster than the process can respond. On the other hand, if the frequency of the input were 0.01 cycles/second, significant variation in the output would result. Also, if the frequency were extremely slow, e.g., one cycle per day, the process would appear to be at steady-state even though in fact it would be changing very slowly. In addition, by analyzing the frequencies of disturbances that pass through a number of controllers, one can evaluate the propagation of variability through a multiple unit process. The frequency response behavior of a control loop can be an important perspective to use to understand the performance of process control systems. While it is not recommended to apply frequency response analysis techniques directly to industrial processes (e.g., tuning control loops), frequency response analysis is still important to the understanding of the feedback control behavior of industrial processes. In addition, important process control terminology is based on frequency response analysis.

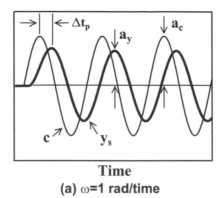

Time
(a) ω=1 rad/time

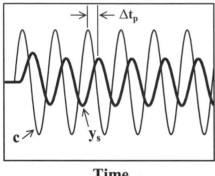

Time
(b) ω=2 rad/time

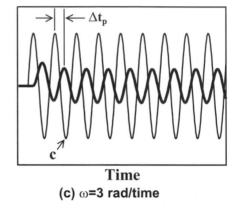

Time
(c) ω=3 rad/time

Figure 8.1 The effect of frequency on the amplitude and phase lag of a FOPDT process.

8.2 Bode Plot

Figure 8.1 shows the dynamic behavior of a FOPDT process model ($K_p = 1$, $\tau_p = 1$, $\theta_p = 0.5$) subjected to sinusoidal inputs with different frequencies. The amplitude of the variations in y_s and the difference in the timing of the peaks in y_s and c at each frequency characterize the frequency response behavior of this process. To normalize the results, the **amplitude ratio** is used, i.e.,

$$A_r = \frac{a_y}{a_c}$$

where a_y is the amplitude of the sinusoidal variation in the controlled variable, y_s, while a_c is the amplitude of the sinusoidal variations in the controller output, c. The time difference between peaks, Δt_p (i.e., the time that c **lags** y_s), can be converted into an angle and is referred to as the **phase angle** of the response, ϕ

$$\phi = \frac{\omega \, \Delta t_p}{2\pi} \times 360°$$

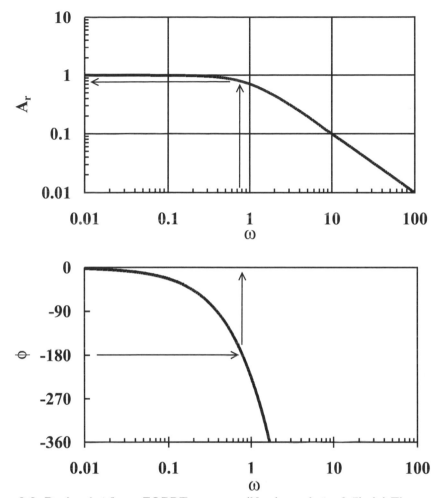

Figure 8.2 Bode plot for a FOPDT process (K_p=1, τ_p=1, θ_p=0.5) (a) The upper plot is the amplitude ratio (b) The lower plot is the phase angle.

where ω is the frequency of the input variations in radians per second. A **Bode plot** of a process is a plot of ϕ and the logarithm of A_r versus the logarithm of ω. Note that these are common logarithms with base 10. Figure 8.2 shows the Bode plot for the previous FOPDT process model. Note that since y_s lags c in Figure 8.1, the phase angle is negative as is shown in Figure 8.2. Therefore, the direct way to generate a Bode plot is to excite the process with sinusoidal inputs of varying frequencies, wait until standing waves have been established, and measure the amplitude ratio and phase angle.

The Bode plot of a process can also be generated by using the transfer function of the process. Consider a first order process

$$G_p(s) \;=\; \frac{K_p}{\tau_p\, s + 1}$$

with a sinusoidal input
$$U(s) = \frac{a_u \omega}{s^2 + \omega^2}$$

Then

$$Y(s) = \frac{K_p \, a_u \, \omega}{(\tau_p s + 1)(s^2 + \omega^2)} = \frac{K_p \, a_u}{\tau_p^2 \omega^2 + 1} \left[\frac{\omega \tau_p^2}{\tau_p s + 1} - \frac{s \omega \tau_p}{s^2 + \omega^2} + \frac{\omega}{s^2 + \omega^2} \right]$$

Then taking the inverse Laplace transform yields

$$y(t) = \frac{K_p \, a_u}{\tau_p^2 \omega^2 + 1} \left[\omega \tau_p \, e^{-t/\tau_p} - \omega \tau_p \, \cos \omega t + \sin \omega t \right]$$

and applying trigonometric relations results in

$$y(t) = \frac{K_p \, a_u \, \omega \tau_p}{\omega^2 \tau_p^2 + 1} \, e^{-t/\tau_p} + \frac{K_p \, a_u}{\sqrt{\omega^2 \tau_p^2 + 1}} \, \sin(\omega t + \phi)$$

where $\phi = \tan^{-1}(-\omega \tau_p)$.

At long time, the exponential term will decay to zero; therefore, the amplitude ratio is given by

$$A_r = \frac{K_p}{\sqrt{\omega^2 \tau_p^2 + 1}}$$

and the phase angle is simply ϕ. Therefore, a Bode plot can also be derived using the transfer function with a sinusoidal input.

Another way to use the transfer function to generate a Bode plot is to substitute $s = i\omega$ into $G_p(s)$ and factor the result into the real and imaginary components, i.e.,

$$G_p(i\omega) = R(\omega) + iI(\omega) \qquad\qquad \textbf{8.1}$$

then
$$A_r = |G_p(i\omega)| = \sqrt{R^2(\omega) + I^2(\omega)}$$

and
$$\phi = \tan^{-1} [I(\omega)/R(\omega)]$$

For example, consider a first order process

$$G_p(i\omega) = \frac{K_p}{i\omega\tau_p + 1}$$

In order to remove i from the denominator, multiply the numerator and denominator each by the complex conjugate of the denominator, i.e., $(1 - i\,\omega\tau_p)$

$$G_p(i\omega) = \frac{-iK_p\,\omega\tau_p + K_p}{\omega^2\tau_p^2 + 1} = \frac{K_p}{\omega^2\tau_p^2 + 1} - i\frac{K_p\,\omega\tau_p}{\omega^2\tau_p^2 + 1}$$

Then using Equation 8.1

$$A_r = \left|G_p(i\omega)\right| = \frac{\sqrt{K_p^2 + K_p^2\,\omega^2\tau_p^2}}{\omega^2\tau_p^2 + 1} = \frac{K_p}{\sqrt{\omega^2\tau_p^2 + 1}} \qquad \textbf{8.2}$$

and $$\phi = \angle G_p(i\omega) = \tan^{-1}(-\omega\tau_p)$$

which agree with the results of the earlier approach and generally is simpler to apply than the previous approach.

Consider a transfer function given by

$$G_p(s) = \frac{G_a(s)\,G_b(s)}{G_c(s)\,G_d(s)}$$

The amplitude ratio is given by

$$A_r = \left|G_p(i\omega)\right| = \frac{\left|G_a(i\omega)\right|\left|G_b(i\omega)\right|}{\left|G_c(i\omega)\right|\left|G_d(i\omega)\right|} \qquad \textbf{8.3}$$

And $\quad \phi = \angle G_p(i\omega) = \angle G_a(i\omega) + \angle G_b(i\omega) - \angle G_c(i\omega) - \angle G_d(i\omega) \qquad \textbf{8.4}$

For example, consider

$$G_p(s) = \frac{K_p}{(\tau_1 s + 1)(\tau_2 s + 1)}$$

Then from Equations 8.2, 8.3, and 8.4

$$A_r = \frac{K_p}{\sqrt{\omega^2 \tau_1^2 + 1}\ \sqrt{\omega^2 \tau_2^2 + 1}}$$

$$\phi = \tan^{-1}(-\omega\tau_1) + \tan^{-1}(-\omega\tau_2)$$

In addition, Bode plots of individual transfer functions can be graphically combined to yield the Bode plot of the product of the transfer functions. Taking the logarithm of Equation 8.3 results in

$$\log A_r = \log|G_a(i\omega)| + \log|G_b(i\omega)| - \log|G_c(i\omega)| - \log|G_d(i\omega)|$$

Since a Bode plot contains the logarithm of A_r, the previous equation shows that the logarithm of A_r of a process composed of the product of several transfer functions is the sum of the logarithms of the A_r's of the individual transfer functions. Likewise, Equation 8.4 indicates that the phase angle of a process composed of the product of several transfer functions is simply the sum of the phase angles of the individual transfer functions. In this way, the Bode plots of complex transfer functions can easily be constructed using the known Bode plots of the individual components. Table 8.1 lists the A_r and ϕ as a function of ω for several commonly encountered transfer functions.

Table 8.1
Amplitude Ratios and Phase Angles for Several Transfer Functions

Transfer Function	A_r	$\phi\,(°)$
K_p	K_p	0
$\dfrac{K_p}{\tau_p s + 1}$	$\dfrac{K_p}{\sqrt{\omega^2 \tau_p^2 + 1}}$	$\tan^{-1}(-\omega\tau_p)$
$\dfrac{K_p}{\tau_p^2 s^2 + 2\tau_p \zeta s + 1}$	$\dfrac{K_p}{\sqrt{(1 - \omega^2 \tau_p^2)^2 + (2\omega\tau_p \zeta)^2}}$	$\tan^{-1}\left(\dfrac{-2\,\omega\tau_p \zeta}{1 - \omega^2 \tau_p^2}\right)$
$e^{-\theta_p s}$	1	$-\theta_p\,\omega\left(\dfrac{360}{2\pi}\right)$
$\dfrac{K_p}{s}$	$\dfrac{K_p}{\omega}$	-90
$K_c\left(1 + \dfrac{1}{\tau_I s}\right)$	$K_c\sqrt{1 + \dfrac{1}{\omega^2 \tau_I^2}}$	$\tan^{-1}\left(\dfrac{-1}{\omega\tau_I}\right)$

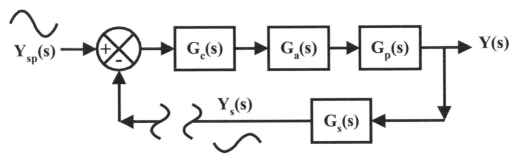

Figure 8.3a Block diagram of a feedback loop with the feedback broken and a sinusoidal variation in the setpoint.

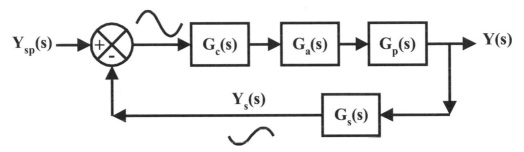

Figure 8.3b Block diagram of a feedback loop with the simultaneously termination of the setpoint variation and the closing of the loop.

8.3 Gain Margin and Phase Margin

Consider the FOPDT process model $(K_p = 1, \tau_p = 1, \theta_p = 0.5)$ that was used to generate the Bode plot shown in Figure 8.2. Further, consider the frequency that corresponds to a phase angle, ϕ, of -180°, i.e., from Figure 8.2 $\omega = 0.79$ radians per time. Figure 8.3a is a schematic of a loop with a sinusoidally varying setpoint with a frequency of 0.79 radians per second. Note that a P-only controller with a gain of 1.0 is used but the feedback of the measurement is broken before it is compared with the setpoint value, i.e., this is an open loop process. Since the amplitude ratio at $\omega = 0.79$ radians per second is 0.78, the amplitude of the variation of the measured value of y is 0.78. Note that since the phase angle is -180°, the sinusoidal variation in the measured value of y is the negative of the setpoint variation, i.e.,

$$y_{sp} = 1.0 \sin(\omega t)$$
$$y_s = -0.78 \sin(\omega t)$$

since $\sin(\omega t - 180°) = -\sin(\omega t)$

Figure 8.3b represents the closing of the feedback loop and the simultaneous replacement of the sinusoidal variation in the setpoint with a constant setpoint. Note

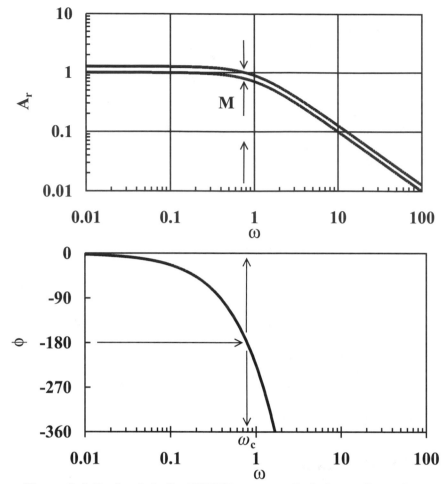

Figure 8.4 Bode plot of a FOPDT process that shows the gain margin.

that since the measured value of the controlled variable is subtracted from the setpoint, the variations in y_s are in phase with the original variations in y_{sp}. Once the loop is closed, the sinusoidal variations are fed back around the loop, but since the amplitude ratio is 0.78, the variation in y_s will damp out with each subsequent cycle of the loop. That is, the second time around the loop y_s will have a sinusoidal amplitude of 0.61 (i.e., $0.78 \cdot 0.78$) and the third time will have an amplitude of 0.48 and so on. If the amplitude ratio were exactly 1.0, the oscillations would be sustained. If the amplitude ratio were greater than 1.0, y_s would grow without bound (i.e., unstable operation). Therefore, the amplitude ratio at a phase angle of -180° indicates the stability of a system and is called the **Bode stability criterion**. The frequency at which the phase angle is equal to -180° is referred to as the **critical frequency**, ω_c.

Figure 8.4 shows the Bode plot of the FOPDT process ($K_p = 1$, $\tau_p = 1$, $\theta_p = 0.5$) for a P-only controller in an open loop configuration. It shows the results for $K_c = 1.0$ and $K_c = 1.28$ which corresponds to underdamped stable operation and sustained oscillations at the critical frequency, respectively. Note that

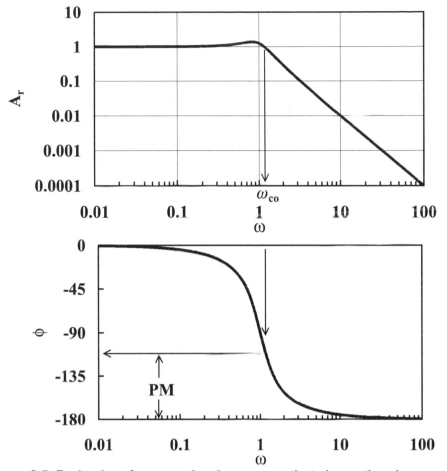

Figure 8.5 Bode plot of a second order process that shows the phase margin.

the difference between the amplitude ratio for $K_c = 1.0$ and $K_c = 1.28$, which is denoted by M in Figure 8.4, is a measure of how close the controller with $K_c = 1.0$ is to the onset of instability. The **gain margin (GM)** is defined by

$$GM \; = \; \frac{1}{A_r^*} \qquad\qquad \textbf{8.5}$$

where A_r^* is the amplitude ratio at $\omega = \omega_c$.

Figure 8.5 shows a Bode plot for a second order process ($K_p = 1$, $\tau_p = 1$, and $\zeta = 0.4$) with a P-only controller with $K_c = 1.0$. The **phase margin (PM)**, is the difference between a phase angle corresponding to an amplitude ratio of 1.0 and a phase angle of -180°, i.e.,

$$PM \; = \; \phi * - (-180°) \qquad\qquad \textbf{8.6}$$

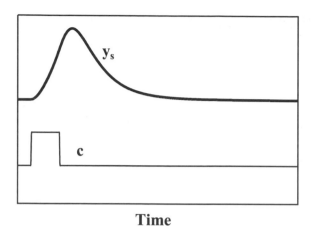

Figure 8.6 Example of a pulse test.

where ϕ^* is the phase angle that corresponds to $A_r=1$. The **crossover frequency**, ω_{co}, is the frequency that corresponds to $A_r=1$. Either gain margins or phase margins can be used to tune controllers. The larger the GM or PM values used for tuning, the more conservatively the controller will be tuned. Typical GM values used for tuning range from 1.4 to 1.8 while PM values typically range from 30° to 45°. GM and PM can be used like the decay ratio was used in Chapter 7 to select the controller tuning criterion, i.e., the more nonlinear a process and the larger the magnitude of disturbance affecting the process, the larger the values of PM or GM that one would use.

8.4 Pulse Test

Earlier in this chapter, several approaches were presented that could be used to develop a Bode plot of a process by testing the process directly or by using the transfer function of the process. A **pulse test** is an experimental approach that can be used to generate a Bode plot of an industrial process without directly using transfer functions. The process considered here will be the combined system of the actuator, process, and the sensor, i.e.,

$$G'_p(s) = G_a(s)G_p(s)G_s(s)$$

Therefore, the input to this process is the output of the controller. For a pulse test, a rectangular pulse (Chapter 4) is used and the resulting measured values of the controlled variable are recorded (Figure 8.6). Note that this is an open loop test and that y_s should return to or near its starting point in the response time of the process if no significant disturbance upset has occurred. The transfer function for this process is given by

$$G'_p(s) = \frac{Y_s(s)}{C(s)} = \frac{\int_0^\infty y'_s(t)e^{-st}\,dt}{\int_0^\infty c'(t)e^{-st}\,dt} \qquad\qquad \textbf{8.7}$$

which is based upon the definition of the Laplace transform with $y'(t)$ and $c'(t)$ being expressed in deviation variable form. The transfer function can be converted into a Bode plot by substituting $s = i\omega$. Thus

$$G'_p(i\omega) = \frac{\int_0^\infty y'_s(t)e^{-i\omega t}\,dt}{\int_0^\infty c'(t)e^{-i\omega t}\,dt} \qquad\qquad \textbf{8.8}$$

Using the Euler identity

$$e^{-i\omega t} = \cos \omega t - i\sin \omega t$$

results in

$$G'_p(i\omega) = \frac{A(\omega) - i B(\omega)}{C(\omega) - i D(\omega)} \qquad\qquad \textbf{8.9}$$

where

$$A(\omega) = \int_0^\infty y'_s(t)\cos\omega t\,dt$$

$$B(\omega) = \int_0^\infty y'_s(t)\sin\omega t\,dt$$

$$C(\omega) = \int_0^\infty c'(t)\cos\omega t\,dt$$

$$D(\omega) = \int_0^\infty c'(t)\sin\omega t\,dt$$

After multiplying by the complex conjugate of the denominator, the real and imaginary components of $G'_p(i\omega)$ are given by

$$R(\omega) = \frac{A(\omega)C(\omega) + B(\omega)D(\omega)}{C^2(\omega) + D^2(\omega)} \qquad\qquad \textbf{8.10}$$

$$I(\omega) = \frac{A(\omega)D(\omega) - B(\omega)C(\omega)}{C^2(\omega) + D^2(\omega)} \qquad\qquad \textbf{8.11}$$

where $R(\omega)$ and $I(\omega)$ are the real and imaginary components of $G'_p(i\omega)$, respectively. Then finally, the amplitude ratio, A_r, and the phase angle, ϕ, can be calculated directly

$$A_r(\omega) = \left|G'_p(i\omega)\right| = \sqrt{R^2(\omega) + I^2(\omega)} \qquad\qquad \textbf{8.12}$$

$$\phi(\omega) = \angle G'_p(i\omega) = \tan^{-1}\left(\frac{I(\omega)}{R(\omega)}\right) \qquad\qquad \textbf{8.13}$$

After the experimental pulse test is generated, Equations 8.9 to 8.13 are applied at each value of ω to generate the Bode plot. That is, a value of ω_1 is selected and the values of $A(\omega_1)$, $B(\omega_1)$, $C(\omega_1)$, and $D(\omega_1)$ are calculated using the pulse test results and a numerical integration method (e.g., the trapezoidal method[1]). Then $R(\omega_1)$ and $I(\omega_1)$ are calculated using Equations 8.10 and 8.11. Finally, $A_r(\omega_1)$ and $\phi(\omega_1)$ are determined from Equations 8.12 and 8.13. Another frequency is selected and the procedure is repeated until the Bode plot is completed.

Once the Bode plot is generated, the Bode plot of a P-only, PI, or PID controller can be combined with it and used to tune a controller to meet gain margin or phase margin specifications. Using the results of Equations 8.3 and 8.4, the Bode plot of the controller can be plotted on the same Bode diagram that was used to plot the Bode plot obtained from the experimental pulse test. Then for a set of tuning parameters, the A_r's and ϕ's for the controller and the process can be added together to yield the overall Bode plot. A_r's are added because they are plotted as logarithms and adding logarithms is equivalent to multiplying the A_r's. In this manner, controller tuning parameters can be adjusted until the desired GM or PM is obtained.

This approach[2] was first used in the 1960's because it allowed for a systematic procedure to tune PID controllers applied to complex industrial processes. This approach to tuning suffers from the following limitations.

1. It requires an open loop response time to complete the pulse test.
2. Disturbances during the test can corrupt the results.
3. Bode plots developed by this approach can be noisy, particularly around the crossover frequency which affects the accuracy of the resulting PM or GM used for tuning.

The ATV method of identification with on-line tuning (Section 7.5) can be applied with much less time and effort and yields more accurate results. As a result, ATV-based tuning is recommended over pulse-based testing for tuning slow responding loops.

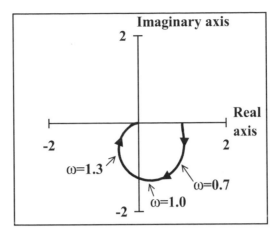

Figure 8.7 Nyquist diagram of a FOPDT process.

8.5 Nyquist Diagram

The **Nyquist diagram** is an alternate method for presenting frequency response behavior. Bode plots present separate curves for the amplitude ratio and phase angle as a function of frequency. The Nyquist diagram presents the frequency response behavior in a more compact form, i.e., with a single curve.

Figure 8.7 shows a Nyquist diagram for a FOPDT process model ($K_p = 1$, $\tau_p = 1$, $\theta_p = 0.5$). Note that the real [$R(\omega)$] and imaginary [$I(\omega)$] components of $G_p(i\omega)$ are plotted in a complex plane for a range of values of frequency, ω. Each point on the Nyquist plot corresponds to a different frequency. A Nyquist plot can be generated by using Equation 8.1 to generate $R(\omega)$ and $I(\omega)$ and plotting them on the complex plane as a function of ω.

8.6 Closed Loop Frequency Response

A Bode plot provides frequency response information about a process or a process and a controller in an open loop form. It is also informative to consider the frequency dependence of a closed loop system.

Figure 8.8 shows a schematic of a closed loop feedback system subjected to a sinusoidally varying disturbance. Figure 8.9 shows the **closed loop frequency response** for a FOPDT process model ($K_p = 1$, $\tau_p = 1$, $\theta_p = 0.5$) and a FOPDT disturbance model ($K_d = 1$, $\tau_d = 1$, $\theta_d = 0.5$) for sinusoidal disturbance changes with a P-only controller ($K_c = 1$). Note that A_r is plotted on a linear scale in Figure 8.9 instead of the log scale used for a Bode plot. The closed loop amplitude ratio, A_r, is defined here as the ratio of the amplitude of the variations in the controlled variable divided by

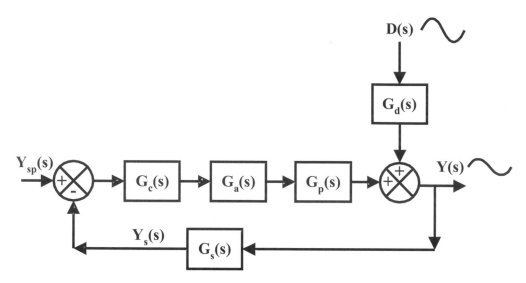

Figure 8.8 Block diagram of a feedback loop that is excited by a sinusoidal disturbance.

the amplitude in the variations in the disturbance. The phase angle is the phase lag between the disturbance and the controlled variable.

At high frequencies, A_r drops off sharply. This results because the process is not fast enough to respond to high frequency variations in the disturbance level and the variations become filtered out (i.e., averaged out by the process). At low frequencies, A_r drops off as well. This is because for very slow varying disturbances the feedback controller has time to absorb the disturbance and maintain operation at the setpoint. At frequencies between these extremes, ω is large enough that the feedback controller is unable to remove all the variations and ω is small enough that the process does not filter out the variations in the disturbance. The peak in the closed loop frequency response is called the **closed loop peak amplitude** and represents the frequency at which the maximum sensitivity to the disturbance occurs. The **bandwidth** (ω_{bw}) of the controller is the largest frequency of the closed loop Bode plot at which the amplitude ratio is equal to 0.707 times the closed loop peak amplitude. The controller band width indicates the upper end of the frequency region at which the controller is most sensitive to disturbances.

Industrial feedback controllers exhibit the same general behavior as shown in Figure 8.9. That is, there is a range of disturbance frequencies that a controller is most sensitive to. Analyzing the closed loop peak amplitudes of the individual loops of a number of processing units in a series can provide insight into the disturbance rejection performance of the overall system. Consider two distillation columns in series (Figure 8.10) where the bottoms of the first column is the feed to the second column. Further assume that the frequency corresponding to the closed loop peak amplitude for the bottom loop of the first column is equal to the frequency corresponding to the closed loop peak amplitude for both the top and bottom composition loops of the second

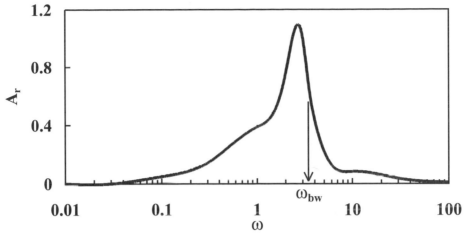

Figure 8.9 The closed loop amplitude ratios for a FOPDT process. Note that A_r is plotted on a linear scale instead of the log scale used for a Bode plot.

column. In this case, the disturbance frequencies that the two loops on the second column are most sensitive to are the same as the frequencies that the bottom loop on the first column is most sensitive to. Therefore, the largest variations in the bottom product would be expected to significantly affect both loops on the second column.

On the other hand, assume that the bottom loop on the first column is much slower than the loops on the second column, i.e., the closed loop peak amplitude for the bottom loop of the first column occurs at a significantly lower frequency than the closed loop peak amplitude for the two loops on the second column (Figure 8.11). For this case, the control loops on the second column should be able to handle the largest variations coming from the first column. From Figure 8.11, one can see that the disturbances that pass through the bottoms controller on the first column (i.e., corresponding to frequencies near the closed loop peak amplitude for the bottom composition controller for the first column) do not significantly affect the control

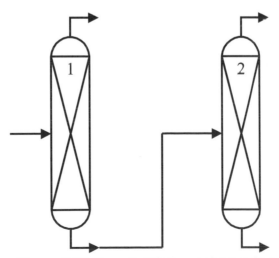

Figure 8.10 Two distillation columns in series.

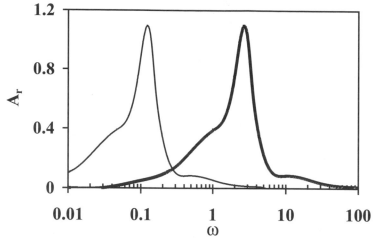

Figure 8.11 Closed loop amplitude ratios for two control loops with very different frequencies corresponding to the closed loop peak amplitude. Thin line-bottom control loop on column 1. Thick line-control loops on column 2.

loops for the second column (i.e., the controllers on the second column have sufficient time to handle these frequencies). For another case, assume that the bottom loop of the first column is much faster than the control loops on the second column. For this case, the largest variations coming from the first column will be filtered out by the slower responding second column. Therefore, qualitatively using closed loop frequency analysis can be helpful in analyzing the propagation of disturbances through a sequence of processing units.

8.7 Summary

The frequency or time scale of inputs to a process can have a significant effect on the resulting closed loop behavior. For example, if high frequency disturbances (i.e., short time variations) enter a process, the process will filter out the variations and the resulting control variable will be relatively unaffected. If low frequency disturbances (i.e., long time variations) enter a process, the feedback controller has ample time to respond to them and deviation from setpoint will be small. Therefore, control systems are typically most sensitive to intermediate frequencies. Frequency response analysis provides a methodology to analyze the frequency dependent characteristics of a process.

Bode plots, which are plots of the $\log(A_r)$ versus $\log(\omega)$ and ϕ versus $\log(\omega)$, are a convenient means to present the frequency dependent characteristics of a process. Bode plots can be generated by (1) directly exciting the process with sinusoidal inputs, (2) applying a sinusoidal input to the transfer function of the process, (3) substituting $s = i\omega$ into the transfer function, and (4) applying a pulse test.

The Bode plot of the combined process and controller can be used to determine the closed loop stability of the system using the Bode stability criterion. In addition, the gain margin and the phase margin can be used as tuning specifications for PID controllers.

Nyquist diagrams are another way to represent the frequency dependent behavior of a process. The Nyquist diagram is a plot of the real and imaginary components of $G_p(i\omega)$ in a complex plane for a range of frequencies.

The closed loop frequency response of a process indicates the disturbance frequencies that the controller is most sensitive to. This information can be used to analyze how disturbances will damp out or propagate from one control loop to another through a sequence of processes.

8.8 Additional Terminology

Amplitude ratio - (A_r) the ratio of the amplitude of the variations in y_s divided by the amplitude of the sinusoidal variations in an input to the process.

Bandwidth - the maximum frequency that corresponds to an A_r that is equal to 0.707 times the closed loop peak amplitude.

Bode plot - a plot of $\log(A_r)$ versus $\log(\omega)$ and a plot of ϕ versus $\log(\omega)$.

Bode stability criterion - states that a process is stable if $A_r < 1$ at the critical frequency.

Closed loop frequency response - a Bode plot for a closed loop process subjected to sinusoidally varying disturbance inputs.

Closed loop peak amplitude - the maximum A_r for a closed loop frequency response.

Critical frequency - the frequency that corresponds to $\phi = -180°$.

Crossover frequency - the frequency that corresponds to $A_r=1$.

Frequency response analysis - the study of the effect of varying input frequencies on process behavior.

Gain margin (GM) - defined by Equation 8.5 and indicates how aggressively a controller is tuned.

Nyquist diagram - the real and imaginary components of $G_p(i\omega)$ plotted on a complex plane for a range of frequencies.

Phase angle - (ϕ) an indication of how much the controller output lags behind the controlled variable.

Phase margin (PM) - given by Equation 8.6 and indicates how aggressively a controller is tuned.

Pulse test - the response of a process to a rectangular pulse input that can be used to develop a Bode plot for an experimental system.

8.9 References

1. Riggs, J.B., *An Introduction to Numerical Methods for Chemical Engineers*, Texas Tech University Press, pp. 136-143 (1994).

2. Hougen, J.O., *Methods for Solving Process Plant Problems*, Instrument Society of America (1996).

8.10 Questions and Exercises

8.1 Even though frequency response analysis is not generally used by industrial process control engineers, why is frequency response analysis important to the understanding of feedback systems?

8.2 Explain what a Bode plot is. Indicate how you would directly generate a Bode plot for the CST thermal mixer.

8.3 Explain using equations how you would generate a Bode plot from the transfer function of a process.

8.4 Using Table 8.1, determine the amplitude ratio and phase angle for a FOPDT process as a function of frequency.

8.5 Using Table 8.1, determine the amplitude ratio and phase angle as a function of frequency for the following transfer function

$$G(s) = \frac{4}{(s+2)(s+5)(s+9)}$$

8.6 Using Table 8.1, determine the amplitude ratio and phase angle as a function of frequency for a PI controller in series with a first order process.

8.7 Explain the Bode stability criterion in your own words.

8.8 How are the gain margin and the phase margin alike and how are they different?

8.9 Describe how the *PM* could be used to tune a PI controller applied to a second order process using the results from Table 8.1

8.11 Explain how a pulse test can be used to identify the Bode plot of an experimental process.

8.12 Describe how a pulse test can be used to tune a controller on an industrial process. Why would you not use this approach on an industrial process?

8.13 Define what a Nyquist diagram is and how it can be generated.

8.14 Define what a closed loop Bode plot is and how it can be used to determine the propagation of variabilities from one processing unit to another.

8.15 What does the bandwidth of a controller indicate?

PART IV

ADVANCED
PID CONTROL

Chapter 9

Cascade, Ratio, and Feedforward Control

9.1 Introduction

This chapter considers cascade, ratio, and feedforward control. The advantage of each of these advanced PID controllers is related to its ability to more effectively reject disturbances than conventional PID controllers. Cascade control rejects specific types of disturbance upsets which can either be measured or unmeasured. Ratio control can effectively handle feed flow rate disturbances for a wide range of processes. Feedforward control is a general methodology for anticipating and correcting for the effect of measured disturbances.

When a disturbance upset affects a conventional PID control loop, all the correction comes from feedback action. That is, no corrective action is taken until the disturbance has affected the process. Return to the everyday control example of driving a car which was presented in Chapter 1. When driving a car, if one were to look only at the car's position on the road when negotiating a turn (e.g., looking right in front of the car), the safe car speed through a turn would have to be greatly reduced compared with the feedforward approach where the driver anticipates the curve. Cascade, ratio and feedforward control provide performance enhancement for chemical process control because in each case corrective action is taken before the disturbance has significantly affected the process. As a result, the amount of corrective action required from the PID controller and the resulting maximum deviation from setpoint and response time of the feedback system can be significantly reduced.

9.2 Cascade Control

Cascade control offers a means of effectively reducing the effect of certain disturbances on the primary control objective of a control loop. Cascade control uses two control loops in tandem (Figure 9.1). The inner loop (A) receives its setpoint from the outer loop (B). The inner loop is used to react to certain disturbances on a high

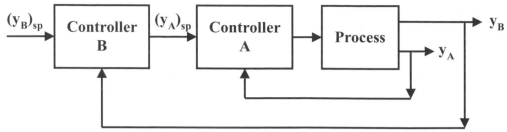

Figure 9.1 Block diagram of a cascade control loop. Controller A is the slave controller and controller B is the master controller.

frequency basis before these disturbances can significantly upset the process. The outer loop is applied to maintain the primary control objective on setpoint.

Cascade Control Examples. Figure 9.2a shows a schematic of a steam heated heat exchanger without cascade control. Assume that the steam supply pressure increases. This would cause an increase in steam pressure in the heat exchanger and result in an increase in the temperature of the process stream leaving the heat exchanger. As the outlet temperature begins to rise, the PID controller on the temperature of the outlet stream would begin to take corrective action by reducing the stem position of the valve on the steam line. By the time the PID controller would start to take corrective action, an excessive amount of heat would have already been transferred from the steam to the process fluid in the heat exchanger. In addition, the inherent deadband of an industrial control valve can affect how accurately the temperature of a high gain process can be controlled if a valve positioner is not used. A high gain for this heat exchanger results if the process exhibits significant changes in the outlet temperature in response to small changes in the steam pressure.

Figure 9.2b shows the steam heated heat exchanger with a cascade control configuration. The pressure control loop is the inner loop and is referred to as the **secondary** or **slave loop**. The temperature control loop is the outer loop and is referred to as the **primary** or **master loop**. Note that the output of the temperature controller for the cascade control case is the setpoint for the pressure controller while the output from the temperature controller for the case without cascade control goes directly to the control valve on the steam line. For the cascade control case, when the steam supply pressure increases, the pressure of steam inside the heat exchanger will increase but the pressure controller will react quickly by closing the valve until the desired pressure of steam in the heat exchanger is reinstated. As a result, the steam pressure disturbance is almost completely absorbed by the slave loop before it can affect the master loop. In addition, the pressure control loop overcomes the detrimental effects of valve deadband by using high frequency feedback action which is discussed in detail in Section 6.5. Note that because the pressure control loop (slave loop) is much faster responding than the temperature control loop (master loop), the pressure control loop can quickly compensate for specific disturbances that affect the steam pressure before they affect the temperature loop.

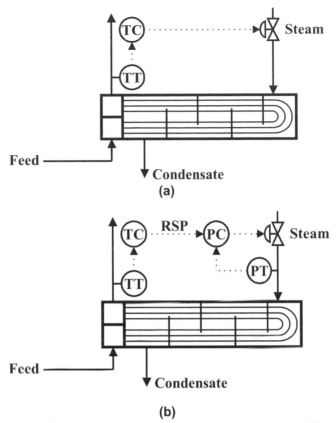

Figure 9.2 Schematic of a steam heated heat exchanger with a temperature controller for controlling the temperature of the exiting process fluid. (a) without cascade and (b) with cascade control.

Figure 9.3a shows the control configuration for a water jacketed exothermic CSTR without cascade control. Changes in the inlet cooling water temperature will result in a reactor temperature change. As a result, when an inlet cooling water temperature change occurs, a significant change in the reactor temperature will occur before changes in the flow rate of the inlet cooling water can be made because the reactor temperature is such a sluggish process. Figure 9.3b shows the CSTR with a cascade configuration. Note that when an inlet cooling water temperature change occurs, a change in the jacket water temperature will occur long before the reactor temperature starts to change. Therefore, the slave loop (i.e., the water jacket temperature loop) can react quickly to inlet cooling water temperature changes, thus significantly reducing the effect of jacket water temperature changes on the reactor temperature control loop.

Figure 9.4 is a multiple cascade configuration that is designed to maintain the impurity level in the bottoms product of a distillation column at its setpoint. The innermost control loop is a flow control loop on the steam to the reboiler. Cascade controllers which use flow controllers as the slave loop are the most commonly used

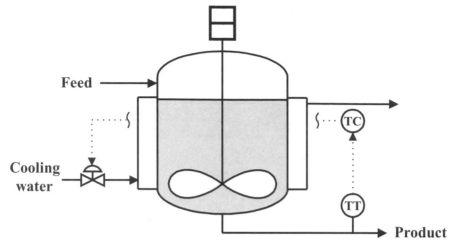

Figure 9.3a Schematic of a CSTR temperature controller without cascade control.

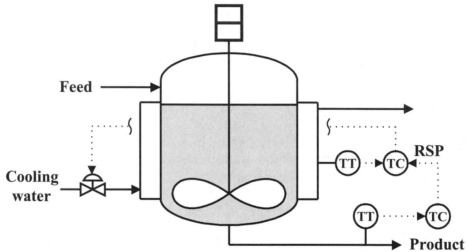

Figure 9.3b Schematic of a cascade temperature controller applied to a CSTR.

form of cascade control in the CPI. The flow controller will provide fast response to steam pressure changes in spite of valve deadband. The setpoint for the flow control loop is set by the tray temperature controller. Tray temperature strongly correlates with product composition for a large class of industrial columns which is an example of inferential control and is discussed in Section 11.2. The advantage of controlling tray temperatures on distillation columns comes from the fact that composition changes are measured much faster using tray temperatures than using on-line analyzers. Moreover, for fast acting columns (i.e., when the reflux ratio is relatively low), feedback control using the GC can result in poor control performance because the resulting deadtime to time constant ratio of the process is too large. For these cases, tray temperature control loops have a much smaller deadtime to time constant ratio due

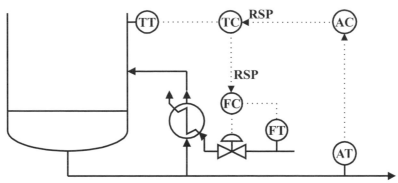

Figure 9.4 Schematic of a multiple cascade configuration applied for bottoms composition control of a distillation column.

to the fast response of temperature sensors, and therefore, tray temperature control loops exhibit better control performance with shorter closed loop response times than control directly off the GC. As the feed composition changes, the proper tray temperature setpoint will change; therefore, adjustments to the setpoint for the tray temperature controllers are made by the composition control loop which is the overall master loop for this cascade arrangement. This multiple cascade arrangement works effectively because the flow control loop is much faster than the temperature control loop which is much faster than the composition control loop.

From an analysis of these examples of cascade control the following conclusions can be drawn:

1. The inner loop (slave loop) must be considerably faster than the outer loop (master loop) for cascade control to be effective.
2. High frequency feedback action of the slave loop eliminates specific disturbances before they can significantly affect the master loop. Since the process responds much faster to the slave loop than to the master loop, the slave loop can absorb specific disturbances much more quickly.

Theoretical Analysis. Figure 9.5 shows a block diagram of a generalized cascade loop. For the heat exchanger example, the inner loop is the pressure control loop where the output of the pressure controller goes directly to the control valve. $G_{ps}(s)$ represents the effect of valve stem position on steam pressure in the heat exchanger. $G_{pm}(s)$ represents the effect of steam pressure on the outlet temperature of the process fluid leaving the heat exchanger. The output of the temperature controller is the setpoint for the pressure controller. Note that the disturbance, $D(s)$, enters the slave loop, and therefore, can be effectively absorbed by the action of the slave loop. The transfer function for the effect of the disturbance $D(s)$ on the master control loop $Y(s)$ can be derived using the properties of a block diagram

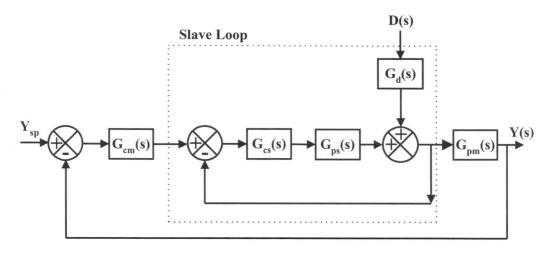

Figure 9.5 Block diagram of a generalized cascade control loop. Note that the actuators and sensors are omitted from this diagram.

$$\frac{Y(s)}{D(s)} = \frac{G_d(s)\,G_{pm}(s)[1+G_{cs}(s)\,G_{ps}(s)]}{1+G_{cs}(s)\,G_{ps}(s)+G_{cm}(s)\,G_{pm}(s)\,G_{cs}(s)\,G_{ps}(s)} \qquad 9.1$$

Assuming first order processes for $G_{pm}(s)$ and $G_{ps}(s)$ and P-only controllers for the slave and master loops, a second order response results with a second order process time constant, τ', given by

$$\tau' = \sqrt{\tau_m\,\tau_s} \qquad 9.2$$

regardless of the controller gains where τ_m is the time constant of the master process $[G_{pm}(s)]$ and τ_s is the time constant of the slave process $[G_{ps}(s)]$. For example, if $\tau_m=1$ and $\tau_s=0.1$, $\tau'=0.3$. That is, the speed of the response for the cascade loop will be about three times as fast as the master loop by itself.

Now consider a FOPDT process model for the slave and master loops:

$$G_{pm}(s) = \frac{1.0\,e^{-0.5s}}{s+1} \qquad 9.3$$

and

$$G_{ps}(s) = \frac{1.0\,e^{-(0.5/r)s}}{s/r+1} \qquad 9.4$$

where r is the relative speed of the slave loop compared to the master loop. Figure 9.6 shows how the relative control performance (ratio of IAE for cascade control divided by IAE without cascade control) varies as a function of r. Note that as r increases (i.e.,

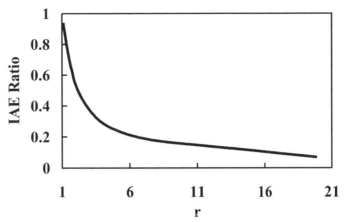

Figure 9.6 The effect of the relative speed of the slave loop compared to the master loop on the relative control performance of cascade control.

the slave loop becomes faster relative to the master loop), the advantage of the cascade loop over a single loop also increases. As a general rule, the slave loop should be at least three times as fast as the master loop to justify the use of cascade control which corresponds to the "knee" of the curve shown in Figure 9.6. In order to obtain this advantage for cascade control, the slave loop **must** be tuned tightly, i.e., allowing only short term deviations from the slave setpoint.

9.3 Ratio Control

Many processes scale directly with the feed rate to the process, e.g., distillation columns and wastewater neutralization. For distillation columns, all the liquid and vapor flow rates within the column are directly proportional to the column feed rate if the product purities are maintained and the tray efficiency is constant. For wastewater neutralization, the amount of reagent necessary to maintain a neutral pH for the effluent varies directly with the flow rate of the wastewater feed, as long as the titration curve of the wastewater remains constant.

When the manipulated variable of a process is, in general, directly proportional to the feed rate, ratio control can significantly reduce the effect of feed rate disturbances on the process. Figure 9.7 shows how a ratio controller can be applied for a general case. Note that when a feed flow rate change is measured, the manipulated variable is proportionally adjusted, i.e., the measured flow rate of the feed is multiplied by the manipulated variable to feed rate ratio (output of the composition controller). Feedback corrections (i.e., changes in the output from the controller) are made to the ratio based on analyzer readings. Figure 9.8 shows a comparison between a conventional feedback controller and a ratio controller. The controlled variable is the overhead composition and the disturbance is the feed rate. Note that the maximum

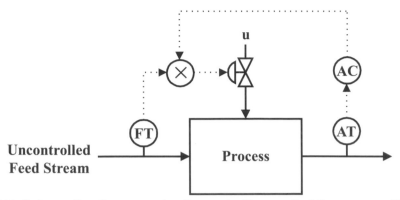

Figure 9.7 Schematic of a general ratio controller applied for composition control.

deviation from setpoint and the settling time for this disturbance are significantly reduced under ratio control.

Figure 9.9 shows the application of ratio control to the effluent pH for a wastewater neutralization process applied in a mixing tank. This controller can effectively handle wastewater feed flow rate changes when the chemical makeup of the wastewater remains relatively constant. Small changes in the chemical makeup of the wastewater can usually be handled by the feedback controller which adjusts the reagent to wastewater ratio to maintain the specified effluent pH.

A schematic of the stripping section of a distillation column with a ratio controller for the bottom products composition is shown in Figure 9.10. This application is similar to ratio control except that dynamic compensation is added to the measured column feed rate. If the steam flow to the reboiler were to be increased immediately for an increase in column feed rate, the corrective action would initially be an over-correction. This results because when a feed rate change occurs, it takes

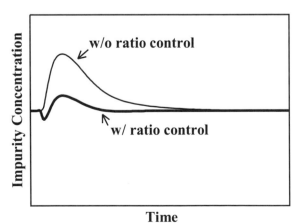

Figure 9.8 Comparison between control performance with and without ratio control for the overhead composition control of a distillation column.

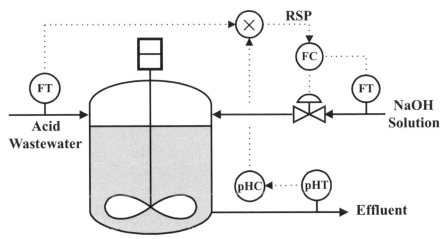

Figure 9.9 Schematic of ratio control applied for pH control of an acid wastewater neutralization process.

some time for the bottom product composition to respond. The purpose of the dynamic compensation (DC) element is to allow for the correct timing for the compensation for feed rate changes. The dynamic element for this case could be simply a lag element, e.g., a digital filter described by Equation 6.21. The wastewater neutralization case (Figure 9.9) does not require dynamic compensation since the process pH response to feed rate changes and its response to NaOH flow rate changes have similar dynamics behavior.

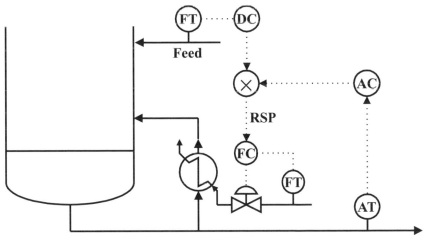

Figure 9.10 Schematic of ratio control for feed rate changes applied to the stripping section of a distillation column.

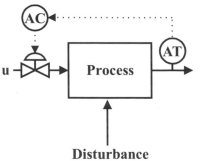

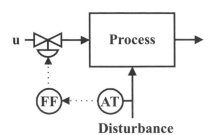

Figure 9.11a Schematic of a feedback controller.

Figure 9.11b Schematic of a feedforward controller.

9.4 Feedforward Control

Feedforward control can be applied to process control loops that are significantly affected by disturbances that are measurable (or estimated) on-line. A feedback controller (Figure 9.11a) reacts to deviations from setpoint caused by the disturbance until the process is returned to setpoint. As was pointed out in Chapter 7, since the proportional and derivative terms are zero during steady-state operation at the setpoint, the integral term in the PID controller is responsible for the long term compensation for disturbances. A feedforward controller (Figure 9.11b) anticipates the effects of a measured change in a disturbance (i.e., a **load change**) and takes corrective action before the disturbance affects the process. In effect, the feedforward controller applies corrective manipulated variable changes corresponding to the integral action that a feedback controller would generate; therefore, when a feedback controller and feedforward controller are used together, the feedback controller has much less "work" to do in order to compensate for a measured disturbance.

Feedforward examples. Figure 9.12a shows a feedback controller applied for the level control of a boiler drum. The feedback controller compares the measured value of the level with the setpoint for the level and adjusts the flow rate of the feedwater to the drum. Therefore, when changes in the demand for steam occur, changes in the drum level will result. If large swings in steam demand occur, a large gain will be required for the feedback controller in order to maintain the level near its setpoint. But for large controller gains, the process is more susceptible to oscillatory behavior in the level and feedwater flow rate to the drum. Also, high gain controllers are sensitive to noisy measurements of the controlled variable, and in this case, level indicators can have significant noise levels.

Figure 9.12b is a schematic of a feedforward controller applied for steam drum level control. The idea is quite simple: if the flow rate of the makeup feedwater is equal to the steam usage, the drum level will remain constant. One is tempted to conclude that the feedforward controller is all that is needed for this application. Unfortunately,

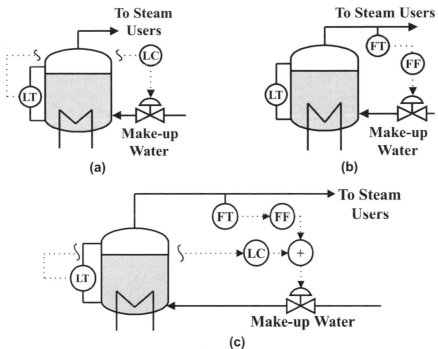

Figure 9.12 Boiler drum level control (a) feedback (b) feedforward (c) feedback and feedforward combined.

the measurements of the steam usage and the feedwater flow rate are not perfectly accurate. Even small errors in measured flow rates will add up over time, leading to one of two undesirable extremes. The drum can fill with water and put water into the steam system or the liquid level can drop, exposing the boiler tubes which can damage these tubes. As a result, neither feedback nor feedforward are effective by themselves for this case. In general, feedforward-only controllers are susceptible to measurement errors and unmeasured disturbances, and as a result, some type of feedback correction is typically required.

Figure 9.12c shows a combined feedforward and feedback controller for the control of the level in the steam drum. Note that the feedforward controller will provide most of the control action required by responding to the measured steam usage. The feedback controller can be a relatively low gain controller since it needs to compensate only for measurement errors and unmeasured disturbances.

Figure 9.13 shows a pipe that is wrapped with resistive tape. The controlled variable is the outlet temperature, T_o, the manipulated variable is the power to the resistive tape, Q, and the measured disturbance is the inlet temperature, T_i. Figure 9.14a shows the effect of a 10 kW increase in Q on the outlet temperature, T_o. Note that T_o responds sluggishly to a change in Q with a response time of seven minutes. Figure 9.14b shows the response of T_o to a 10°C increase in the inlet temperature, T_i. Note

Figure 9.13 Drawing of a pipe wrapped with resistive heating tape.

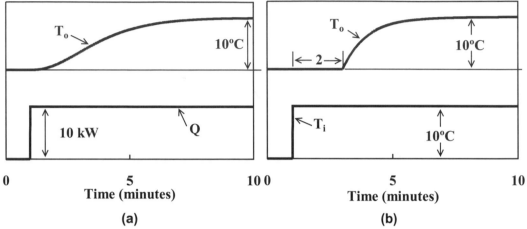

(a)   **(b)**

Figure 9.14 Outlet temperature response for a step change in (a) Q and (b) T$_i$.

that the response of T_o for a change in T_i can be represented as a FOPDT process with two minutes of deadtime.

Consider a step decrease of 20°C in T_i. It is obvious that Q should be increased by 20 kW to compensate for the 20°C drop in the inlet temperature. Figure 9.15 shows the response if the 20 kW increase is applied when the inlet temperature drop occurs. The deviation from setpoint is due to dynamic mismatch between the

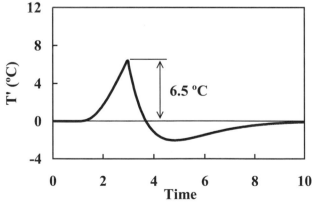

Figure 9.15 Change in the outlet temperature for feedforward control without dynamic compensation.

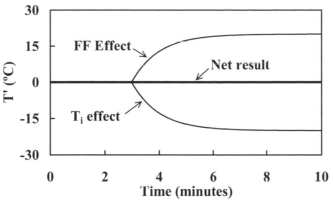

Figure 9.16 Perfect feedforward control for a step change in the inlet temperature.

response of the process to changes in Q and the response of the process to changes in T_i. Figure 9.16 shows the case with no dynamic mismatch, i.e., mirror image responses of T_o to Q and to T_i. In this case, the feedforward action would provide perfect compensation. Perfect feedforward control is not possible but considering it helps better to understand feedforward control. The results of a dynamically compensated feedforward controller are shown in Figure 9.17 along with the results without dynamic compensation. The methodology for applying dynamic compensation for a feedforward controller will now be addressed.

General feedforward controller. The previous examples demonstrate how feedforward controllers can be developed from an analysis of the process. A more generalized feedforward controller design procedure can also be used. Consider a block diagram for a generalized feedforward controller shown in Figure 9.18. The disturbance is measured by a sensor with a dynamic response given by $G_{ds}(s)$. The feedforward controller $[G_{ff}(s)]$ uses the measured value of the disturbance to calculate its feedforward correction $[C_{ff}(s)]$. The feedforward correction affects the actuator

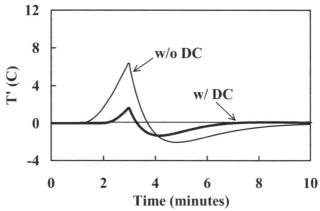

Figure 9.17 Comparison between feedforward control with and without dynamic compensation (DC).

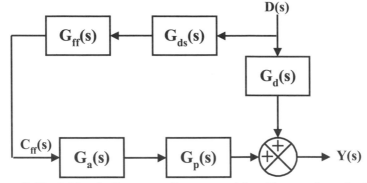

Figure 9.18 A block diagram of a general feedforward controller.

which in turn changes the manipulated variable level which changes the controlled variable. Notice that the controlled variable changes are due to changes in the feedforward controller output, $C_{ff}(s)$, and in the disturbance, $D(s)$.

$$Y(s) = C_{ff}(s)G_a(s)G_p(s) + D(s)G_d(s) \qquad \textbf{9.5}$$

The feedforward controller determines the control action $C_{ff}(s)$, i.e.,

$$C_{ff}(s) = G_{ff}(s)G_{ds}(s)D(s) \qquad \textbf{9.6}$$

where $G_{ds}(s)$ represents the sensor on the measured disturbance, then

$$Y(s) = D(s)G_{ds}(s)G_{ff}(s)G_a(s)G_p(s) + D(s)G_d(s)$$

Since we want to design a feedforward controller that keeps the process at setpoint in spite of disturbances, we set $Y(s)$ equal to zero and solve for $G_{ff}(s)$ yielding

$$G_{ff}(s) = \frac{-G_d(s)}{G_{ds}(s)G_a(s)G_p(s)} \qquad \textbf{9.7}$$

This equation gives us a means of directly determining the feedforward controller using a model of the effect of the disturbance on the process and a model of the effect of the manipulated variable on the process. Let's assume that we have FOPDT models for $G_d(s)$ and the product $G_{ds}(s)\ G_a(s)\ G_p(s)$, i.e.,

$$G_{ds}(s)G_a(s)G_p(s) = \frac{K_p\, e^{-\theta_p s}}{\tau_p\, s + 1}$$

$$G_d(s) = \frac{K_d\, e^{-\theta_d s}}{\tau_d\, s + 1}$$

Then the application of Equation 9.7 using the FOPDT models yields

$$G_{ff}(s) = -\frac{K_d(\tau_p s+1)\, e^{-\theta_d s}}{K_p(\tau_d s+1)\, e^{-\theta_p s}} = \frac{K_{ff}(\tau_{ld}\, s+1)\, e^{-\theta_{ff} s}}{(\tau_{lg}\, s+1)} \qquad \textbf{9.8}$$

where the feedforward controller gain is given by

$$K_{ff} = \frac{-K_d}{K_p} \qquad \textbf{9.9}$$

The lead of the feedforward controller, τ_{ld}, is

$$\tau_{ld} = \tau_p \qquad \textbf{9.10}$$

the lag of the feedforward controller, τ_{lg}, is

$$\tau_{lg} = \tau_d \qquad \textbf{9.11}$$

and the deadtime of the feedforward controller is

$$\theta_{ff} = \theta_d - \theta_p \qquad \textbf{9.12}$$

Equation 9.8 represents a **lead/lag element**, a standard feature on a DCS. A feedforward controller can be implemented on a DCS by applying a lead/lag element function with the proper values of $K_{ff}, \tau_{ld}, \tau_{lg}$, and θ_{ff} to measured changes in the disturbance. The results in Figure 9.17 were obtained by applying a feedforward controller using the lead/lag element represented by Equation 9.8.

Tuning. Tuning a feedforward controller involves selecting the values of $K_{ff}, \tau_{ld}, \tau_{lg}$, and θ_{ff}. Equations 9.9 to 9.12 can be used to estimate these tuning parameters if FOPDT models are available. Since identifying $G_d(s)$ can be difficult, it is usually advisable to field tune feedforward controllers. The following field tuning procedure is recommended.

1. Make initial estimates of $K_{ff}, \tau_{ld}, \tau_{lg}$, and θ_{ff} based on process knowledge.
2. Under open loop conditions, adjust K_{ff} to minimize deviation from setpoint after a disturbance has had its steady-state effect on the process. Figure 9.19a shows the dynamic response of a feedforward controller for a step change in the disturbance based on initial feedforward controller settings and after K_{ff} has been adjusted to eliminate offset.
3. By analyzing the dynamic mismatch, adjust θ_{ff}. The direction of the deviation should indicate whether the feedforward correction is applied too soon or too late causing dynamic mismatch. Figure 9.19b shows the feedforward control performance after θ_{ff} is tuned.

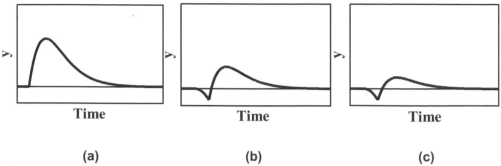

(a)   **(b)**   **(c)**

Figure 9.19 Tuning results for a feedforward controller for a step change in the disturbance. (a) Results for initial settings with correct feedforward gain. (b) Results after deadtime tuned. (c) Final tuning results.

4. Finally, adjust $(\tau_{ld} - \tau_{lg})$ until approximately equal areas above and below the setpoint result.   Figure 9.19c shows the results after $(\tau_{ld} - \tau_{lg})$ is adjusted. It is recommended to adjust the difference between τ_{ld} and τ_{lg} since this difference (the relative dynamics of the process to manipulated variable and disturbance changes) has a profound effect on the shape of the response.

Overview. Table 9.1 summarizes the advantages and disadvantages of feedforward and feedback control. Note that feedforward and feedback control are complementary, i.e., they each can overcome the disadvantages of the other so that together they are superior to either method alone. Feedforward control does not offer a significant advantage for fast responding processes because a feedback-only controller can usually absorb disturbances efficiently for these cases. But for slow responding processes or processes with significant deadtime, by the time a feedback-only controller starts to respond to the effects of a disturbance, the process can already be severely upset. For these cases, the effect of the disturbance can cause the controlled variable to change significantly from its setpoint resulting in relatively large process parameter changes $(K_p, \tau_p,$ and $\theta_p)$ and in some cases this can lead to closed loop instability. When feedforward is added to a slow process or a process with significant deadtime, the deviation of the controlled variable from setpoint can be significantly reduced resulting in smaller process parameter changes. Therefore, feedforward can provide   significantly more reliable feedback control performance when the feedforward control performance compensates for a major disturbance to the process. In general, feedforward is useful when (1) feedback control by itself is not satisfactory, i.e., for slow responding processes or processes with significant deadtime, and (2) the major disturbance to a process is measured on-line.

Table 9.1 Comparison of Feedback and Feedforward Control

Feedback

Advantages	Disadvantages
1. Does not require a measurement of the disturbance.	1. Waits until the disturbance has affected the process before taking action.
2. Can effectively reject disturbances for fast responding process.	2. Susceptible to disturbances when the process is slow or when significant deadtime is present.
3. Simple to implement.	3. Can lead to instability of the closed loop system due to nonlinearity.

Feedforward

1. Compensates for disturbances before they affect the process.	1. Requires the measurement of the disturbance.
2. Can improve the reliability of the feedback controller by reducing the deviation from setpoint.	2. Does not compensate for unmeasured disturbances.
3. Offers noticeable advantages for slow processes or processes with significant deadtime.	3. Since it is a linear based correction, its performance will deteriorate with nonlinearity.

Feedforward control provides a linear correction and therefore can provide only partial compensation to a nonlinear process. Nevertheless, feedforward control can be effective when properly implemented since it can reduce the amount of feedback correction required. When tuning a feedforward controller for a nonlinear process, care should be taken to ensure that the feedforward controller is tuned considering both increases and decreases in the disturbance level. For example, if the feedforward controller is tuned for a certain size increase in the disturbance, it may work quite well for that case but actually contribute to poorer performance when a different size disturbance decrease is encountered. Figure 9.20 shows how a feedforward controller and a feedback controller are combined. Note that the changes in the manipulated variable calculated by the feedforward and feedback controllers are simply added.

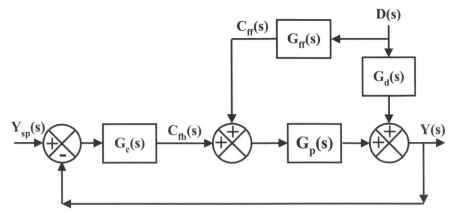

Figure 9.20 Block diagram of a combined feedforward and feedback controller. Note that the actuator and sensor are omitted.

Figure 9.21 shows the effect of the ratio of τ_{ld} / τ_{lg} on the dynamic response of a lead/lag element. Note that when τ_{ld} / τ_{lg} is greater than one, overcompensation is used. That is, when the process responds faster to the disturbance than to the controller output, larger than steady-state changes in the controller output are required in order to compensate for dynamic mismatch. On the other hand, when τ_{ld} / τ_{lg} is less than one, the application of the controller output is more gradual, eventually approaching its steady-state level. That is, when the process responds faster to the controller output than to the disturbance, a more gradual increase in the controller output level can be used to compensate for a disturbance. Figure 9.22 shows the effect of τ_{lg} on the dynamic response of a lead/lag element for which the ratio of lead to lag is maintained constant at a value of 2. Note that the case with the larger value of the lag requires a longer time to settle to the steady-state value.

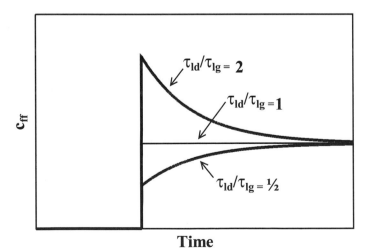

Figure 9.21 The effect of the ratio of τ_{ld} to τ_{lg} on the dynamic response of a lead/lag element. c_{ff} is the output from the feedforward controller.

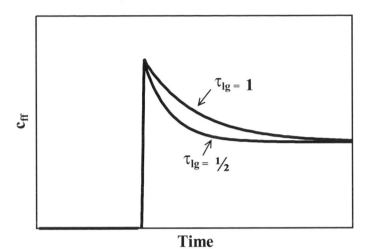

Figure 9.22 The effect of τ_{lg} on the dynamic response of a lead/lag element. c_{ff} is the output of the feedforward controller.

Consider how Equation 9.8 can be used to develop a feedforward controller for a measured flow rate disturbances (F_2) to a CST thermal mixer (Figure 3.6). Since $G_d(s)$ and $G_p(s)$ have the same dynamic behavior (i.e., deadtime and time constant)

$$G_{ff}(s) = K_{ff}$$

which is referred to as a **static feedforward controller** since it has no dynamic compensation.

Example 9.1 Feedforward Control Applied to Endothermic CSTR

Problem Statement. Apply a feedforward controller to the endothermic CSTR for feed temperature changes.

Solution. Using open loop step tests, the following FOPDT models were developed for $G_d(s)$ and $G_p(s)$

$$G_d(s) = \frac{0.381 \ e^{-5.62s}}{6.57 \ s + 1} \ (^\circ C / ^\circ C)$$

$$G_p(s) = \frac{1.50 \times 10^{-4} \ e^{-4.31s}}{10.7 \ s + 1} \left(\frac{^\circ C}{cal \ / \ s} \right)$$

where time constants and deadtimes are reported in seconds. The feedforward controller was tuned for a 100°C increase in feed temperature (T_0). It was determined

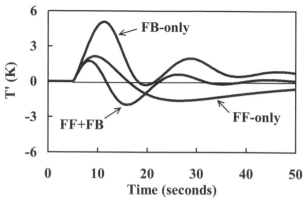

Figure 9.23 Comparison among feedforward (FF-only), feedback (FB-only), and combined feedforward and feedback (FF+FB) for a disturbance upset.

by using a static-only feedforward controller (i.e., no dynamic compensation) that the K_{ff} should be increased in order to eliminate offset at steady-state; therefore, K_{ff} was set at -1.09×10^4 cal/sec/°C. Next, θ_{ff} was evaluated and it was found that θ_{ff} should be set to zero. Due to the positive deviations of the reactor temperature from setpoint, τ_{ld} was increased from 10.7 s (i.e., τ_p) to 12.9 s which reduced the maximum deviation from setpoint without resulting in excessive negative deviations. τ_{lg} was maintained equal to τ_d or 6.57 seconds. Figure 9.23 shows the results for a step increase in T_0 from 400 K to 500K for the feedforward controller, a feedback controller, and the combined feedforward and feedback controller. It should be noted that the open loop effect of this disturbance results in a 38K increase in reactor temperature while the combined feedforward and feedback controller had a maximum deviation of only 1.7K. The results in Figure 9.23 show that combined feedforward and feedback outperform either feedforward or feedback alone. Note that the feedforward-only controller significantly reduces the initial deviation from setpoint compared to the feedback-only controller but is sluggish in returning to the setpoint. The combined feedforward and feedback controller uses the feedforward action to reduce the initial deviation from setpoint and uses the feedback action to quickly settle at the setpoint. Figure 9.24 shows a schematic representing a combined feedforward and feedback controller applied to the endothermic CSTR.

9.5 Summary

Cascade, ratio, and feedforward control are each designed to reduce the effect of disturbances on feedback control performance. Since disturbances tend to undermine controller reliability, cascade, ratio, and feedforward can contribute to controller performance and reliability when they are properly implemented.

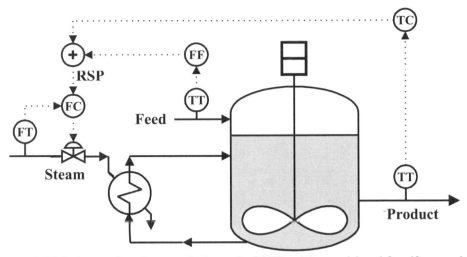

Figure 9.24 Schematic of an endothermic CSTR with combined feedforward and feedback control.

Cascade control involves applying two controllers in tandem instead of using a single control loop. The control loops are arranged such that the master loop provides the setpoint for the slave loop. Since the slave loop responds faster than the master loop, the slave loop is able to more effectively reject certain disturbances than if the master loop were applied by itself.

Ratio controllers can effectively handle process feed rate changes for processes that generally scale with feed rate. For ratio controllers, the controller selects the manipulated stream flow rate to feed flow rate ratio. Then this ratio is multiplied by the measured feed rate to give the setpoint for the flow controller on the manipulated stream. In certain cases, dynamic compensation is required for the proper implementation of ratio control.

Feedforward control offers significant benefits to a feedback controller (1) when the process is slow responding or when significant deadtime is present and (2) the major disturbances to a process are measurable. A feedforward controller is typically implemented using a lead/lag element.

9.6 Additional Terminology

Lead/lag element - the ratio of two FOPDT transfer function models which is defined by Equation 9.8.
Load change - a change in the disturbance level to a process.
Master loop - the outer loop for a cascade controller. Also, the slowest loop in a cascade arrangement.

Primary loop - the outer loop for a cascade controller. Also, the slowest loop in a cascade arrangement.

Secondary loop - the inner loop for a cascade controller. Also, the fastest loop in a cascade arrangement.

Slave loop - the inner loop for a cascade controller. Also, the fastest loop in a cascade arrangement.

Static feedforward controller - a feedforward controller which contains only a gain, i.e., it contains no dynamic compensation.

9.7 Questions and Exercises

9.1 What do cascade, ratio and feedforward control have in common?

9.2 What relationship between the master and slave loop is required for effective cascade control?

9.3 Draw a schematic showing a process controlled with and without cascade control for a case not presented in this text.

9.4 Consider the fixed bed reactor (Figure 10.6) in which the feed is preheated by a gas-fired heater similar to Figure 10.14. The current control configuration has a temperature controller on the outlet from the fixed bed reactor setting the setpoint for the flow controller on the gas flow to the furnace. Draw a schematic showing a further application of cascade control (i.e., beyond flow control on the gas flow rate) that would provide improved control for this process for changes in the heating value of the gas fired to the heater.

9.5 Is a typical flow control loop on a DCS part of a cascade arrangement? Explain your reasoning.

9.6 Consider a heat exchanger that cools a process stream using a liquid refrigerant. The process stream is on the tube-side of the exchanger and the liquid refrigerant is maintained as a level on the shell-side. Note that the vast majority of the heat transfer from the refrigerant to the process stream occurs from the liquid refrigerant due to the larger heat transfer coefficient for the liquid than for the vapor refrigerant. As heat is transferred from the process stream to the liquid refrigerant, the refrigerant boils and leaves the heat exchanger as a vapor. The cascade control configuration has a temperature controller on the exit of the process stream setting the setpoint for the level controller on the liquid level of refrigerant in the exchanger. The level controller sets the valve position for a valve on the inlet flow of liquid refrigerant to the heat exchanger. What advantage does this cascade control arrangement have compared to having the output of the temperature controller go directly to the valve on the liquid refrigerant?

9.7 What kinds of processes benefit from ratio control?

9.8 When is dynamic compensation required and when is it not required for ratio control?

9.9 Draw a schematic for the rectifying section of a distillation column in which the ratio of distillate product rate to column feed rate is set by a composition controller on the overhead product. Remember to set up a level control scheme for the accumulator. (See Figure 1.12).

9.10 Draw a schematic for the rectifying section of a distillation column in which the ratio of reflux flow rate to distillate flow rate is set by a composition controller on the overhead product. (See Figure 1.12). (Hint: Use a level controller to set either the reflux flow rate or the distillate flow rate and determine the other flow rate using the ratio).

9.11 Draw a schematic by modifying Figure 3.13 so that the CSTR is equipped with a vent stream so that light impurities do not accumulate in the vapor space above the reaction mixture in the reactor. Add a ratio controller that adjusts the ratio of the flow rate of the vent stream to the reactor feed flow rate in order to maintain the composition of the light component in the reactor vapor space at a prescribed setpoint.

9.12 Draw a schematic of a ratio controller applied to the CST thermal mixer (Figure 3.6) in which the ratio controller for the temperature sets the ratio of F_1 to F_2.

9.13 How are ratio control and feedforward control alike and how are they different?

9.14 Draw a schematic of a control system that would provide the same function as the ratio control system shown in Figure 9.10 using a combined feedforward and feedback controller.

9.15 For a feedforward controller using a lead/lag element, what kinds of systems will result in a lead that is larger than its lag?

9.16 Consider the steam heated heat exchanger (Figure 3.16). Draw a schematic for this process for combined feedforward and feedback control where the feedforward disturbance is the temperature of the process stream entering the heat exchanger.

9.17 Consider the level process shown in Figure 3.11. Draw a schematic for this process for combined feedforward and feedback control where the feedforward disturbance is the inlet flow to the tank.

9.18 Apply and tune a feedforward controller to each of the following process simulators that are provided with this text. Develop FOPDT models of $G_p(s)$ and $G_d(s)$ using step test applied to the simulators. From these models, make initial guesses of the tuning parameters for the feedforward controller. Fine tune the feedforward controller and show results for a series of step changes in the measured disturbance.

    a. CST thermal mixer   b. CST composition mixer

    c. Endothermic CSTR   d. Heat exchanger

Chapter 10

PID Enhancements

10.1 Introduction

This chapter is concerned with enhancements to PID controllers that are designed to overcome the effects of measurement deadtime, process nonlinearity, and process constraints. Inferential control can greatly reduce the effect of measurement deadtime, scheduling of controller tuning can compensate for process nonlinearity, and override/select control provides a direct means to use PID controls on systems that encounter process constraints. When the desired manipulated variable is not directly controllable, computed manipulated variable control can be used.

10.2 Inferential Control

To this point, it has been assumed that the sensor in a control loop provides a direct measurement of the controlled variable. In fact, the output of the sensor only correlates with the value of the measured variable. For example, from Chapter 2, a thermocouple exposed to a process stream at a specific temperature will generate a millivolt signal that correlates strongly with the temperature of the process stream. Likewise, the level in a tank can be inferred from the pressure difference between the top and the bottom of a vessel and a flow rate can be estimated from the pressure drop across an orifice plate. In this section, it will be shown that **easily measured quantities, such as pressures, temperatures, and flow rates, can be effectively used to infer quantities which are more difficult to measure, such as compositions, molecular weight, and extent of reaction**. Then, the inferred value of the controlled variable can be used as the value of the controlled variable in a feedback control loop, greatly reducing the associated measurement delay.

There are three main reasons for using inferential measurement of a controlled variable:

1. Excessive analyzer deadtime undermines the performance of the feedback loop.   In Chapter 7, it was shown that when the deadtime to time constant ratio exceeds 0.5, deadtime reduces the aggressiveness of the controller, and therefore, this

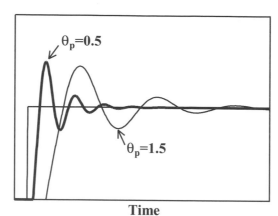

Figure 10.1 Setpoint tracking performance showing the effect of deadtime on closed loop performance.

reduces the resulting performance of the feedback controller. Figure 10.1 shows the setpoint tracking performance for two FOPDT processes (K_p=1, τ_p=1, θ_p=0.5; K_p=1, τ_p=1, θ_p=1.5). Both systems were tuned for QAD, but the process with the larger deadtime results in a much longer response time than the lower deadtime process. Certain techniques, such as **Smith Predictors**, have been developed to directly compensate for the deadtime of a process using process models. Smith predictors have been studied extensively in academia, but have been rarely applied industrially because the incremental improvement provided by the Smith predictor is generally much less than the improvement associated with an inferential measurement. In addition, Smith predictors are typically difficult to implement and their effectiveness is sensitive to modeling errors; therefore, inferential measurements are the industrial method of choice for counteracting large measurement delays for controlled variables. Inferential measurements can greatly reduce the measurement deadtime because they use measurements (e.g., temperatures, pressures, and flows) that have relatively low levels of measurement deadtime.

2. The total cost (i.e., the purchase price and maintenance cost) of an on-line analyzer can be excessive. Since inferential measurements are typically based on temperature, pressure, and flow measurements, they are much less expensive to install and maintain.

3. An on-line analyzer may not be available. In that case, an inferential measurement may be the only option for feedback control.

For an inferential control to be effective, the inferential measurement must correlate strongly with the controlled variable value and this correlation should be relatively insensitive to unmeasured disturbances. Following are several examples that illustrate how inferential measurements can be effectively applied in the CPI.

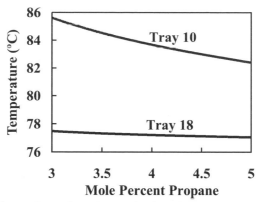

Figure 10.2 The effect of product impurity level on two different tray temperatures.

Inferential Temperature Control for Distillation. Tray temperatures correlate very well with product compositions for many distillation columns; therefore, inferential control of distillation product composition is a widely used form of inferential control. Figure 10.2 shows the correlation between propane content in the bottoms product and the tray temperature for two trays in the stripping section of a propane/butane binary column. Since this is a binary separation, the temperature and pressure of a tray define the composition on that tray. The largest temperature change for a fixed change in the bottom product composition occurs for tray number 10; therefore, the temperature of tray 10 could be used to infer the product purity of this column. Figure 10.3 shows the arrangement for inferential temperature control of the bottom product composition for this column. Note that the tray temperature controller is cascaded to a flow controller.

For a multicomponent distillation column, the tray temperature does not define the product composition. For example, the liquid on a tray can have the same

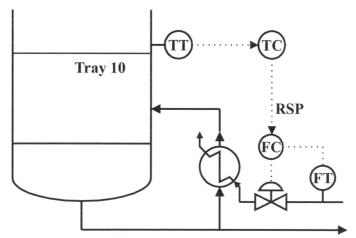

Figure 10.3 Schematic for inferential control of the bottoms product composition of a distillation column.

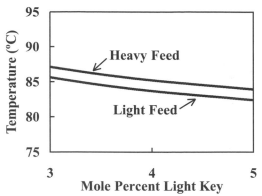

Figure 10.4 The effect of feed composition on the correlation between tray temperature and impurity level in the bottoms product.

concentration of light and heavy keys with different relative amounts of heavy non-key and light non-key and the resulting equilibrium temperature will change significantly. That is, as the amount of heavy non-key is increased and the amount of light non-key is decreased, the tray temperature will increase even though the proportions of light and heavy keys remain unchanged. Figure 10.4 shows a tray temperature in the stripping section of a multicomponent distillation column for different ratios of heavy non-key to light non-key as a function of the light key in the bottom product (i.e., a light and a heavy feed). Note that the two curves are parallel to each other with a difference of about 2°C. As a result, controlling a tray temperature to a fixed temperature will result in offset as the feed composition changes. In order to remove this offset, a composition controller that uses an on-line composition analyzer can be cascaded to the tray temperature control loop (Figure 10.5). In certain cases, laboratory analysis results which are taken once a shift or once per day are used by the operator to select the setpoint for the temperature controller in an effort to remove the aforementioned offset.

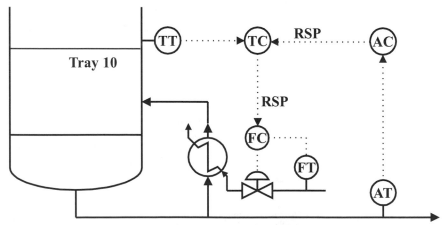

Figure 10.5 Schematic of an analyzer controller cascaded to a temperature controller for bottoms composition control of a distillation column.

Figure 10.6 Schematic of a fixed bed reactor.

Inferential Reaction Conversion Control. Consider an adiabatic fixed bed reactor (Figure 10.6). For a single irreversible reaction, $A \rightarrow B$, the macroscopic energy balance assuming no phase change is given by

$$X_A C_{A_{in}} (-\Delta H_{rxn}) = \rho C_P (T_{out} - T_{in}) \qquad \textbf{10.1}$$

where X_A is the fractional conversion of reactant A, $C_{A_{in}}$ is the inlet concentration of A to the reactor, ΔH_{rxn} is the heat of reaction, ρ is the average density of the process stream, C_P is the average heat capacity of the process stream, T_{out} is the temperature of the outlet stream from the reactor, and T_{in} is the temperature of the inlet stream to the reactor. Rearranging Equation 10.1

$$X_A = \frac{\rho C_P}{C_{A_{in}} (-\Delta H_{rxn})} (T_{out} - T_{in}) \qquad \textbf{10.2}$$

Note that this relationship is not affected by changes in the feed rate although feed rate will affect T_{out} and thus X_A. In an industrial reactor, there will be heat losses, side reactions, and variations in the physical parameters; therefore, the assumed inferential relationship will be

$$X_A = a(T_{out} - T_{in}) + b$$

A plot of the experimental data for a reactor (X_A, T_{out}, and T_{in}) can be used to determine a and b as well as check the validity of this functional form. Note that the temperature difference across the reactor needs to be large enough that temperature measurement noise does not significantly affect the results of the measured temperature drop for this approach to be effective. Note that once a and b are identified, the inlet temperature (T_{in}) can be adjusted to maintain a fixed reaction conversion, X_A. Periodically composition measurements for the product leaving the reactor can be made and the

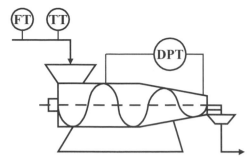

Figure 10.7 Schematic of a polymer extruder.

results used to update the value of b in the previous equation since a is less likely to change significantly compared with b.

Inferential Measurement of the Molecular Weight of a Polymer.

Figure 10.7 shows a schematic for a polymer extruder. An extruder is a screw device that forces a polymer melt through a set of dies creating a number of polymer strands. From fluid dynamics, it is known that the pressure drop across the extruder is directly related to the viscosity of the polymer. Further, as the molecular weight of the polymer increases, its viscosity increases. In addition, the temperature of the polymer melt inside the extruder also affects the viscosity.

The procedure for estimating the molecular weight of a polymer is as follows. First, the flow rate, F, and pressure drop across the extruder, ΔP, are measured. Then a fluid dynamic relationship is used to calculate the corresponding viscosity of the polymer melt at the prevailing temperature, T, i.e.,

$$\mu(T) = f_1(\Delta P, F)$$

Then the viscosity is corrected for temperature so that the viscosity of the melt is calculated at a standard temperature, T_o.

$$\mu(T_o) = f_2[T, \mu(T)]$$

Finally, a correlation between $\mu(T_o)$ and the molecular weight of the polymer melt is developed using laboratory measurements of the molecular weight (M_{wt}) for a range of $\mu(T_o)$ values, i.e.,

$$M_{wt} = f_3[\mu(T_o)]$$

Therefore, from measurements of the flow rate of the polymer melt, the pressure drop, and the temperature, the molecular weight of the polymer can be estimated on-line. This value can be used by a feedback controller to make adjustments to the polymer reactor in order to control the molecular weight of the polymer product. Without this inferential estimator, samples of the extruded polymer would have to be tested in the laboratory requiring in the range of 10 hours to perform each test. Since the residence time of the reactor/extruder process can be less than 1 hour, a 10 hour analysis deadtime would make feedback molecular weight control extremely difficult if not impossible. The samples, which are taken 1-3 times per day, could be used to make corrections to the correlation functions used to infer molecular weight.

Soft Sensors Based on Neural Networks. In electric power generating stations, restricting the NO_x (nitrogen oxide compounds) emissions from the flue gas to acceptable levels is important because NO_x compounds contribute to air pollution. Typically on-line analyzers are used to measure the NO_x in the flue gas from the boilers. Occasionally, the NO_x analyzers on a boiler will fail. If the NO_x level is not measured, the power companies must pay a fine for emissions. Instead of installing additional on-line NO_x analyzers which are quite expensive, a number of power companies have applied a type of inferential estimator to predict the NO_x level in their flue gas.

Instead of using one or two process measurements, all the measured process conditions (e.g., fuel feed rate, oxygen in the flue gas, heating value of the fuel, ambient air temperature, etc.) have been empirically correlated to predict the NO_x concentration in the flue gas. The empirical correlation is based on training an **artificial neural network** to predict the flue gas NO_x concentration from all the available data. A network with three input nodes, four nodes in the hidden layer, and one output node is shown schematically in Figure 10.8. Inputs to each node are summed and the resultant is transformed by a nonlinear function to calculate the node output. Weights are multiplied by the values that pass through them and are selected to emphasize or de-emphasize individual inputs to a node. Note that for Figure 10.8 there is a total of 16 adjustable weights for the neural network that can be selected such that the neural network matches the available process data. As a result, neural networks can be used as empirical nonlinear input/output models. A neural network for a NO_x analyzer could have over 500 weights (adjustable parameters). This inferential NO_x analyzer is also referred to as a **soft sensor** since the neural network

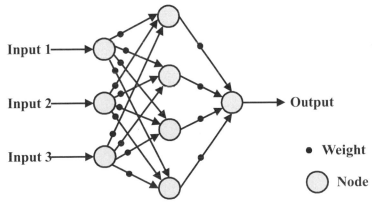

Figure 10.8 Diagram of a network with three input nodes, four nodes in the hidden layer, and one output node.

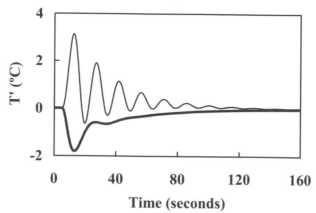

Figure 10.9 The effect of feed composition upsets on the PI feedback behavior for the endothermic CSTR. Thin line is for a feed composition decrease and thick line is for a feed composition increase.

software along with the process measurements are used to provide the on-line measurement.

10.3 Scheduling Controller Tuning

In Chapter 7, it was demonstrated that nonlinear process behavior can result in a controller becoming unstable in certain situations and in others it can become extremely sluggish (see Figure 10.9). For example, if the process gain increases by over 100%, the controller is likely to become unstable and if the process gain decreases by 50% or more the process can be expected to behave sluggishly. Tuning PID controllers for the case with the largest process gain can eliminate unstable operation, but at the expense of largely sluggish performance. As pointed out in Chapter 7, it is the combination of the magnitude of the disturbances and the inherent process nonlinearity that determine the degree of observed process nonlinearity. For a number of processes, certain measurements directly indicate whether the process parameters have increased or decreased and by how much; therefore, **scheduling of the controller tuning based on process measurements can be an effective means of compensating for process nonlinearity**. The controlled variable and the feed rate are examples of such key process measurements that can typically be used to schedule the controller tuning.

CSTR. Consider a CSTR in which the reaction rate constant is represented by an Arrenhius rate expression, i.e.,

$$k = k_o \, e^{-E/RT}$$

Figure 10.9 shows a PI controller tuned for the endothermic CSTR with Arrhenius temperature dependence for a region near the setpoint for a feed composition decrease

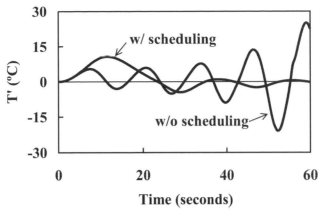

Figure 10.10 Comparison between a conventional PI controller and a PI controller with scheduling of the controller tuning for a severe feed composition upset for the endothermic CSTR.

and a feed composition increase. A feed composition decrease causes the reactor temperature to increase and a feed composition increase causes the reactor temperature to decrease. Note that when the reaction temperature increases, the closed loop response begins to ring and when the temperature decreases, the closed loop response becomes sluggish.

Now consider an approach where the controller aggressiveness is adjusted based on the reactor temperature. That is, the PID tuning factor, F_T, is scheduled as a function of the reactor temperature (Table 10.1). Figure 10.10 shows a comparison between a conventional PI controller and a PI controller with scheduling the controller

Table 10.1	
Scheduling of Controller Tuning for the CSTR Case	
$(T - T_{sp})$	F_T
- 4	1.4
- 2	1.6
0	1.8
2	2.8
4	3.8
6	4.8
8	5.8
10	6.8

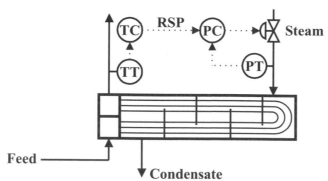

Figure 10.11 Schematic of a heat exchanger for which the outlet temperature is controlled by the steam pressure.

tuning for a severe feed composition upset for the endothermic CSTR. For the scheduled controller, F_T (Equation 7.14) is adjusted based on the error from setpoint according to Table 10.1. For this case, scheduling of the controller tuning was able to prevent the feedback controller from going unstable while a conventional PI controller was not. The slow movement towards setpoint indicates that not enough integral action is used when the reactor temperature is below setpoint. Scheduling the entire set of controller parameters can provide the correct integral action for each temperature region. This can be accomplished by tuning the controller at several different reactor temperatures and using the results to schedule the tuning parameters.

Heat Exchanger. Consider the heat exchanger shown in Figure 10.11. As the feed to the heat exchanger flows through the tube bundle, it is heated by steam condensing on the shell side. As the feed rate changes, the residence time of the feed in the tubes exposed to the steam changes. Figure 10.12 shows the open loop responses for three different feed rates for a step change in the setpoint of the steam pressure controller. The feed rate is represented by the average fluid velocity (v) in the tubes. Note that both the gain and the dynamic response change as the feed rate is changed. Table 10.2 list the FOPDT parameters for each flow rate. Note that the gain and the deadtime each change by a factor of about 2.5. Using these FOPDT parameters, the PI Cohen and Coon settings (Table 7.8) for each flow rate are also listed in Table 10.2. Note that the controller gain changes by a factor of 5 while the reset time changes are more gradual. It is clear from these results that it is not reasonable to expect one set of PI controller settings to work effectively for significant changes in the feed rate to this heat exchanger. For example, if the temperature controller for the outlet of the heat exchanger were tuned for $v=7$ ft/s, when the feed rate is reduced to $v=4$ ft/s, the controller becomes unstable. Conversely, if the controller were tuned for the low flow rate condition, it would perform sluggishly for the high flow rate conditions. Figure 10.13 shows results with and without scheduling of the controller tuning based on feed rate for a step decrease in the feed rate corresponding to a change in the velocity through the tubes from 7 to 4 ft/s. Note that the controller without scheduling was tuned for a feed rate corresponding to $v= 7$ ft/s.

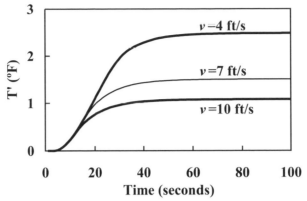

Figure 10.12 Open loop response for a heat exchanger for different feed rates.

Table 10.2			
FOPDT and PI Tuning Parameters for the Heat Exchanger Case as a Function of Feed Rate			
	v=4 ft/s	v=7 ft/s	v=10 ft/s
K_p	0.25	0.15	0.11
τ_p	10.7	9.9	10.0
0_p	10.2	5.8	4.0
K_c	4.2	10.8	21.3
τ_I	12.0	8.8	7.3

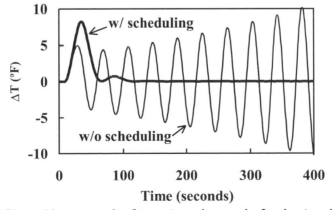

Figure 10.13 Closed loop results for a step change in feed rate with and without scheduling of the controller tuning for the heat exchanger case.

Non-stationary Behavior. Consider a wastewater neutralization process. If the titration curve of the wastewater and the other process parameters remain fixed, the process is referred to as **stationary**. On the other hand, if the titration curve changes, the process is **non-stationary**. In the case of this pH control example, changes in the titration curve can have an overwhelming effect on the process gains. There are many more examples of non-stationary behavior that result in much more gradual process gain changes. The following are several examples of non-stationary behavior in the CPI:

1. Catalyst deactivation
2. Heat exchanger fouling
3. Fouling of trays in a distillation column
4. Feed composition changes that affect the process parameters (K_p, τ_p, and θ_p)

These effects can be large enough that controller retuning is required. If an overall tuning factor, F_T, has been used, one can adjust F_T in a straightforward manner in order to compensate for the non-stationary behavior. Control methods that adjust controller tuning to adapt to non-stationary behavior are referred to as **adaptive control** techniques. Adaptive control techniques can be effectively applied for processes that vary slowly. That is, an adaptive controller would be expected to handle gradual catalyst deactivation that occurs over several days, but would not be expected to handle sharp changes in catalyst activity that occur within an hour. A number of commercially available adaptive controllers are referred to as **self-tuning controllers** and can usually be installed on a DCS. While there is a range of approaches used for self-tuning controllers, they are generally limited to processes that vary in a gradual, consistent manner.

10.4 Override/Select Control

Constraints are a natural part of industrial process control. As processes are pushed to produce as much product as possible, process limits will inevitably be encountered. When an upper or lower limit on a manipulated variable is encountered, or when an upper or lower value of a controlled or output variable from the process is reached, it can become necessary to apply different control loops than were previously used. That is, **effective industrial controller implementation requires that safeguards be installed to prevent the process from violating safety, environmental, or economic constraints.** These constraints can be met using override/select controls.

Consider the furnace fired heater shown in Figure 10.14. Under normal operating conditions, the fuel flow rate is adjusted to control the exit temperature of the process fluid. As the feed rate of the process fluid is increased, the furnace tube temperature will increase. At some point, the upper limit on furnace tube temperature (an operational constraint) will be encountered. The fuel flow rate to the furnace must

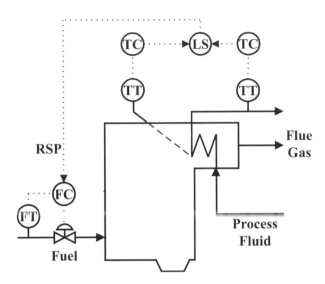

Figure 10.14 A schematic of a furnace fired heater with low select firing controls.

be adjusted in order to keep the furnace tube temperature from exceeding its upper limit. If the tube temperature constraint is exceeded, damage to the furnace tubes will result, significantly reducing their useful life. Figure 10.14 shows that the output of both control loops (the temperature controller on the process fluid and the temperature controller on the furnace tube temperature) are combined and the lower fuel feed rate is actually applied. The "LS" symbol in Figure 10.14 is called a **low select (LS)** and indicates that the lower fuel feed rate is chosen. When the feed rate is sufficiently low that the temperature of the process fluid can be controlled to setpoint, the output of the process fluid temperature controller will be selected since it is lower than the output of the tube temperature controller. Likewise, when the tube temperature approaches its upper limit, the output of the tube temperature controller will be selected. Therefore, there are two separate loops that use fuel flow rate as a manipulated variable and the LS controller switches between them as the flow rate of the process fluid changes.

Flooding of a distillation column can result as the feed to a column is increased. The onset of flooding is usually identified when the pressure drop across the column or a portion of the column increases sharply. When the pressure drop across the column reaches an upper safe limit (usually identified by operational experience), the reboiler duty is switched from controlling the bottom product composition to maintaining operation at the maximum pressure drop across the column (Figure 10.15). Note that a LS controller is used for this application as well. When the feed rate is reduced while operating at maximum differential pressure across the column, the impurity of the bottoms product will move below its setpoint and the reboiler duty called for by the composition control loop will be less than that called for by the differential pressure controller and the LS controller will use the output from the composition controller. As a result, the control loop is switched when the column

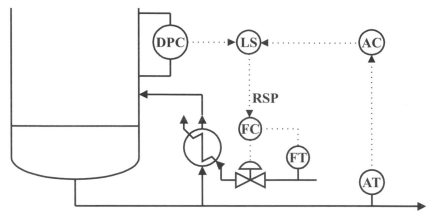

Figure 10.15 Schematic of the stripping section of a distillation column with low select controls applied to prevent flooding of the column.

differential pressure reaches its upper limit and switches back when the bottom product is overpurified. Two separate control loops use reboiler duty as a manipulated variable and the LS controller switches between them as the feed rate to the process changes.

A **high select (HS)** controller (Figure 10.16) can be used to control the maximum temperature in a fixed-bed reactor even when the maximum reactor temperature can occur at different locations in the reactor. The HS controller chooses the largest temperature measurement from a number of temperature measurements and the largest reading is sent to the temperature controller. In this manner, the highest reactor temperature can be controlled. Low select (LS) controllers can also be used where the lowest reading is selected from several readings.

Figure 10.17 shows a distillation column that reaches an upper limit on the reboiler duty. When the remote setpoint for the steam flow rate to the reboiler is consistently greater than the measured steam flow, an override controller switches to

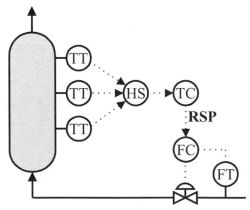

Figure 10.16 Schematic of a fixed-bed reactor a with high select controller applied to control the maximum reactor temperature.

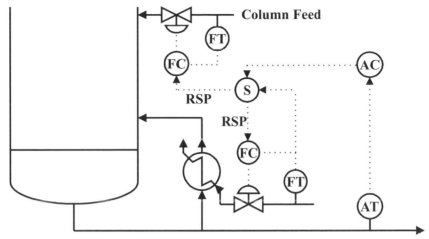

Figure 10.17 Schematic of the stripping section of a distillation column with override/select control to maintain bottom product purity when a maximum reboiler constraint is encountered.

using the column feed rate as a manipulated variable in order to keep the bottom product purity on specification. When the column feed rate is adjusted back to its normal level and the control valve on the steam to the reboiler is no longer **saturated** (i.e., fully open), the control configuration is changed so that the reboiler duty is manipulated to control the bottom product purity. This is an example of override selection of a secondary manipulated variable when the primary manipulated variable reaches a limit (becomes saturated).

For furnaces, it is important to ensure that excess air is always supplied with the fuel in order to prevent the formation of carbon monoxide (CO), a serious safety hazard. Furnaces are normally equipped with CO sensors that will shut down the furnace if CO levels exceed specified limits. **Cross-limiting firing controls** (Figure 10.18) are designed to reduce the likelihood that CO will be formed during changes in the firing rate to the furnace. In the case in which the firing rate is increased, the air feed rate is increased immediately and the fuel feed rate will follow the air flow rate in order to ensure that combustion occurs with excess air. Note that the fuel to air ratio is applied so that the fuel firing rate can be used in the air flow control loop. An increase in the firing rate signal will not directly affect the fuel control loop due to the LS, but the air flow control loop will accept the firing rate increase due to the HS; therefore, the setpoint for the air flow controller will increase immediately. As the air flow rate increases , the fuel flow rate corresponding to the increased air flow rate is transferred to the LS which sends it on to the fuel flow controller as its setpoint; therefore, the fuel flow rate will begin to increase, but only after the air flow rate in order to ensure that excess air is present during this transient. Similarly, when the firing signal is decreased, it will not directly affect the air flow due to the HS, but the setpoint for the fuel flow rate controller will decrease immediately due to the LS. As the measured value of the fuel flow rate decreases, the HS will choose the measured fuel flow; therefore, excess air will be maintained during a firing rate decrease.

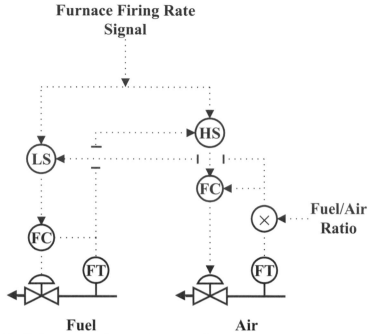

Figure 10.18 Schematic of cross-limiting firing controls which are designed to prevent CO formation during changes in the furnace firing rate.

10.5 Computed Manipulated Variable Control

In certain cases, it is not possible to directly adjust the desired manipulated variable for a particular process. For example, consider the reboiler on a distillation column that uses waste heat in the form of quench water (water used to cool hot gases) to provide reboiler duty (Figure 10.19). The inlet temperature of the quench water can vary over a considerable range which results in a disturbance for the distillation column. When the inlet temperature increases, extra boilup will result for the column and the bottoms product will become overpurified. The composition controller on the bottoms product can eventually compensate for this disturbance, but disturbances in the inlet temperature of the quench water will affect the variability in the products produced by the distillation column. The desired operation of the reboiler would have the composition controller setting the reboiler duty directly. For steam heated reboilers, the reboiler duty is directly related to the steam flow rate, but for the case under consideration the reboiler duty changes with inlet temperature as well as the flow rate of the quench water. The solution is to use a steady-state energy balance on the quench water to calculate the flow rate of the quench water that provides the desired reboiler duty. That is,

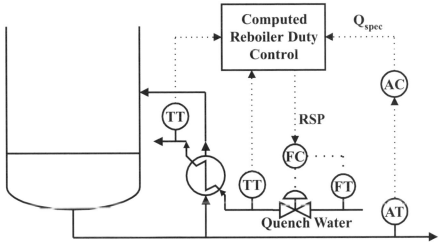

Figure 10.19 Schematic for applying computed reboiler duty control for a distillation column.

$$F_{sp} = \frac{Q_{spec}}{C_p\,(T_{in} - T_{out})}$$

10.3

where F_{sp} is the setpoint for the flow controller on the quench water to the reboiler, Q_{spec} is the reboiler heat duty specified by the bottom product composition controller, C_p is the heat capacity of the quench water, T_{in} and T_{out} are the measured inlet and outlet temperatures of the quench water, respectively. In this manner, as the inlet and outlet temperatures change for the quench water, its flow rate can be adjusted accordingly before it affects the product compositions of the distillation column. Figure 10.19 shows how computed variable control can be applied to this case. Note that the inlet and outlet temperatures along with the specified reboiler duty are input to the computation block where Equation 10.3 calculates the required flow rate which in turn is passed on as the setpoint for the flow controller on the quench water.

Computed manipulated variable control can also be used to control a furnace that uses two different grades of fuel. Consider a process that produces a low heating value gas as a byproduct. It is desirable to burn all the low heating value gas in a furnace which is used to heat a process stream. Unfortunately, the product rate of the low heating value gas is not sufficient to provide all the heat duty for the furnace; therefore, natural gas is also fed to the furnace and the flow rate of natural gas is adjusted to control the temperature of the process stream leaving the furnace. Since the flow rate of the low heating value gas varies over a wide range, it represents a major disturbance for the temperature controller on the process stream leaving the furnace. A computed manipulated variable controller can be used to calculate the required flow rate of natural gas necessary to meet the heat duty requirements specified by the temperature controller using an energy balance for the heat duty of the furnace along with the heats of combustion for the low heating value gas and the natural gas. In this manner, flow rate changes in the low heating value gas can be readily compensated by the computed variable controller. Note that these two cases demonstrate that computed manipulated variable control is an effective means of providing heat duty control in certain cases. By contrast, inferential control, which was presented in Section 10.2, uses calculations involving several process measurements to estimate the values of difficult to measure controlled variables.

Distillation columns can be particularly sensitive to sharp changes in ambient conditions due to weather fronts or to thundershowers since both of these cases can cause significant increases in the reflux subcooling. This results because the ambient air conditions can have a significant effect on the temperature of the condensed liquid products from the overhead for a large number of distillation columns. Decreases in the reflux temperature cause an increase in the amount of liquid that is condensed out of the vapor when the reflux is added to the top of the column. This can be understood by recognizing that the vapor and liquid on the top tray are at very nearly the same temperature; therefore, when subcooled reflux is added to the top of a column, some of the vapor must be condensed in order to raise the temperature of the reflux to the temperature of the top tray. The reflux added to the column (external reflux) and the reflux that results from condensing some of the vapor by the subcooled reflux make up the internal reflux for the column. Decreases in the reflux temperature caused by thunderstorms can produce sharp changes in the flow rate of the internal reflux which directly affects the purity of the column products since the internal vapor/liquid rates determine the separation produced by a distillation column. As a result, it is much more desirable to control the internal reflux flow rate than the external reflux flow rate when thunderstorms or weather fronts can have a significant effect on the internal reflux flow rate of a column.

Equating the heat lost by the condensing vapor to the heat required by the subcooled reflux results in the following equation

$$C_p F_{ex} (T_{oh} - T_r) = \Delta F_{int} \Delta H_{vap}$$

where C_p is the heat capacity of the reflux, T_{oh} is the overhead temperature, T_r is the subcooled reflux temperature, F_{ex} is the external reflux flow (the setpoint for the flow controller on the reflux), ΔF_{int} is the change in the reflux caused by the condensing vapor, and ΔH_{vap} is the heat of vaporization of the vapor. ΔF_{int} combines with the external reflux to form the internal reflux. Then the equation for the internal reflux flow rate (F_{int}) is given by

$$F_{int} = F_{ex} (1 + C_p [T_{oh} - T_r]/\Delta H_{vap})$$

This equation can be rearranged to calculate the external reflux that maintains a specified internal reflux control (F_{int}^{spec}), i.e.,

$$F_{ex} = \frac{F_{int}^{spec}}{1 + C_p (T_{oh} - T_r)/\Delta H_{vap}}$$

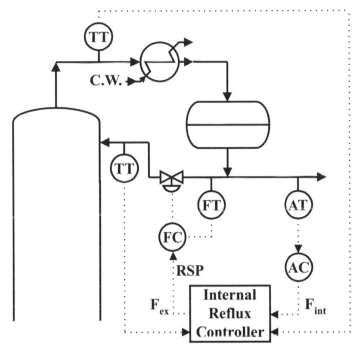

Figure 10.20 Schematic of an internal reflux controller applied for composition control of the overhead of a column.

This approach is called internal reflux control and is shown schematically in Figure 10.20. Note that the composition controller outputs the internal reflux flow rate and the internal reflux controller calculates the external reflux flow rate which is used as the setpoint for the flow controller on the reflux.

10.6   Summary

Inferential control uses fast responding process measurements, such as pressures, temperatures and flow rates, to estimate the value of the controlled variable. Less deadtime associated with the measurement of the controlled variable results and better feedback control performance is obtained.

When the characteristics of a process (K_p, τ_p, and θ_p) change significantly with the value of a measured process variable, scheduling of the controller tuning parameters can be applied and results in improved control performance and reliability. For these cases, scheduling of the tuning parameters allows for the variation in the controller tuning as the process conditions change in order to maintain stable controller performance without sluggish behavior.

Override/select control switches between control loops when process constraints are encountered. High and low select controllers are applied to cases where the same manipulated variable is used by two different control loops in order to observe process constraints. Override controls switch between manipulated variables and possible control loops as process conditions change in order to meet the operational objectives of the process.

Computed manipulated variable control can be used when direct manipulation of the desired manipulated variable is not possible. For these cases, process measurements are used to calculate the flow rate that can be adjusted to maintain the desired manipulated variable at its prescribed level.

10.7   Additional Terminology

Adaptive controller - a controller that adjusts its tuning parameters on-line in response to changes in the process.
Artificial neural networks   - (ANN) a special class of nonlinear empirical models.
Cross-limiting firing controls - firing controls based on low and high selects that maintain excess air during changes in the firing rate to a furnace.
HS - high select controller.
Inferential control - the use of readily measured quantities, such as pressures, flows, and temperatures, to estimate on-line the values of the controlled variables for control purposes.
LS - low select controller.
Non-stationary process - a process whose characteristics (K_p, τ_p, θ_p) change due to disturbances entering the process.
Saturated control valve- a control valve that is fully open or closed.
Self-tuning control - a controller that adjusts its tuning parameters on-line in response to changes to the process.
Smith predictor - an approach that uses a process model to reduce the effects of deadtime.
Soft sensor - an algorithm that estimates the value of difficult to measure process variables using correlation functions based on available process measurements.
Stationary process - a process whose process characteristics (K_p, τ_p, θ_p) remain constant with time.

10.8 Questions and Exercises

10.1 Why are inferential measurements used industrially?

10.2 How do you determine what tray temperature should be used to infer the product composition of a distillation column?

10.3 Indicate how an energy balance on a CSTR can be used to estimate the amount of conversion occurring in the reactor. What assumptions and limitations would this inferential estimator have?

10.4 Explain how a neural network can be trained and then used as a soft sensor.

10.5 The operating pressure of a distillation column has a significant effect on the temperatures of the trays of the column. Indicate how a tray temperature used to infer the product composition can be compensated for pressure changes. Assume that the tray temperature varies linearly with column pressure. Indicate how you would determine all unknown parameters.

10.6 Construct an inferential estimate of the fouling of the heat exchanger shown in Figure 10.11. Indicate how this estimator could be used to schedule cleaning of the tube bundle.

10.7 How does scheduling controller tuning prevent a nonlinear process from going unstable or behaving sluggishly?

10.8 How do you determine whether or not scheduling of the tuning parameters of a controller will be effective?

10.9 Identify a process for which scheduling of the controller tuning parameter is likely to be beneficial. Outline how the scheduling of the controller tuning parameters could be accomplished. Choose a system not described in the text.

10.10 What is the difference between a low select controller and an override controller?

10.11 Consider the accumulator for a distillation column for which the distillate product flow rate is used to control the accumulator level and the reflux flow rate is used to control the composition of the overhead product similar to Figure 1.12. Draw a schematic showing select controls that will prevent the level from exceeding 95% and prevent the level from becoming less than 5% by overriding the composition controller on the overhead when the level is too high or too low.

10.12 Consider the stripping section of a distillation column shown in Figure 9.10. Modify this schematic by adding override controls that will prevent the column pressure from exceeding its upper limit by overriding the composition controller when the pressure reaches its upper limit.

10.13 Consider the stripping section of a distillation column shown in Figure 9.10. Under certain conditions the column will flood if the steam addition rate is not restricted and under other conditions excess steam flow to the reboiler will cause the maximum temperature limit on the reboiler to be exceeded resulting in severe fouling of the reboiler. Draw a schematic showing the override/select controls that will simultaneously prevent the column from flooding and from exceeding the upper limit on the reboiler temperature.

10.14 From your fluids course, you know that the mass flow rate of a gas through an orifice meter is dependent on the pressure drop across the orifice plate and the temperature and pressure of the gas. Therefore, if the temperature and pressure of a gas change significantly, using the pressure drop across an orifice meter as a measurement of flow rate can result in significant error. Devise a computed manipulated variable controller for the mass flow rate of a gas for which the temperature and pressure of the gas change significantly. List all the necessary equations and draw a schematic showing the computed mass flow rate controller.

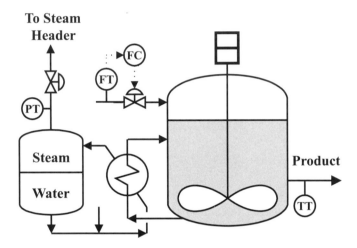

10.15 Consider the schematic shown above for an exothermic CSTR in which the heat produced by the reactor is used to generate steam [after W.L. Luyben, *Process Modeling, Simulation and Control for Chemical Engineers*, Second Edition, McGraw-Hill, p. 292 (1990)]. Draw a schematic for this process including each of the following control features:

a. The level in the steam drum is controlled by the make-up water.

b. The pressure of the steam drum is controlled by the valve on the steam line to the steam header.

c. The temperature controller for the reactor is cascaded to the steam pressure control loop.

d. The level in the reactor is controlled by the product flow rate.

e. A low level in the steam drum overrides the setpoint for the flow controller on the feed to the reactor and cuts back on the feed to the reactor.

f. A high reactor temperature overrides the setpoint for the flow controller on the feed to the reactor and cutback on the feed to the reactor.

Chapter 11

PID Implementation Issues

11.1 Introduction

This chapter is concerned with several techniques that have been developed in order to solve PID implementation problems. Anti-reset windup procedures protect against integral windup when a manipulated variable reaches an upper or lower limit or when either of two control loops can be used to select the same manipulated variable (e.g., override/select control). Bumpless transfer is a strategy for bringing a controller on-line in a manner that does not unduly upset the process. Split-range flow control uses two separate flow control loops in order to provide precise flow metering over a wider range of flow rates than a single flow control loop can provide.

11.2 Anti-Windup Strategies

Figure 11.1a shows the manipulated and controlled variables for a standard PI controller for which the manipulated variable reaches its upper limit, i.e., the control valve is fully open or fully closed which is referred to as a saturated control valve. This can occur when a large disturbance enters the process. Since the manipulated variable cannot be increased further, the PI controller is unable to return the controlled variable to its setpoint. As long as there is an error between the controlled variable and its setpoint, the integral term in the PI controller (Equation 6.9) will continue to accumulate which is referred to as **reset windup** or **integral windup**. After some time, the disturbance level returns to its original value. At this point, integral windup in the PI controller keeps the manipulated variable at its maximum level even though the value of the controlled variable is now above its setpoint. In effect, before the process can return to steady-state, an equal area above the setpoint must be generated to compensate for area "A" shown in Figure 11.1a.

This behavior results because the integral is allowed to continue accumulating after control of the process has been lost (i.e., the **manipulated variable saturates**). Figure 11.1b shows the same case as Figure 11.1a except that when the manipulated variable saturates, the integral is not allowed to accumulate (**windup**). Note that when control returns to the process (i.e., when the manipulated variable is no longer saturated), the controlled variable moves directly back to its setpoint and does not

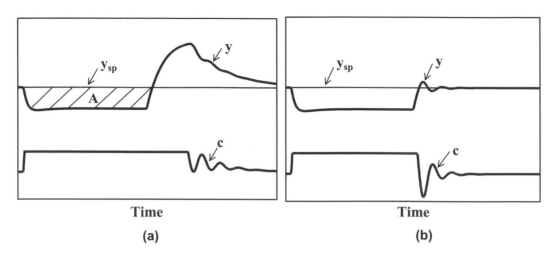

Figure 11.1 Response of a feedback system to a saturated manipulated variable. (a) Conventional PI controller. (b) PI controller with anti-reset windup.

exhibit prolonged deviations from setpoint as before. Because the integral action was turned off when the manipulated variable became saturated, the PI controller does not have to generate an area equivalent to area "A" above the setpoint.

Anti-reset windup can be implemented by simply not allowing the integral to accumulate when the manipulated variable is saturated. The manipulated variable is saturated when the control valve on the line supplying the manipulated variable is either closed or fully open. A saturated control valve can be identified when there is sustained offset between the manipulated variable level requested by the flow controller and the actual flow rate of the manipulated variable.

Clamping the Controller Output. Since DCS's use the velocity form of the PID controller, the output from the controller can be restricted or "clamped" so that it does not become less than 0% or more than 100%. In most cases, clamping the controller output will prevent severe reaction to reset windup, but clamping the controller output will still allow some degree of windup to occur.

Internal Reset Feedback. Figure 11.2a shows a block diagram for a conventional PI controller. Figure 11.2b shows a block diagram for **internal reset feedback**. Applying a balance around the summation block in Figure 11.2b for the internal reset feedback case yields

$$K_c E(s) + F(s) = C(s)$$

where
$$F(s) = \frac{C(s)}{\tau_I s + 1}$$

Substituting and collecting terms result in

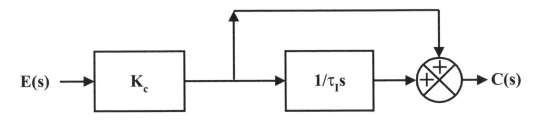

Figure 11.2a Block diagram of a conventional PI controller.

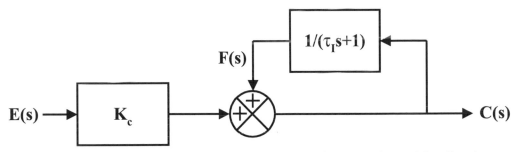

Figure 11.2b Block diagram of a PI controller with internal reset feedback.

$$C(s)\left[1-\frac{1}{\tau_I \, s+1}\right] = K_c \, E(s)$$

Collecting terms and solving for $C(s)$ yields

$$C(s) = K_c\left[1+\frac{1}{\tau_I \, s}\right] F(s)$$

which is the transfer function for a PI controller; therefore, internal reset feedback (Figure 11.2b) is equivalent to PI control (Figure 11.2a). Internal reset feedback will also windup since it is equivalent to a conventional PI controller, but since $C(s)$ can be clamped, it does not windup past 100% or below 0%. Therefore, internal reset feedback does not offer any advantage over using the velocity form of the PI controller and clamping the controller output. It is, however, a natural step from internal reset feedback to external reset feedback which is superior to controller output clamping.

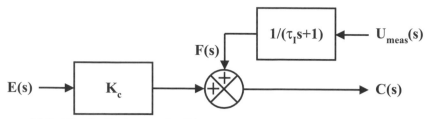

Figure 11.3 Block diagram of a PI controller with external reset feedback.

External Reset Feedback. Figure 11.3 shows a block diagram for **external reset feedback**. Note that for this case the measured value of the manipulated variable instead of the output from the controller is fed back through the filter to the summation block. The advantage of external reset feedback is that shortly after the manipulated variable saturates, i.e., $F(s)$ becomes constant, reset windup is turned off and $C(s)$ becomes constant. For internal reset feedback, reset windup continues until the controller output reaches 0% or 100%. As a result, external reset feedback turns off the integral action much sooner than internal reset feedback. The disadvantage of external reset feedback is that a measurement of the manipulated variable value is required which is not available in all cases. It should be pointed out that the measured value of the manipulated variable must be scaled so that it has the same units as the controller output (i.e., %). It is a standard control practice to apply some type of anti-windup strategy (e.g., external reset feedback or turning off the integral when the manipulated variable saturates) to all control loops that use integral action to prevent reset windup. This is essential for override/select loops because when one loop is controlling the process, the other is not in service; therefore, the inactive loop can experience severe windup if anti-reset windup measures are not taken.

11.3 Bumpless Transfer

Figure 11.4 shows the process behavior with and without **bumpless transfer**. Without bumpless transfer, if the controller is turned on when the controlled variable is far removed from setpoint, the controller will take immediate action and drive the process to setpoint in an underdamped fashion. In certain cases, the controlled variable can be far enough away from setpoint and the process can be sufficiently nonlinear that the control loop becomes unstable. Even if the control loop does not become unstable, the abrupt action of the feedback controller can significantly upset other control loops on the process. As a result, operators find that the behavior of a controller without bumpless transfer is generally unacceptable particularly for key loops such as composition and temperature control loops.

For bumpless transfer, there are two types of setpoints: the true setpoint which corresponds to the desired operating point and the internal setpoint that is used for bumpless transfer (Figure 11.5). When a control loop is turned on, the setpoint used by the controller is actually different than the true setpoint when applying bumpless

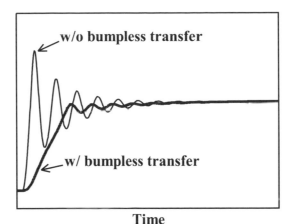

Figure 11.4 The startup response of a feedback system (a) without bumpless transfer and (b) with bumpless transfer.

transfer. When the controller is turned on, the internal setpoint is set equal to the current controlled variable value; therefore, there is no change in the manipulated variable level. After this, the internal setpoint is ramped toward the true setpoint and the process begins moving toward the true setpoint in a gradual fashion. After the internal setpoint reaches the true setpoint value, it will remain constant. By selecting a proper setpoint ramping rate, smooth and consistent startups for control loops will result.

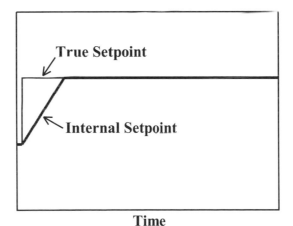

Figure 11.5 Comparison between the true setpoint and the internal setpoint for the bumpless transfer example.

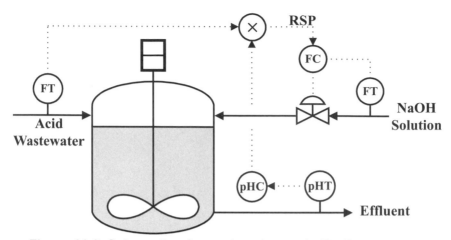

Figure 11.6 Schematic of a wastewater neutralization process.

11.4 Split-Range Flow Control

Consider the wastewater neutralization process shown in Figure 11.6. The titration curve for the wastewater is shown in Figure 11.7. In order to control the pH to ± 1.0 pH units at a setpoint of pH 7, the base flow rate must be metered accurately to within ±0.5%. A single flow control loop with a control valve with a positioner can meet this metering precision. But if the total flow rate of base were to range from 0.1 to 10 gallons per minute, one flow control loop could not simultaneously meter the base flow rate to within ±0.5% at 0.1 and 10 gallons per minute.

Two flow control loops that work together can meet this requirement as shown in Figure 11.8. At low flow rates, the large control valve is closed and the flow control

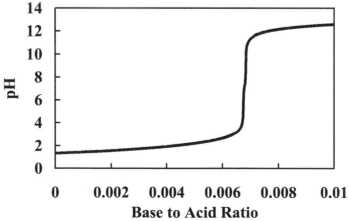

Figure 11.7 Titration curve for a strong acid/strong base system.

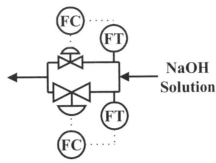

Figure 11.8 Schematic of a split range flow controller.

loop with the smaller control valve can accurately meter the low flow operation. As the total flow increases, the smaller control valve will begin to approach saturation. Before this happens, the flow control loop with the larger control valve comes into service. At large flow rates (i.e., greater than 1 GPM), the small control valve is completely open and the flow control loop with the larger valve is accurately metering the base flow rate. This is an example of **split-range flow control** which is used when accurate flow control is required over a wider operating range than one control valve can provide.

11.5 Summary

Reset windup can occur when a control valve saturates. External reset feedback or turning off the integral action when a control valve saturates will eliminate reset windup. Bumpless transfer provides a smooth startup procedure for a control loop by ramping the setpoint from the initial value of the controlled variable to its desired final value. Split-range flow control uses two flow control loops in parallel each with different sized control valves so that the overall system provides accurate flow control over a much wider range of flow rates than a single flow control loop could provide.

11.6 Additional Terminology

Anti-reset windup - approaches that prevent reset windup, e.g., external reset feedback.

Bumpless transfer - a startup procedure used to gradually bring a control loop into service.

Clamping - restricting the output of a controller to be less than a maximum amount (e.g., 100%) and greater than a minimum amount (e.g., 0%).

External reset feedback - an anti-windup approach that uses the measured value of the manipulated variable.

Integral windup - the accumulation of the integral of the error from setpoint caused by an uncontrollable error from setpoint.

Internal reset feedback - an anti-windup approach that does not use the measured value of the manipulated variable.

Reset windup - the accumulation of the integral of the error from setpoint caused by an uncontrollable error from setpoint.

Saturated manipulated variable - a manipulated variable that is either at its maximum or minimum value.

Split-range flow control - using two flow control loops in parallel, one with a smaller valve than the other in order to provide precise flow metering over a wide range of flow rates.

Windup - the accumulation of the integral of the error from setpoint caused by an uncontrollable error from setpoint.

11.7 Questions and Exercises

11.1 In your own words, explain how windup occurs and what problems it causes.

11.2 Show that internal reset feedback is equivalent to conventional control for a PI controller.

11.3 What advantage does internal reset feedback have over using the velocity form of the PID controller and clamping the controller output?

11.4 What is the advantage of external over internal reset feedback?

11.5 If you were applying an anti-windup strategy that turned off the integral when a control valve saturated, how would you determine whether or not a control valve was saturated?

11.6 Explain how bumpless transfer is applied and indicate what its advantages are.

11.7 Why do operators prefer bumpless transfer?

11.8 When should you use split-range flow control?

PART V

CONTROL OF MIMO PROCESSES

Chapter 12

PID Controllers Applied to MIMO Processes

12.1 Introduction

A multiple-input/multiple-output (MIMO) process has two or more inputs and two or more outputs. A two input/two output system is shown schematically in Figure 12.1. Note that c_1 affects both y_1 and y_2 and c_2 affects both y_1 and y_2. When both inputs affect both outputs the process is referred to as a **coupled** process. MIMO processes are frequently encountered in the CPI.

This chapter considers the application of PID controllers to coupled MIMO processes. A key issue when applying PID controllers to MIMO systems is deciding which manipulated variable should be used to control which controlled variable. This is referred to as choosing the **manipulated/controlled variable pairings** [(c, y) pairings] or the **control configuration**. The factors that affect the choice of (c, y) pairings are analyzed in this chapter. In addition, a strategy for tuning PID controllers that are applied to MIMO processes is presented as well as an introduction to decoupling. In this chapter, the transfer function $G'(s)$ is used for simplicity to represent the combined effect of the actuator, process, and sensor [$G_a(s)$ $G_p(s)$ $G_s(s)$].

12.2 SISO Controllers and (c, y) Pairings

Figure 12.2 shows two **single loop PID controllers** applied to a two input/two output process (2×2 system). Applying single loop PID controllers to a MIMO process is called **decentralized control**. Note that the coupling in this 2×2 system causes the two control loops to interact. That is, while control loop 1 adjusts c_1 to keep y_1 at its setpoint, it upsets control loop 2. Likewise, the operation of control loop 2 can act as an upset for control loop 1. Figure 12.3 shows schematically the coupling effect of control loop 2 (indicted by heavy lines) as an additive disturbance to control loop 1. The coupling effects of control loop 1 are also represented as an additive disturbance to control loop 2. For this 2×2 example, when tuning control loop 1, the effects of

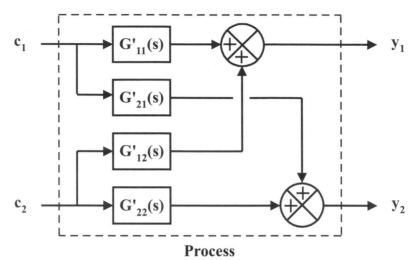

Process
Figure 12.1 Block diagram of a two input/two output process.

control loop 2 must be taken into account and vice-versa. When tuning single loop PID controllers applied to a MIMO process, one must take into account the effects of coupling.

The selection of pairings for a decentralized controller can have a dramatic effect on the resulting overall control performance. Consider the 2×2 process represented by transfer function models shown in Table 12.1. Note that using c_1 to control y_1 and c_2 to control y_2 has the advantage that the magnitude of coupling is relatively small. The steady-state process gain for the effect of c_1 on y_1 is 1.0 and for

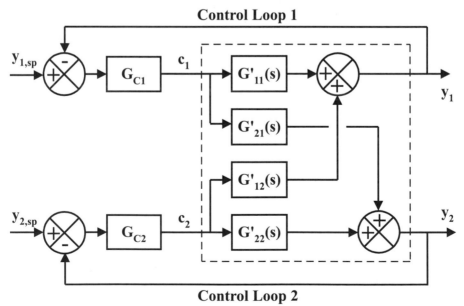

Figure 12.2 Block diagram of a 2 × 2 process with single loop controllers applied (decentralized control).

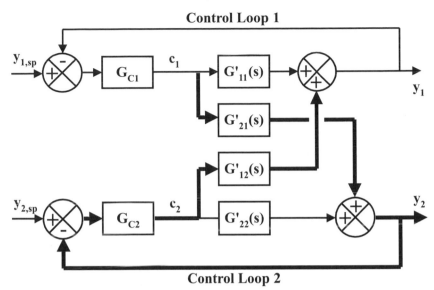

Figure 12.3 A block diagram of a 2 × 2 process with single loop controllers showing the coupling effect of loop 2 on y_1 for changes in c_1.

the effect of c_2 on y_2 is 2.0 while the gain for the effect of c_1 on y_2 is 0.05 and for the effect of c_2 on y_1 is 0.1. As a result, relatively small changes in c_1 and c_2 are called for by the feedback controllers since the process gains are relatively large and the resulting coupling would be relatively low in magnitude. On the other hand, if c_1 were chosen to control y_2 and c_2 to control y_1, large changes in c_1 and c_2 would be required by the feedback controllers due to the low process gains. Then the resulting coupling would be severe.

	c_1	c_2
Table 12.1		
Transfer Function Models for a Two Input/Two Output Process.		
y_1	$\dfrac{1.0}{10s+1}$	$\dfrac{0.1}{10s+1}$
y_2	$\dfrac{0.05}{10s+1}$	$\dfrac{2.0}{10s+1}$

There are three factors that determine the best pairings for a MIMO process: coupling, dynamic response, and the sensitivity to disturbances. Each of these factors will be considered separately in the next three sections.

12.3 Steady-State Coupling

Bristol[1] developed the **Relative Gain Array (*RGA*)** which is a measure of steady-state coupling. The *RGA* for a 2×2 system is given by

$$RGA = \begin{pmatrix} \lambda_{11} & \lambda_{12} \\ \lambda_{21} & \lambda_{22} \end{pmatrix}$$

where

$$\lambda_{11} = \frac{\left(\dfrac{\Delta y_1}{\Delta c_1}\right)_{c_2}}{\left(\dfrac{\Delta y_1}{\Delta c_1}\right)_{y_2}} \qquad\qquad \lambda_{12} = \frac{\left(\dfrac{\Delta y_1}{\Delta c_2}\right)_{c_1}}{\left(\dfrac{\Delta y_1}{\Delta c_2}\right)_{y_2}}$$

$$\text{12.1}$$

$$\lambda_{21} = \frac{\left(\dfrac{\Delta y_2}{\Delta c_1}\right)_{c_2}}{\left(\dfrac{\Delta y_2}{\Delta c_1}\right)_{y_1}} \qquad\qquad \lambda_{22} = \frac{\left(\dfrac{\Delta y_2}{\Delta c_2}\right)_{c_1}}{\left(\dfrac{\Delta y_2}{\Delta c_2}\right)_{y_1}}$$

where

$$\left(\dfrac{\Delta y_i}{\Delta c_j}\right)_{c_k}$$

represents the steady-state change in y_i resulting from a change in c_j while keeping c_k constant and

$$\left(\dfrac{\Delta y_i}{\Delta c_j}\right)_{y_k}$$

represents the steady-state change in y_i for a change in c_j while keeping y_k constant. The numerator of λ_{11} in Equation 12.1 is simply the open loop gain for the effect of c_1 on y_1, i.e., the steady-state gain in $G_{11}(s)$, and this can be determined by implementing a change in c_1 and measuring the resulting steady-state change in y_1 while control loop 2 is open (Figure 12.4). The denominator of λ_{11} is the gain between c_1 and y_1 while keeping y_2 at its setpoint which requires that the second loop be closed (Figure 12.5). If no coupling is present, the numerator of λ_{11} will equal the denominator. As a result, the closer λ_{11} is to 1.0, the less steady-state coupling a configuration will have.

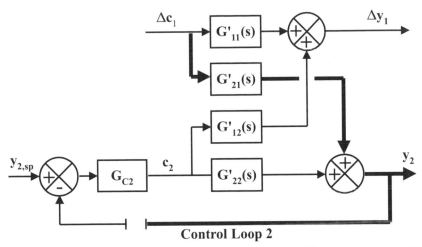

Figure 12.4 Block diagram for the determination of the numerator of λ_{11}.

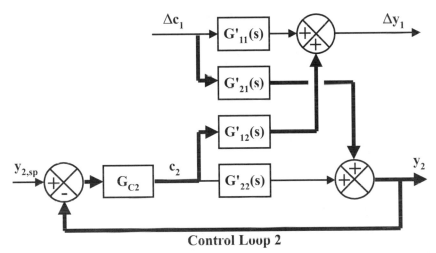

Figure 12.5 Block diagram for the determination of the denominator of λ_{11}.

Consider the system represented by Table 12.1. The steady-state gain matrix for this process is given by

$$\boldsymbol{K} = \begin{pmatrix} K_{11} & K_{12} \\ K_{21} & K_{22} \end{pmatrix} = \begin{pmatrix} 1.0 & 0.1 \\ 0.05 & 2.0 \end{pmatrix}$$

Consider λ_{11}. The numerator is the open loop gain of the first transfer function or 1.0. The evaluation of the numerator of λ_{11} is shown schematically in Figure 12.4. In order to calculate the value of

$$\left(\frac{\Delta y_1}{\Delta c_1} \right)_{y_2}$$

consider a change in c_1 of 1.0. From Figure 12.5, the net effect on y_1 will be the combined effect of the primary response and the result of coupling. The primary response is the product of Δc_1 and K_{11} or 1.0. The result of coupling is calculated by using the various steady-state gains. The effect of Δc_1 on y_2 is given by

$$\Delta y_2 = \Delta c_1 K_{21} = 0.05$$

The (c_2, y_2) control loop must compensate for this change in y_2; therefore, the required change in c_2 is given by

$$\Delta c_2 = \frac{-\Delta y_2}{K_{22}} = -0.025$$

Finally, the effect of Δc_2 on y_1 is given by

$$\Delta y_1 = \Delta c_2 K_{12} = -0.0025$$

which represents the coupling result for a Δc_1 change.

Therefore, the total effect is the sum of the primary effect and the coupling effect, i.e.,

$$\left(\frac{\Delta y_1}{\Delta c_1} \right)_{y_2} = \frac{1 - 0.0025}{1.0} = 0.9975$$

Then λ_{11} is given by

$$\lambda_{11} = \frac{1.0}{0.9975} = 1.0025$$

which indicates that this pairing is highly decoupled.

For a 2×2 system using the steady-state gain values, the value of λ_{11} is given by

$$\lambda_{11} = \frac{K_{11}}{K_{11} - \dfrac{K_{12} K_{21}}{K_{22}}} = \frac{1}{1 - \dfrac{K_{12} K_{21}}{K_{11} K_{22}}} \qquad \textbf{12.2}$$

In this example, the effect of coupling worked in the opposite direction to the primary action where the primary action in this case is given by K_{11}. As a result, λ_{11} is greater than unity. When the primary action and the coupling effect act in the same direction, λ_{11} is less than one. This can be understood by recognizing that when both effects act in the same direction, the denominator of Equation 12.2 will be greater than the numerator.

For the system represented in Table 12.1, if c_1 were used to control y_2 and c_2 were used to control y_1, the steady-state gain matrix would become

$$K = \begin{pmatrix} 0.1 & 1.0 \\ 2.0 & 0.05 \end{pmatrix}$$

Using Equation 12.2 yields

$$\lambda_{11} = \cfrac{1}{1 - \cfrac{2}{0.005}} = -0.0025$$

which is λ_{12} for original pairing scheme. It can be shown that

$$\lambda_{11} + \lambda_{12} = 1$$

Likewise,

$$\lambda_{21} + \lambda_{22} = 1$$

It can also be shown that

$$\lambda_{11} + \lambda_{21} = 1$$

and

$$\lambda_{12} + \lambda_{22} = 1$$

These results show that the sum of any row or any column is equal to unity. As a result,

$$\lambda_{11} = \lambda_{22}$$

and

$$\lambda_{12} = \lambda_{21} = 1 - \lambda_{11}$$

As a result, determining that

$$\lambda_{11} = 1.0025$$

sets

$$\lambda_{22} = 1.0025$$
$$\lambda_{12} = -0.0025$$
$$\lambda_{21} = -0.0025$$

Therefore, once λ_{11} is determined, all the other λ's are specified for a 2×2 system. As a result, the *RGA* for a 2×2 is typically reported as a single number (i.e., λ_{11}). In addition, if the pairing of c_1 and c_2 are switched, the *RGA* value is simply unity minus the *RGA* (λ_{11}) value for the original pairing.

Consider the *RGA* for a 3×3 system

$$RGA = \begin{pmatrix} \lambda_{11} & \lambda_{12} & \lambda_{13} \\ \lambda_{21} & \lambda_{22} & \lambda_{23} \\ \lambda_{31} & \lambda_{32} & \lambda_{33} \end{pmatrix}$$

where

$$\lambda_{12} = \frac{\left(\dfrac{\Delta y_1}{\Delta c_2} \right)_{c_1, c_3}}{\left(\dfrac{\Delta y_1}{\Delta c_2} \right)_{y_2, y_3}}$$

Note that the gain in the numerator is based upon keeping c_1 and c_3 constant while the gain in the denominator is based upon keeping y_2 and y_3 constant. The closer the diagonal elements of the *RGA* are to unity, the more decoupled the process will be. In addition, the sum of λ's in any row or any column is equal to unity, therefore, for a 3×3 system, the *RGA* requires the determination of four of the nine possible λ's.

12.4 Dynamic Factors in Configuration Selection

For the 2×2 system represented in Table 12.1, all the input/output relationships have the same dynamic behavior; therefore, a steady-state analysis is sufficient. Consider the transfer function representation of a 2×2 system shown in Table 12.2. The steady-state *RGA* (λ_{11}) for this system is 0.94 using Equation 12.2 which indicates that the control loop pairings listed in Table 12.2 are proper.

Table 12.2		
Transfer Function Representation of a 2×2 System with Dynamic Coupling		
	c_1	c_2
y_1	$\dfrac{1.0}{100s+1}$	$\dfrac{0.3}{10s+1}$
y_2	$\dfrac{-0.4}{10s+1}$	$\dfrac{2.0}{100s+1}$

But notice that the effect of c_1 on y_1 and the effect of c_2 on y_2 have much slower dynamics than the effect of c_1 on y_2 and the effect of c_2 on y_1 (i.e., the coupling). That is, the time constants for the diagonal responses are ten times larger than the time constants for the off-diagonal terms. As a result, when changes in c_1 are made to correct for deviations in y_1 from its setpoint, changes in y_2 will result long before y_1 can be corrected. Then the (c_2, y_2) control loop will make changes in c_2 to correct for the coupling. Once again, due to the dynamic differences, y_1 will respond to the coupling much faster than y_2 can be corrected. The (c_1, y_1) control loop will respond to these additional changes in y_1 and the coupling process will continue. This is an example of **dynamic coupling**. Figure 12.6 shows the dynamic response of y_1 and y_2 for a setpoint change in y_1 for the original (c, y) pairings and for the reverse pairings, i.e., (c_1, y_2) and (c_2, y_1). Note that the control performance of the reverse pairings is far superior even though the steady-state RGA of the reverse pairing is only 0.06.

The dynamic RGA^2 can be used to assess the effect of dynamics on coupling. The dynamic RGA is calculated by substituting $s = i\omega$ into each transfer function

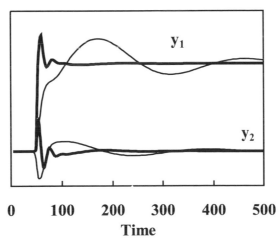

Figure 12.6 Response to a setpoint change in y_1 for the original pairings (thin line) and the reverse pairings (thick line) for Table 12.2.

comprising the input/output model. For a specific frequency, the magnitude of each transfer function (Equation 8.1) and the corresponding *RGA* at that frequency is calculated using Equation 12.2 where the transfer function magnitudes are used instead of the static gains. In this manner, the *RGA* can be plotted as a function of frequency. At very low frequencies, the dynamic *RGA* will approach the steady-state *RGA* value. Therefore, a comparison of dynamic *RGA*'s at intermediate frequencies will distinguish dynamic coupling effects.

Consider the calculation of the dynamic *RGA* for the 2×2 process represented in Table 12.2. Since each of the transfer functions in Table 12.2 is for a first order process, the magnitude of $G_p(i\omega)$ for a general first order process is simply A_r and is given by Equation 8.2

$$\left| G_p(i\omega) \right| = \frac{K_p}{\sqrt{\tau_p^2 \, \omega^2 + 1}}$$

Then using Equation 12.2, the dynamic *RGA* for the (c_1, y_1) pairing listed in Table 12.2 is given by

$$\lambda_{11}(\omega) = \frac{1}{1 + \dfrac{100^2 \, \omega^2 + 1}{16.7 \, (10^2 \, \omega^2 + 1)}}$$

Likewise, the dynamic *RGA* for the opposite pairing is given by

$$\lambda_{11}(\omega) = \frac{1}{1 + \dfrac{16.7 \, (10^2 \, \omega^2 + 1)}{100^2 \, \omega^2 + 1}}$$

Figure 12.7 shows the dynamic *RGA*'s for each of these cases. Note that for frequencies above 0.1 radians per unit time, which correspond to faster closed loop control performance, the reverse pairing is preferred which is consistent with the simulation results shown in Figure 12.6.

Since transfer function models are not usually available for industrial processes, it is recommended to qualitatively use the results of this section when choosing (c, y) pairings. That is, **when selecting a manipulated variable for a particular controlled variable, choose a manipulated variable that causes the controlled variable to exhibit a relatively fast dynamic response, i.e., choose pairings that have a relatively low effective time constant and a relatively low effective process deadtime**. It is important to remember to use your understanding of the process to guide your analysis.

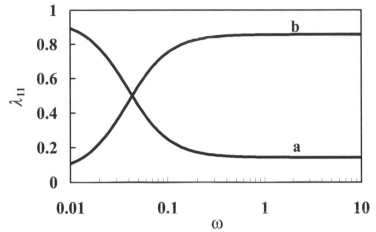

Figure 12.7 Dynamic RGA for the original pairings (a) and the reverse pairings (b) for the process represented in Table 12.2.

12.5 Sensitivity to Disturbances

In general, each possible configuration has a different sensitivity to a particular disturbance. Consider the distillation column shown in Figure 12.8. The reflux flow rate, L, is used to control the overhead composition and the boilup rate, V, which is set by the reboiler duty, is used to control the bottom composition. Since L and V are used for composition control, the distillate flow rate, D, is used to control the accumulator level and the bottoms flow rate, B, is used to control the reboiler level. This configuration is referred to as the (L,V) configuration since L is used to control the

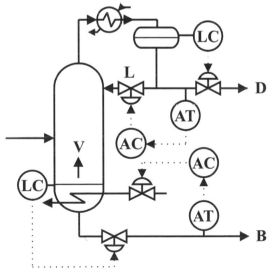

Figure 12.8 Schematic of a distillation column with the (L,V) configuration. Note that control valves represent flow control loops in this figure.

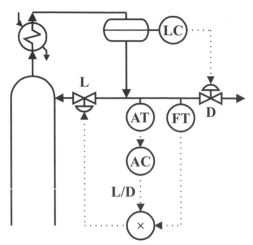

Figure 12.9 Schematic of a reflux ratio controller applied for the control of the overhead composition. Note that control valves represent flow control loops in this figure.

overhead product composition and V is used to control the bottoms product composition. Consider the (L/D, V/B) configuration. Figure 12.9 shows how the reflux ratio, L/D, can be applied to control the overhead product composition. Note that a ratio controller is used for the composition controller and D is used to control the level in the accumulator. In a similar manner, the boilup ratio V/B can be used to control the bottoms product composition. That is, a V/B ratio controller can be used to control the bottoms product composition while the bottoms product flow rate B is used to control the level in the reboiler. Figure 12.10 shows the "open loop" response of a distillation column to a step increase in the light component composition in the feed for the (L,V) and ($L/D,V/B$) configurations. In this case open loop response refers to placing the composition control loops in open loop while maintaining the level controller in closed loop operation. Note that the (L,V) configuration is less sensitive to feed composition changes than the ($L/D,V/B$) configuration. As a result, the (L,V)

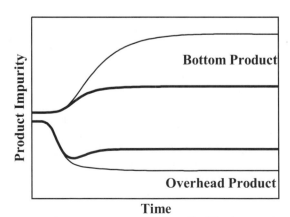

Figure 12.10 The open loop response of a distillation column with the (L,V) configuration (thick line) and the ($L/D,V/B$) configuration (thin line) to a step change in feed composition.

configuration is less affected by feed composition changes than the $(L/D, V/B)$ configuration.

From an analysis of the previous sections it can be concluded that **it is the combined effect of coupling, dynamic behavior, and sensitivity to disturbances that determines the control performance for a particular control configuration for a MIMO process**. Process control engineers typically rely upon their understanding of the process and their experience when selecting a control configuration for a MIMO process.

Example 12.1 Configuration Selection for a C_3 Splitter

Problem Statement. Evaluate the configuration selection problem for a C_3 splitter. A C_3 splitter separates a feed mixture primarily composed of propane and propylene into polymer grade propylene (< 0.5% propane) and a fuel grade propane (approximately 2% propylene).

Solution. The nomenclature used here refers to a particular configuration as (c_1, c_2) where c_1 is assumed to be the controller output that is used to control the overhead composition and c_2 is the controller output that is used to control the bottoms composition. If we limit ourselves to controlling the overhead composition with L, D, or L/D (the reflux ratio) and the bottoms composition with V, B, or V/B (the boilup ratio), there are a total of nine possible configurations. Here we will limit the discussion to the following configurations: (L, B), (L, V), $(L/D, V/B)$, and (D, V).

The steady-state RGA's for each of the configurations considered here are listed below:

Configuration	RGA (λ_{11})
(L, B)	0.94
(L, V)	25.3
$(L/D, V/B)$	1.70
(D, V)	0.06

Based upon these results, the (L, B) and $(L/D, V/B)$ configurations appear the most promising. Even though the RGA value of (L, B) is considerably closer to unity than the RGA value of $(L/D, V/B)$, Shinskey[3] recommends RGA values between 0.9 and 3.0 for distillation columns indicating that RGA values greater than unity are preferred over RGA values less than one.

The dynamics of distillation columns can be understood by recognizing that product composition changes result from changes in the vapor/liquid traffic in the column. That is, changing L or V directly affects the column vapor/liquid traffic and this has the most immediate effect on the product composition. On the other hand, changes in B and D must depend on the level controllers to change the vapor/liquid traffic of the column; therefore, the dynamic response of the product compositions is significantly slower when B and D are changed compared with changing L and V. The dynamic response to changes in L/D and V/B are intermediate between L and V on the fast side and B and D on the slow side. For example, the dynamics of changes in L/D are faster than changes in D but slower than changes in L. Based upon this analysis, (L, B) would be expected to perform better for the overhead composition control than for the bottoms, but there is no clear winner between the (L, B) and the $(L/D, V/B)$ configurations with regard to the overall dynamic response.

Table 12.3 shows the relative changes in each manipulated variable for a change in feed composition. This table is based on steady-state results in which the product compositions are maintained at a constant level. A lower relative change for a manipulated variable indicates a reduced sensitivity to feed composition changes for that manipulated variable. Note that L, L/D, and V show the least sensitivity to feed composition changes.

Table 12.3	
Relative Changes in the Manipulated Variables in Order to Maintain the Product Purities for a 5 mole % Increase in Feed Composition.	
Manipulated Variable	**Percentage Change**
L	4.2
D	7.4
L/D	-3.0
V	4.4
B	-16.8
V/B	25.5

Table 12.4 lists the integral absolute error (IAE) for each configuration for each product for a feed composition upset. A lower IAE value indicates closer control to setpoint. Note that the (L, B) configuration provided the best overall control performance especially for the overhead product. This is consistent with the observations that L is dynamically fast and relatively insensitive to feed composition changes coupled with the relatively moderate steady-state coupling as indicated by the *RGA*.

The (L, V) configuration has the advantages of fast overall dynamics and insensitivity to feed composition upsets. These advantages are negated by the extreme degree of steady-state coupling as indicated by its steady-state RGA value. The control performance of the (L, V) configuration is the poorest of the four configurations listed in Table 12.4. The $(L/D, V/B)$ configuration has a good steady-state *RGA* and dynamic characteristics, but is particularly sensitive to feed composition upsets for the bottom composition control loop. As a result, its performance is inferior to the (L, B) configuration. The steady-state RGA value of the (D, V) configuration indicates that this configuration will not function properly. In fact, the control performance of the (D,V) configuration is quite reasonable, i.e., the IAE's for the (D,V) configuration were only about 30% larger than those for the (L,B) configuration which is not a great deal of difference in control performance.

Table 12.4		
Control Performance (IAE) for a Step Change in Feed Composition		
Configuration	**IAE for Overhead**	**IAE for Bottoms**
L,B	0.067	1.49
L,V	0.250	13.3
L/D,V/B	0.095	2.00
D,V	0.098	1.91

For complex configuration selection problems, such as distillation columns, the previous analysis is helpful but does not always guarantee that the best configuration will be identified. The performance differences between reasonable configuration choices and the best configuration can be substantial. Therefore, in these cases, the use of detailed dynamic simulations for the analysis of the control performance of feasible configurations is recommended wherever possible.

12.6 Tuning Decentralized Controllers

The recommended tuning procedure for a single PID loop can be extended to tuning the single loop PID controllers applied for decentralized control of a MIMO process. The first step in tuning a decentralized controller is to apply ATV tests for each manipulated variable/controlled variable pair. While an ATV test is being applied to one loop, the other loops should be maintained in an open loop condition.

Next, determine if any of the loops are significantly faster responding than the other loops. This can be done by comparing the values of the ultimate periods, P_u, obtained in the ATV tests. If the smallest value of P_u is five times smaller or more than the next largest P_u, that loop should be first implemented by itself before tuning the other loops. It can be tuned as a single PID loop as discussed in Chapter 7. Then ATV tests on the remaining loops should be rerun with the tuned fast loop in service (closed loop operation). Then the remaining control loops can be tuned using the following procedure.

Assume that it is required to tune PI controllers on a 2×2 MIMO process. The ATV results are used to select the controller gain and reset time based on, for example,

Zeigler-Nichols tuning. Then a single tuning factor, F_T, is applied to the tuning parameters for **both control loops**.

$$\left.\begin{array}{l} K_c = K_c^{ZN} / F_T \\ \tau_I = \tau_I^{ZN} \times F_T \end{array}\right\} \text{ First control loop}$$

$$\left.\begin{array}{l} K_c = K_c^{ZN} / F_T \\ \tau_I = \tau_I^{ZN} \times F_T \end{array}\right\} \text{ Second control loop} \qquad\qquad \textbf{12.3}$$

F_T is adjusted until the proper dynamic response is obtained. For example, setpoint changes in y_1 and/or y_2 can be used to select the proper value of F_T. Alternatively, the value of F_T can be adjusted to provide reliable performance of the controllers based on day-to-day controller operating performance. While tuning, if the closed loop response is sluggish, decrease the value of F_T. Likewise, if the controller exhibits periods of ringing, increase the value of F_T.

After F_T has been adjusted to tune the set of decentralized PI controllers, fine tuning of the controller settings should be used. For example, if one observes that one of the control loops is slow to settle at setpoint in a manner similar to Figure 7.6a, an increase in integral action for that loop should be tested. If one of the loops exhibits ringing, derivative action should be tested to determine if it will improve the feedback control performance of that loop. In the latter case, derivative action should be tuned in the manner that was described in Chapter 7.

12.7 Decouplers

Decouplers are designed to reduce the detrimental effects of coupling. Figure 12.11 shows two decouplers [$D_1(s)$ and $D_2(s)$] applied to a two-input/two-output process. D_1 is designed to reduce the effects of changes in c_2 on y_1 while D_2 is designed to reduce the effects of changes in c_1 on y_2.

Consider the design of D_1. The effect of changes in c_2 on y_1 is given by

$$G_{12}'(s)C_2(s)$$

The corrective action on y_1 from D_1 is given by

$$D_1(s)G_{11}'(s)C_2(s)$$

The objective of the decoupler is to eliminate the effect of coupling; therefore, the sum of the previous two terms is set to zero, i.e.,

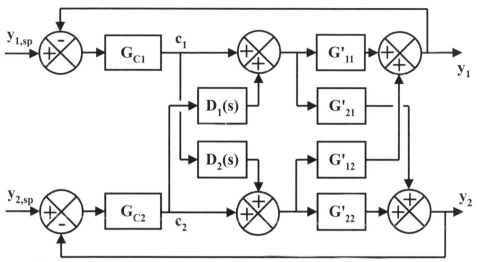

Figure 12.11 **Block diagram of a two-input/two-output process with two-way decoupling.**

$$G'_{12}(s)C_2(s)+D_1(s)G'_{11}(s)C_2(s)=0$$

Solving for $D_1(s)$ yields

$$D_1(s)=\frac{-G'_{12}(s)}{G'_{11}(s)}\qquad\qquad\textbf{12.4}$$

Using a similar analysis

$$D_2(s)=\frac{-G'_{21}(s)}{G'_{22}(s)}\qquad\qquad\textbf{12.5}$$

The decoupler $D_1(s)$ can be viewed as a "feedforward" correction to y_1 for disturbances caused by changes in c_2. Note that Equations 12.4 and 12.5 are similar to the general equation for a feedforward controller (Equation 9.7) where $G'_{12}(s)$ corresponds to $G_d(s)$ and $G'_{11}(s)$ corresponds to $G_p(s)$.

Figure 12.11 shows a 2×2 system with two decouplers which is referred as a **two-way** or **complete decoupler**. Two-way decouplers are rarely used industrially because many times they result in poorer control performance than conventional control without decouplers. This results because two-way decouplers can be sensitive to nonlinearity and modeling errors in the decouplers. On the other hand, **one-way** or **partial decouplers** (Figure 12.12) are much more reliable and are more frequently used industrially. One-way decouplers are particularly useful when the key controlled variable of a MIMO process suffers from significant coupling.

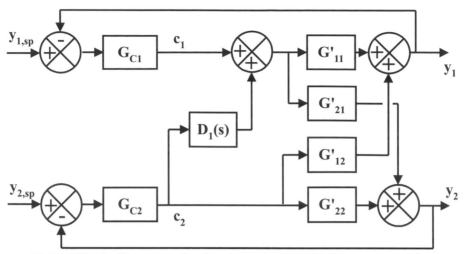

Figure 12.12 Block diagram of a two-input/two-output process with one-way decoupling to reduce the effect of u_2 on y_1.

12.8 Summary

The combined effect of coupling, dynamic behavior, and sensitivity to disturbances determines the best control configuration for a decentralized controller applied to a MIMO process. The steady-state RGA and the dynamic RGA can be used to assess the steady-state and dynamic coupling, respectively, for a particular control configuration. It is desirable to choose (c,y) pairings such that each y responds quickly to changes in the c that it is paired with. Each control configuration for a MIMO process has its own specific sensitivity to disturbances. Once a control configuration is selected, the decentralized controllers can be tuned using an extension of the ATV tuning procedure recommended for a single PID control loop. One-way decouplers can be beneficial when the most important controlled variable in a MIMO process suffers from significant coupling from one or more of the other loops.

12.9 Additional Terminology

Complete decoupling - a decoupler for each controlled variable.
Control configuration - the particular pairing of manipulated and controlled variables for a MIMO process.
Coupling - control loops on a MIMO process that affect each other.
Decentralized control - applying single loop PID controllers to a MIMO process.
Dynamic coupling - coupling that includes dynamic differences between various input/output pairs. It can be evaluated using the dynamic RGA.

Manipulated/controlled variable pairings - the choice of which manipulated variable is used to control each controlled variable.
One-way decoupler - one decoupler applied to a MIMO process.
Partial decoupler - fewer decouplers applied than the number of controlled variables.
RGA - the relative gain array which indicates the degree of steady-state coupling.
Single loop PID controllers - PID controllers that are applied to a MIMO process.
Two-way decoupler - two decouplers applied to a 2×2 process.

12.10 References

1. Bristol, E.H., *IEEE Trans Auto. Con.*, AC-11, p. 133 (1966).
2. McAvoy, T.J., *Interaction Analysis*, Instrument Society of America, pp. 190-192 (1983).
3. Shinskey, F.G., *Distillation Control*, 2nd Edition, McGraw-Hill, pp. 154-165 (1984).

12.11 Questions and Exercises

12.1 Why is it important to choose a good pairing of manipulated and controlled variables when applying control to a MIMO process?

12.2 Explain how the steady-state *RGA* is a measure of steady-state coupling.

12.3 When is the steady-state *RGA* the best criterion for selecting (c,y) pairings?

12.4 Why is dynamic coupling important to the performance of a control system on a MIMO process?

12.5 Why is the sensitivity of a configuration to disturbances important in the selection of a control configuration for a MIMO process?

12.6 Consider the thermal mixing tank shown in Figure 3.6. Assuming perfect level control, consider that the two manipulated variables are the F_1 and F_2 and that the two controlled variables are the total product flow rate and the product temperature. Determine the steady-state RGA for pairing F_1 to control the product temperature and F_2 to control the total flow rate. Would the dynamic RGA provide additional insight into this problem over the steady-state *RGA*? What configuration would you recommend and why?

12.7 Consider the MIMO version of the endothermic CSTR included with the text. Assuming perfect level control, there are two manipulated variables, F and Q, and two controlled variables, T and C_A. Recommend a control configuration for this case and justify your answer using a quantitative analysis.

12.8 Using the MIMO version of the CST thermal mixer included with the text, tune a set of decentralized PI controllers for this process using setpoint change in the total flow rate and the product temperature. Test the tuning using a step disturbance upset.

12.9 Using the MIMO version of the endothermic CSTR included with the text, tune a set of decentralized PI controllers for this process using setpoint changes in the reactor temperature and the product composition. Test the tuning using a step disturbance upset.

12.10 Using the MIMO version of the CST thermal mixer, apply and tune a one-way decoupler to reduce the effects of the product flow rate loop on the product temperature. Retune the decentralized PI controllers and test the controller performance using a step disturbance test.

12.11 Using the MIMO version of the endothermic CSTR, apply and tune a one-way decoupler to reduce the effects of the product composition loop on the product temperature. Retune the decentralized PI controllers and test the controller performance using a step disturbance test.

Chapter 13

Multivariable Controllers

13.1 Introduction

In Chapter 12, the application of conventional PID controllers to a multivariable (MIMO) process was presented. In this chapter, the use of **multivariable controllers** for the control of MIMO systems is considered. Multivariable controllers, also known as **centralized controllers**, can use all available process measurements (i.e., manipulated variables, disturbances, and controlled variables) simultaneously to determine the values of all the manipulated variables for control of a MIMO process. Since multivariable controllers typically use MIMO process models, they are also known as **model-based controllers**. Model-based controllers can also be applied to SISO systems.

A diagram comparing a multivariable controller and a conventional decentralized PI controller is shown in Figure 13.1. The multivariable controller in this case uses y_1 and y_2 to simultaneously calculate u_1 and u_2. The multivariable model used in the multivariable controller considers the effect of u_1 on y_1 and y_2 and the effect of u_2 on y_1 and y_2 when determining the control action; therefore, the multivariable controller provides decoupling. If the multivariable model considers the effect of disturbances on the process, it can also provide feedforward compensation for measured disturbances. Further, if the model used by the multivariable controller is a nonlinear model, the multivariable controller can directly compensate for the nonlinearity of the process.

This chapter will introduce a class of linear multivariable controllers known as **model predictive controllers**. In addition, a couple of nonlinear multivariable controllers will also be overviewed. Since multivariable controllers normally act as supervisory controllers, in this chapter the controller output will be assumed to be the setpoint for the flow controller on u and will be designated as u.

13.2 Model Predictive Control

Model predictive control (**MPC**) is the most widely used form of multivariable control. It has been estimated[1] that there are more than 3,000 industrial

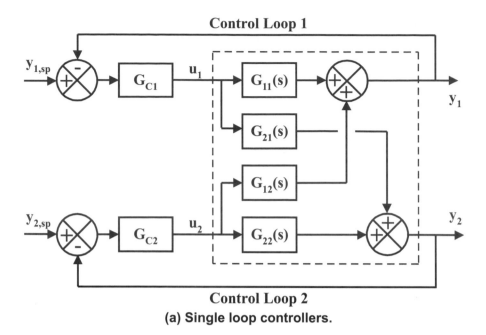

Control Loop 1

Control Loop 2

(a) Single loop controllers.

(b) A centralized controller

Figure 13.1 A comparison of single loop PID controllers and a multivariable controller applied to a 2 × 2 MIMO process.

MPC applications worldwide. **Dynamic matrix control**[2] (**DMC**) is the most popular form of MPC. This section will consider DMC applied to a SISO process and show how it can be extended to MIMO processes.

       Discrete Time Step Response Models. DMC uses **discrete time step response models** of the process to calculate control action. Previously, we used transfer function models to represent the effect of the manipulated variable on the controlled variable, $G_p(s)$. The same information contained in $G_p(s)$ can be represented

using a discrete time step response model. Consider a FOPDT process
($K_p = 1$, $\tau_p = 1$, $\theta_p = 1$). The step response for $\Delta u = 1$ applied at $t = 0$ is shown in
Table 13.1 for discrete points in time. Note that these results are based on a fixed
sampling time, ΔT_s, of 1.0. Note that a_i is constant for i greater than or equal to 7 since
the step response is complete after 7 sampling time intervals. The generalized discrete
time step response model of a process can be obtained from a step test using the
following equation

$$a_i = \frac{y'(t_i)}{\Delta u(t_0)} \qquad \textbf{13.1}$$

assuming that the process is at steady state at $t - t_0$ and a single step input change is
made at $t = t_0$. Note that a_i is called a step response coefficient. The values of the
coefficients of the **step response model**, a_i, for this case are also listed in Table 13.1.
The equation for the step response model can be obtained by rearranging Equation
13.1.

$$y'(t_i) = y(t_i) - y(t_0) = a_i \Delta u(t_0) \qquad \textbf{13.2}$$

Due to the flexible form of Equation 13.1, a wide range of complicated dynamic
behavior (e.g., inverse action) can easily be represented using this approach.

Table 13.1				
Step Response and Step Response Coefficients for a FOPDT Process **($K_p = 1$, $\tau_p = 1$, $\theta_p = 1$) for a Step Change in u.**				
Time	Sample Number, i	$\Delta u(t)$	$y'(t)$	a_i
0	0	1	0	0
1	1	0	0	0
2	2	0	0.63	0.63
3	3	0	0.87	0.87
4	4	0	0.95	0.95
5	5	0	0.98	0.98
6	6	0	0.99	0.99
7	7	0	1.00	1.00
8	8	0	1.00	1.00

The Dynamic Matrix. Equation 13.2 can be used to predict the behavior of
$y(t)$ for a series of $\Delta u(t)$ moves by applying the Principle of Superposition. The
Principle of Superposition states that the total effect of a number of $\Delta u(t)$ moves on $y(t)$

is equal to the sum of the effect of each individual $\Delta u(t)$. Assume that $y(t_0)$ is known and $y(t)$ is at steady state at $t = t_0$ and that a series of $\Delta u(t_i)$ moves are made into the future, then using Equation 13.2 applying the principle of superposition

$$
\begin{aligned}
y(t_1) - y(t_0) &= a_1 \Delta u(t_0) \\
y(t_2) - y(t_0) &= a_2 \Delta u(t_0) + a_1 \Delta u(t_1) \\
y(t_3) - y(t_0) &= a_3 \Delta u(t_0) + a_2 \Delta u(t_1) + a_1 \Delta u(t_2) \\
&\vdots \\
y(t_n) - y(t_0) &= a_n \Delta u(t_0) + a_{n-1} \Delta u(t_1) + a_{n-2} \Delta u(t_2) + \ldots
\end{aligned}
$$
$$\tag{13.3}$$

For example, consider the equation for $y'(t_3)$. The contribution of $\Delta u(t_0)$ to $y(t_3)$ uses a_3 when applying Equation 13.2. In order to consider the effect of $\Delta u(t_1)$, Equation 13.2 must be time shifted backwards, ΔT_s; therefore, the coefficient applied to $\Delta u(t_1)$ is a_2. Another way to consider this problem is that since $\Delta u(t_1)$ is applied at $t = t_1$, using Equation 13.2 to model the effect of $\Delta u(t_1)$ requires that i in Equation 13.2 be set equal to 2. Then similarly, to calculate the effect of $\Delta u(t_2)$ on $y(t_3)$, a_1 should be used. Equation 13.3 can be more compactly expressed by

$$
y'(t_n) = y(t_n) - y(t_0) = \sum_{i=1}^{n} a_i \Delta u(t_{n-i})
$$
$$\tag{13.4}$$

Equation 13.3 or Equation 13.4 can be put into matrix form. Consider the case in which n moves in $\Delta u(t_i)$ are made into the future and the step response models have m coefficients (i.e., a_i's). Then from Equation 13.3,

$$
\begin{bmatrix}
y'(t_1) \\
y'(t_2) \\
y'(t_3) \\
\vdots \\
y'(t_n)
\end{bmatrix}
=
\begin{bmatrix}
a_1 & 0 & 0 & \ldots & 0 \\
a_2 & a_1 & 0 & & \\
a_3 & a_2 & a_1 & & \\
\vdots & & & & \\
a_m & a_m & a_m & \ldots & a_1
\end{bmatrix}
\begin{bmatrix}
\Delta u(t_0) \\
\Delta u(t_1) \\
\Delta u(t_2) \\
\vdots \\
\Delta u(t_{n-1})
\end{bmatrix}
$$
$$\tag{13.5}$$

assuming that $n > m$. n is the **prediction horizon** or the number of ΔT_s steps into the future for which the model is used to predict the behavior of the controlled variable and m is the **model horizon** or the number of ΔT_s steps used by the step response model. For a DMC controller, n is sometimes set equal to $1.5m$. Note that a_i for $i > m$ is equal to a_m. Equation 13.5 can also be written as

$$
y' = A \Delta u
$$
$$\tag{13.6}$$

Table 13.2

Prediction of *y(t)* using a Step Response Model for a Series of Manipulated Variable Changes.

Time	Sample Number, i	$u(t_i)$	$\Delta u(t_i)$	$y(t)$
0	0	1.0	0	1.0
1	1	2.0	1.0	1.0
2	2	3.0	1.0	1.0
3	3	2.0	-1.0	1.63
4	4	2.0	0.0	2.50
5	5	1.0	-1.0	2.19
6	6	0.0	-1.0	2.06
7	7	1.0	1.0	1.39
8	8	2.0	1.0	0.51
9	9	2.0	0.0	0.82
10	10	2.0	0.0	1.57

The matrix **A** is calculated from the coefficients of the step response model and is dimensioned (n,n), i.e., there are n rows and n columns, and is called the **dynamic matrix**. The dynamic matrix can be used to calculate the dynamic behavior of the process in response to future changes in $\Delta u(t_i)$.

The value of Equation 13.6 stems from the fact that it can be used to calculate the dynamic behavior of y for a series of input changes. Table 13.2 shows how the convolution model developed in Table 13.1 can be applied to a series of manipulated variable changes using Equation 13.4. Consider the application of Equation 13.4 to calculate $y(t_7)$ for this case

$$y(t_7) = y(t_0) + a_1 \Delta u(t_6) + a_2 \Delta u(t_5) + a_3 \Delta u(t_4) + a_4 \Delta u(t_3)$$
$$+ a_5 \Delta u(t_2) + a_6 \Delta u(t_1) + a_7 \Delta u(t_0)$$

Using the numerical values of these terms results in

$$y(t_7) = 1.39$$

These results are based on assuming that the process is at steady state at $t = t_0$ (i.e., $\Delta u(t_i) = 0$, $i = -7$ to -1 since based upon Table 13.1 the process takes seven ΔT_s steps to reach steady-state). In this manner, the effect of a complicated set of manipulated variable changes on $y(t)$ can be conveniently modeled using discrete time step response models.

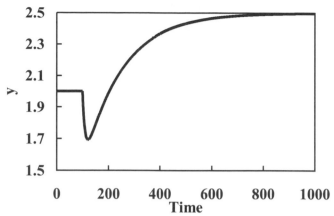

Figure 13.2 Dynamic response of a complex process.

Table 13.3					
Coefficients for Convolution Model of Complex Process Response $(\Delta T_s = 20)$					
i	a_i	i	a_i	i	a_i
1	-0.31	11	0.27	21	0.44
2	-0.26	12	0.30	22	0.45
3	-0.17	13	0.32	23	0.45
4	-0.09	14	0.34	24	0.46
5	-0.02	15	0.36	25	0.46
6	0.05	16	0.38	26	0.47
7	0.10	17	0.40	27	0.47
8	0.15	18	0.41	28	0.48
9	0.20	19	0.42	29	0.48
10	0.23	20	0.43	30	0.48

Figure 13.2 shows a step response for a more complicated process. Table 13.3 lists the coefficients of the step response model of this process. While this modeling approach can be effectively applied to a large number of industrial processes, it is a linear model, and as a result, can result in significant **process/model mismatch** for nonlinear processes. Process/model mismatch is the error between the model prediction and the actual process response.

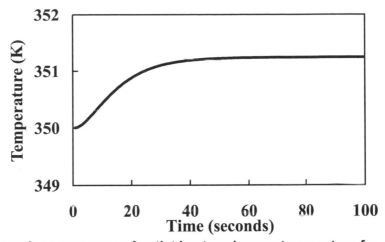

(a) The open loop response of outlet heat exchanger temperature for a 10% step increase in the heat duty.

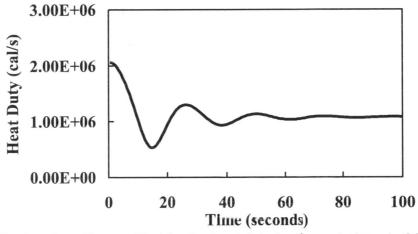

(b) The input profile specified for the heat duty for the endothermic CSTR.

Figure 13.3 Step response and input data specification for the Example 13.1.

Example 13.1 Step Response Model Identification and Prediction.

Problem Statement. For the step response shown in Figure 13.3a which is based on a 10% increase in heat duty for the heat exchanger for the endothermic CSTR (Section 3.5), predict the controlled variable response for the input sequence shown in Figure 13.3b. Assume that the controlled variable is initially at steady state at 350 K.

Solution. First, the step test results should be used to identify the step response model parameters, a_i. The coefficients of the convolution model are obtained by applying Equation 13.4 to the step response results. The coefficients of the step response model are listed in Table 13.4.

Time (sec)	i	a_i	$\Delta u(t_i)$	$y(t_i)$
		Table 13.4		
		Results for Example 13.1		
0	0	0	1.07×10^6	350.00
5	1	2.07×10^{-6}	-7.45×10^6	352.21
10	2	6.10×10^{-6}	-4.87×10^5	354.98
15	3	9.79×10^{-6}	4.09×10^5	354.92
20	4	1.26×10^{-5}	3.43×10^5	354.41
25	5	1.45×10^{-5}	-7.37×10^4	354.56
30	6	1.57×10^{-5}	-2.21×10^5	355.80
35	7	1.65×10^{-5}	-4.54×10^4	356.50
40	8	1.69×10^{-5}	1.23×10^5	356.23
45	9	1.72×10^{-5}	6.55×10^4	356.06
50	10	1.75×10^{-5}	-4.33×10^4	356.40
55	11	1.76×10^{-5}	-5.30×10^4	356.57
60	12	1.77×10^{-5}	9.30×10^3	356.61
65	13	1.77×10^{-5}	3.61×10^4	356.51
70	14	1.77×10^{-5}	8.04×10^3	356.53
75	15	1.77×10^{-5}	1.10×10^3	356.64

Next, the input sequence is approximated by a series of step changes and the results are listed as $\Delta u(t_i)$ in Table 13.4. Then Equation 13.1 is applied to predict the time behavior of the reactor temperature. These results are also listed in Table 13.4.

Moving Horizon Algorithm. Figure 13.4 illustrates the key features of a moving horizon control algorithm. Note that all the previous controlled variable and manipulated variable values are fixed and known. The manipulated variable moves and the resulting controlled variable values into the future remain unknown at this point. The moving horizon controller chooses the future manipulated variable values in order to regulate the controlled variable to its setpoint using the step response model and the previous inputs.

After one control interval has expired, a new controlled variable value is available as well as the last change in manipulated variable value. Once again, the controller recalculates the sequence of manipulated variable values into the future to meet the control objective. In this manner, even though the complete sequence of

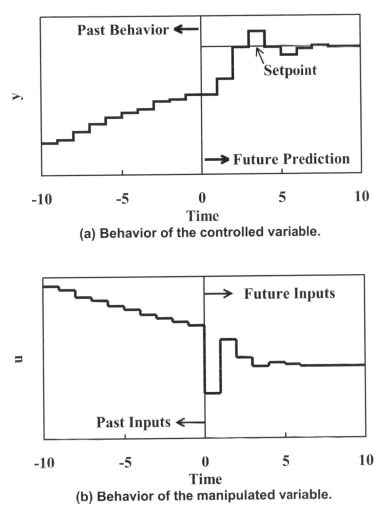

(a) Behavior of the controlled variable.

(b) Behavior of the manipulated variable.

Figure 13.4 Controlled and manipulated variable profiles for a moving horizon controller.

control moves into the future is calculated at each control interval, only the first move is actually implemented before a new sequence of inputs is determined. The key feature of this approach is that at each control interval a sequence of control moves into the future is considered as well as the previous input sequence when determining the next change in the manipulated variable value.

Prediction Vector. Up until this point, we have assumed that $y(t_0)$ was at steady state and that manipulated variable changes are made only for $t \geq t_0$. For a control application, this assumption is not realistic since manipulated variable changes at $t < t_0$ are likely to exist as shown in Figure 13.4. As a result, the effect of the previous input changes ($\Delta u(t)$ for $t < t_0$) must be taken into account in order to properly model the future behavior of the controlled variable ($y(t)$ for $t > t_0$).

The **prediction vector, y^P**, contains the values of $y(t)$ for $t > t_0$ if no future manipulated variable changes are made ($\Delta u(t) = 0$ for $t \geq t_0$). The prediction vector contains the effects of previous manipulated variable changes on future controlled variable values.

Assume that the process has a model horizon, m. That is, after m time steps, an input change has had its total steady-state effect on the process. For example, for the step response model listed in Table 13.1, m is equal to 7; therefore, a_i is constant for $i \geq 7$ for this case.

Applying Equation 13.4 to calculate the prediction vector at $t = t_1$ results in

$$y^P(t_1) = y(t_{-m}) + a_{m+1}\Delta u(t_{-m}) + a_m \Delta u(t_{-m+1}) + a_{m-1}\Delta u(t_{-m+2})$$
$$+ \ldots\ldots + a_3\Delta u(t_{-2}) + a_2\Delta u(t_{-1}) + a_1\Delta u(t_0)$$

where the negative subscripts indicate the number of sampling intervals before t_0 and assuming that the process is at steady state at $t = t_{-m}$. Also note that the coefficients of $\Delta u(t_{-m})$ and $\Delta u(t_{-m+1})$ are both a_m since $a_{m+1} = a_m$. Also, $\Delta u(t_0)$ is zero for the prediction vector; therefore,

$$y^P(t_1) = y(t_{-m}) + a_m \Delta u(t_{-m}) + a_m \Delta u(t_{-m+1}) + a_{m-1}\Delta u(t_{-m+2})$$
$$+ \ldots\ldots + a_3\Delta u(t_{-2}) + a_2\Delta u(t_{-1})$$

Likewise, $y^P(t_2)$ is given by

$$y^P(t_2) = y(t_{-m}) + a_m \Delta u(t_{-m}) + a_m \Delta u(t_{-m+1}) + a_m \Delta u(t_{-m+2}) + a_{m-1}\Delta u(t_{-m+3})$$
$$+ \ldots\ldots + a_4\Delta u(t_{-2}) + a_3\Delta u(t_{-1})$$

In this manner, $y^P(t_n)$ is given by

$$y^P(t_n) = y(t_{-m}) + a_m \Delta u(t_{-m}) + a_m \Delta u(t_{-m+1}) + \ldots\ldots + a_m \Delta u(t_{-2}) + a_m \Delta u(t_{-1})$$

where n is the number of ΔT_s moves into the future that are modeled and where $n > m$. The prediction vector, y^P, can be expressed in matrix form,

$$
\begin{bmatrix} y^P(t_1) \\ y^P(t_2) \\ \vdots \\ y^P(t_n) \end{bmatrix} = \begin{bmatrix} y(t_{-m}) \\ y(t_{-m}) \\ \vdots \\ y(t_{-m}) \end{bmatrix} + \begin{bmatrix} a_m & a_m & a_{m-1} & a_{m-2} & \ldots\ldots & a_3 & a_2 \\ a_m & a_m & a_m & a_{m-1} & \ldots\ldots & a_4 & a_3 \\ \vdots & & & & & & \\ a_m & a_m & a_m & a_m & \ldots\ldots & a_m & a_m \end{bmatrix} \begin{bmatrix} \Delta u(t_{-m}) \\ \Delta u(t_{-m+1}) \\ \vdots \\ \Delta u(t_{-1}) \end{bmatrix}
$$

or $\qquad\qquad\qquad y^P = y(t_{-m}) + A^P \Delta u^P \qquad\qquad\qquad\qquad$ **13.7** where $y(t_{-k})$ is the value of the controlled variable at $t = t_o - k\,\Delta T_s$. Then the values of $y(t)$ for $t > t_o$ can be calculated by combining the prediction vector with the effects of future control moves (Equation 13.6)

$$ y = y^P + A\Delta u \qquad\qquad \textbf{13.8} $$

Equation 13.8 is subject to a number of factors that undermine its accuracy: (1) errors in identifying the coefficients of the discrete time step response model, (2) unmeasured disturbances, (3) nonlinear behavior, and (4) not a steady-state process at $t = t_{-m}$. If Equation 13.8 were used for control, offset would result due to these sources of process/model mismatch.

Using Equation 13.7, $y^P(t_0)$ is calculated by

$$ y^P(t_o) = y(t_{-m}) + a_m \Delta u(t_{-m}) + a_{m-1}\Delta u(t_{-m+1}) + \dots\dots + a_2 \Delta u(t_{-2}) + a_1 \Delta u(t_{-1}) $$

The error between the measured value of $y(t_0)$ and the predicted one, $y^P(t_0)$, can be used to adjust Equation 13.8 to make it more accurate. Thus, the error between the measured and predicted value of $y(t_0)$ is given as

$$ \varepsilon = y(t_0) - y^P(t_0) $$

Then,

$$ y = y^P + A\Delta u + \varepsilon^{\mathrm{T}} \qquad\qquad \textbf{13.9} $$

where

$$ \varepsilon^T = [\varepsilon\ \ \varepsilon\ \ \varepsilon\dots\varepsilon] $$

so that the predicted value of $y(t)$ agrees with the latest value of controlled variable $[y(t_0)]$. When Equation 13.9 is used in a DMC controller, offset is eliminated.

DMC Control Law. The DMC control law is based on minimizing the error from setpoint. The objective function, Φ, is the sum of the square of the errors from setpoint for the prediction horizon (i.e., n steps into the future).

$$ \Phi = \sum_{i=1}^{n} [y_{sp} - y(t_i)]^2 \qquad\qquad \textbf{13.10} $$

Equation 13.9 shows that $y(t_i)$ is made up of three parts: the prediction vector (i.e., the effect of past inputs), the effects of future inputs, and the process/model mismatch correction term. Note that only the effect of future moves can be changed by the controller; therefore, combining y_{sp}, y^P, and ε into

$$ E(t_i) = y_{sp} - y^P(t_i) - \varepsilon \qquad\qquad \textbf{13.11} $$

results in

$$\Phi = \sum_{i=1}^{n} [E(t_i) - y_c(t_i)]^2 \qquad\qquad \textbf{13.12}$$

where $\qquad\qquad y_c = A \Delta u$

The objective of the DMC controller is to choose the control moves, $\Delta u(t_i)$ for n moves into the future such that Φ is minimized.

Perfect control (i.e., $\Phi = 0$), which is based upon assuming that $y_c(t_i)$ is the mirror image $E(t_i)$, is given by

$$\Delta u = A^{-1}E \qquad\qquad \textbf{13.13}$$

But this result is not realistic since it assumes that y_c can be moved instantaneously. In addition, Equation 13.13 is valid only when the number of dependent variable is equal to the number of input variables. Instead, we can choose the set of control moves that minimizes the sum of the squares of the errors from setpoint. This solution can be obtained analytically by differentiating Equation 13.12 with respect to Δu and setting the result equal to zero,

$$\frac{\partial \Phi}{\partial \Delta u} = A^T (A \Delta u - E) = 0 \qquad\qquad \textbf{13.14}$$

Solving for Δu

$$\Delta u = (A^T A)^{-1} A^T E \qquad\qquad \textbf{13.15}$$

which is the control law for a DMC controller. This equation does not assume instantaneous changes in y_c and can be applied in cases in which the number of dependent variables is different from the number of independent variables. Note that $(A^T A)^{-1} A^T$ is equal to A^{-1} when A is a square matrix. Therefore, once the step response model and the prediction vector are calculated, the DMC controller can be formulated directly using Equation 13.15.

Equation 13.15 results in very aggressive control because it is based on minimizing the deviation from setpoint without regard to the changes in the manipulated variable levels. That is, if Equation 13.15 is applied, excessively sharp changes in u will result which is not desirable operationally. Normal levels of process/model mismatch combined with the aggressive nature of Equation 13.15 can easily yield unstable control performance. In addition, $(A^T A)^{-1}$ can be ill-conditioned due to process/model mismatch and deadtime in the process model. These problems can be overcome by adding the diagonal matrix, Q^2, to $A^T A$ in Equation 13.15 resulting in the following

$$\Delta u = (A^T A + Q^2)^{-1} A^T E \qquad\qquad \textbf{13.16}$$

where Q is the move suppression matrix and is a diagonal matrix with positive elements, i.e.,

$$Q = \begin{bmatrix} q & 0 & 0 & \dots & 0 \\ 0 & q & 0 & \dots & 0 \\ 0 & 0 & q & \dots & 0 \\ \vdots & \vdots & \vdots & & \\ 0 & 0 & 0 & \dots & q \end{bmatrix}$$

where q is called the **move suppression factor** and is a positive number. The larger the value of q, the more Φ is penalized for changes in the manipulated variable; therefore, q can be used as a tuning parameter and it will determine the aggressiveness of the DMC controller. In general, the more nonlinear a process and the larger the magnitude of the disturbances, the larger the value of q that should be used.

Model Identification. In the previous examples, the step response model parameters were calculated directly from a step test. In an industrial setting, it is difficult to conduct a step test while keeping all other inputs constant, particularly for MIMO applications. Moreover, it is better to use a number of step tests to identify "average" coefficients for the step response model, particularly in light of the nonlinearity associated with industrial processes and the presence of unmeasured disturbances.

For model identification, the controlled variable and manipulated variable values are known for a sequence of discrete times. The objective function for identification is given by

$$\Phi - \sum_{i=1}^{k} [y_s(t_i) - y(t_i)]^2 \qquad \qquad \textbf{13.17}$$

where k is the number of process measurements available for parameterizing the model, $y_s(t_i)$ are the measured values of the controlled variable, and $y(t_i)$ is the value of the controlled variable at t_i calculated from the step response model parameters. Note that the better the step response models of the process the smaller the resulting value of Φ. The values of the coefficients of the step response model are calculated such that Φ is minimized. Due to the linear nature of $y(t_i)$, the a_i's can be calculated explicitly using matrix algebra.

When developing the plant tests that are used for model identification, it is not necessary to make a set of complete step tests. In fact for most MIMO systems, such an approach would require a prohibitive amount of time. Moreover, during plant tests, it is important to keep the controlled variables within specified operating ranges. One way to accomplish this is to make Δu changes at each of the following intervals:

$$\tfrac{1}{4} T_{ss}, \ \tfrac{1}{2} T_{ss}, \ \tfrac{3}{4} T_{ss}, \ T_{ss}, \ \tfrac{5}{4} T_{ss}$$

where T_{ss} is the open loop time to steady state (the open loop response time of the process). This approach also develops models for a range of input frequencies. Note that

$$T_{ss} = m \Delta T_s$$

Extension to MIMO Processes. Extending DMC to MIMO processes is relatively straightforward. Augmented vectors and matrices are used to apply DMC to MIMO processes using Equation 13.16. For example, the augmented dynamic matrix, A, is given by

$$A = \begin{bmatrix} A_{11} & A_{12} & \cdots & A_{1,j} \\ A_{21} & A_{22} & & A_{2,j} \\ \vdots & & & \\ A_{k,1} & A_{k,2} & \cdots & A_{k,j} \end{bmatrix}$$

where j is the number of manipulated variables and k is the number of controlled variables. Consider a two input/two output process. A_{11} is the dynamic matrix for y_1 as affected by u_1 and A_{12} is the dynamic matrix of y_1 as affected by u_2, etc. For illustration purposes, consider

$$A_{11} = \begin{bmatrix} 1 & 2 \\ 3 & 4 \end{bmatrix} \qquad A_{12} = \begin{bmatrix} 5 & 6 \\ 7 & 8 \end{bmatrix}$$

$$A_{21} = \begin{bmatrix} 9 & 10 \\ 11 & 12 \end{bmatrix} \qquad A_{22} = \begin{bmatrix} 13 & 14 \\ 15 & 16 \end{bmatrix}$$

Then the multivariable dynamic matrix is given by

$$A = \begin{bmatrix} 1 & 2 & 5 & 6 \\ 3 & 4 & 7 & 8 \\ 9 & 10 & 13 & 14 \\ 11 & 12 & 15 & 16 \end{bmatrix}$$

Also, the MIMO manipulated variable vector is given by the following augmented vector

$$\Delta u = \begin{bmatrix} \Delta u_1 \\ \Delta u_2 \\ \vdots \\ \Delta u_j \end{bmatrix}$$

For example, if

$$\Delta u_1 = \begin{bmatrix} 1 \\ 2 \end{bmatrix} \qquad \Delta u_2 = \begin{bmatrix} 3 \\ 4 \end{bmatrix}$$

Then

$$\Delta u = \begin{bmatrix} 1 \\ 2 \\ 3 \\ 4 \end{bmatrix}$$

The **A** matrix requires inversion for the application of the DMC control law and it can be quite large for certain MIMO DMC controllers. Consider the case with 10 manipulated variables, 10 controlled variables, and a prediction horizon of 100 sampling intervals, then the MIMO dynamic matrix would be dimensioned 1000×1000. There have been a large number of industrial DMC applications that are considerably larger than this example.

An additional issue that must be addressed when applying DMC to MIMO processes is how to prioritize the various control objectives. DMC controllers use controlled variable weighting which allows the user to assign a relative weighting to each of the controlled variables. A controlled variable weighting matrix, **W**, is added to the DMC control law (Equation 13.16)

$$\Delta u = (A^T W^2 A + Q^2)^{-1} A^T W^2 E \qquad\qquad \textbf{13.18}$$

where **W** is an augmented diagonal matrix which contains diagonal matrices, W_i, which contains the same element, w_i, on its diagonal. w_i is the relative weighting factor for the i-th controlled variable.

13.3 Nonlinear Multivariable Controllers

There is a variety of nonlinear multivariable controllers[3]. In this section, two nonlinear controllers will be outlined: generic model control and nonlinear model predictive control. For both cases it will be assumed that a SISO nonlinear model is known, i.e.,

$$\frac{dy}{dt} = f(y, u, d, p) \qquad\qquad \textbf{13.19}$$

where y is the controlled variable, f is a nonlinear function, u is the manipulated variable, d is the measured disturbance, and p is the model parameter.

Generic Model Control. Generic model control (GMC)[4] uses the current process conditions along with the nonlinear model (Equation 13.19) to calculate the control action without regard to the future behavior of the process, i.e., a **single-step-ahead controller**.

The GMC control law is given by

$$K_c\left[(y_{sp}-y) + \frac{1}{\tau_I}\int_0^t(y_{sp}-y)\,dt\right] = f(y,u,d,p) \qquad \textbf{13.20}$$

where K_c is the controller gain and τ_I is the reset time. All parameters in Equation 13.20 are known except u; therefore, Equation 13.20 is solved directly to calculate the value of u. K_c and τ_I are analogous to the tuning parameters for a PI controller; therefore, PI tuning techniques can be applied to tune GMC controllers[5].

The model parameter, p, can be calculated using steady-state data at steady-state

$$\frac{dy}{dt} = f(y,u,d,p) = 0 \qquad \textbf{13.21}$$

and therefore, using the steady-state values of y, u, and d, p can be calculated directly using this equation. The extension of GMC to MIMO systems is direct. For MIMO systems, there is an equation similar to Equation 13.20 for each controlled variable and $f(y, u, d, p)$ is a multivariable model. GMC can be effective for the control of processes that exhibit severe nonlinearity in the process gain but have simple first order dynamics (e.g., certain CSTR's and batch reactors).

Nonlinear Model Predictive Control. Nonlinear model predictive control (NLMPC) is a direct extension of linear MPC except that nonlinear dynamic models are used instead of linear dynamic models. NLMPC is a moving horizon controller that chooses a sequence of inputs that minimize the objective function over the prediction horizon, n, but only implements the first control move at each control interval. NLMPC chooses control moves into the future that minimize the following objective function, Φ

$$\Phi = \sum_{i=0}^{n-1}[y_{sp}-y(t_i)]^2 + \sum_{i=0}^{n-1}q[\Delta u(t_i)]^2 \qquad \textbf{13.22}$$

where q is the move suppression factor, and $y(t_i)$ is calculated using the control action, $\Delta u(t_i)$, and the nonlinear dynamic model [Equation 13.19]. The solution of this optimization problem requires a nonlinear optimization algorithm whereas the objective function for linear MPC can be solved analytically using matrix equations. The number of degrees of freedom for the optimization problem for NLMPC is equal to the number of control moves into the future (i.e., n, the prediction horizon) times the number of manipulated variables.

For MIMO problems, the numerical application of NLMPC may not be feasible. That is, the computer time required to minimize Φ and thus calculate the next control step can be excessively long, thus rendering NLMPC ineffective. The key factors in this problem are the total number of degrees of freedom for the optimization problem and the computer time required to integrate the model equations over the prediction horizon. NLMPC can be applied to cases that exhibit severe gain and dynamic nonlinearity for which accurate and computationally efficient models are available.

13.4 Summary

Multivariable controllers use measured values of the manipulated variables, the controlled variables, and disturbances to simultaneously calculate all the manipulated variable levels for the control of MIMO processes. Multivariable controllers can provide decoupling, feedforward compensation, and compensation for nonlinear behavior.

DMC is the most popular form of linear multivariable control and is based on discrete time step response models of the process to calculate control action. The DMC controller uses the coefficients of the step response model, the previous input history, and the latest measured value of the controlled variable to calculate the next manipulated variable value using a moving horizon control approach. A move suppression factor is used to tune the DMC controller to provide reliable control performance.

GMC is a single-step-ahead controller that uses tuning parameters that are analogous to conventional PI controllers and is useful for processes that have significant gain nonlinearity with well-behaved dynamics. NLMPC extends DMC to nonlinear control using a moving horizon control approach and is a more general nonlinear model-based controller. The computational requirements for NLMPC can make its application impractical at this time for many industrial applications.

13.5 Additional Terminology

Centralized controller - a controller which uses all the available process information to select control action for a MIMO process.

Discrete time step response model - the discrete time behavior of a process to a unit step change in an input variable.

Dynamic matrix control (DMC) - a linear model predictive controller that uses step response models of the process to select control action.

Dynamic matrix - the A matrix in the DMC controller which is constructed from the coefficients of the step response model.

Generic model control (GMC) - a single-step-ahead nonlinear multivariable controller.

Model-based controller - a controller that chooses control action based upon a model of the process.

Model horizon (m) - the number of sampling intervals used to model a step response of the process.

Moving horizon algorithm - a control approach that calculates future control moves based on a process model and the input history.

Model predictive control (MPC) - a controller that uses a process model to calculate control action by determining a sequence of inputs that regulates the process to setpoint.

Move suppression factor (q) - the tuning factor for a DMC controller that determines the aggressiveness of the controller.

Multivariable controller - a controller which uses all the available process information to select control action for a MIMO process.

Nonlinear model predictive control (NLMPC) - MPC using nonlinear process models.

Prediction vector (y^p) - the future values of the controlled variable if no changes in the manipulated variable are made.

Prediction horizon (n) - the number of sampling intervals into the future in which the model is used to predict the behavior of the controlled variable.

Process/model mismatch - the difference between the model predictions for the controlled variable and the actual process behavior.

Sampling interval - the time period between the calculations of control action.

Single-step-ahead controller - a controller that calculates the current control action without predicting the future behavior of the process.

Step response model - the discrete time response of a process to a unit step change in an input variable.

13.6 References

1. Quin, S. J. and T. A. Badgwell, "An Overview of Industrial Model Predictive Control Technology", *Proceed of the Fifth International Conference on Chemical Process Control*, AIChE Symposium Series Number 316, Vol 93, p. 232 (1997).

2. Cutler, C. R. and B. L. Ramaker, "Dynamic Matrix Control - A Computer Control Algorithm", *Proceed of the Joint Automatic Control Conference*, San Francisco (1980).

3. Bequette, B. W., "Nonlinear Control of Chemical Processes: A Review", *Ind. Eng. Chem. Res.*, Vol 30, p. 1391 (1991).

4. Lee, P. L. and G. R. Sullivan, "Generic Model Control", *Computers Chem. Eng..*, Vol 12, p. 573 (1988).

5. Flathouse, S. E. and J. B. Riggs, "Tuning GMC Controllers using the ATV Procedure", *Computers Chem. Eng.*, Vol 20, p. 979 (1996).

13.7 Questions and Exercises

13.1 For each of the following simulators provided with this text, develop a step response model. First, determine the open loop response time for the process. Choose ΔT_s so that m is equal to 10. Finally, develop the step response model for the process.

    a. CST thermal mixer   b. CST composition mixer

    c. Endothermic CSTR   d. Heat exchanger

13.2 Using the results for 13.1, predict the output variable as a function of time for a series of 10 inputs changes. Use the same series of inputs on the process simulator and plot these results along with the step response model results on the same graph.

Chapter 14

Multiunit Controller Design

14.1 Introduction

The previous material in this text has been concerned with the control of a single control loop or control of a single MIMO process. This chapter addresses the problem of applying the approaches that were developed for SISO and MIMO processes to a multiple unit process which is composed of a number of unit operations connected together forming an overall processing unit. A typical multiple unit process could include a reactor followed by several distillation columns. The reactor converts the feed into product and the distillation columns separate the product from the byproducts and the unconverted feed. The control engineer is responsible for implementing controls on this multiunit process so that the process meets its operational objectives, e.g., produces a specified production rate of product with impurity levels less than the specified limits while maintaining maximum profitability in a safe and reliable fashion in the face of a variety of process disturbances. In order to accomplish this task, the control engineer must have a command of the single unit control techniques, but must also be able to coordinate all the single unit controls so that the multiunit process functions properly.

In an effort to optimize the designs of plants (i.e., develop designs that maximize profit generation), heat recovery and material recycle are being used frequently in process design. By using product streams to preheat feed streams and by using the condenser of one column to provide reboiler duty for another column, less energy is required to produce the same amount of product. Also, recycling unreacted feed components increases overall conversion and reduces the material costs for the products. Both heat recovery and material recycle can provide superior steady-state economic performance, but can result in much more difficult processes to control. The following approach to control design is recommended for both recycle processes and systems that utilize once-through sequential processing. This approach is based on the control design procedure presented by Luyben et. al.[1].

14.2 Approach

Following is the recommended approach for undertaking the control design problem for multiunit processes. This approach is developed assuming that no instrumentation or controls are in place. Obviously, many control projects involve a revamp of existing controls; therefore, certain items, such as sensor selection and actuator location can already be completed and are not likely to be modified unless compelling reasons are identified. While this approach was developed for multiunit processes, it can also be applied to single unit systems as well.

1. Identify process objectives. The steady-state and dynamic objectives of the process should first be identified. These include product rate specifications, product variability requirements, process selectivity, product grade specifications, environmental constraints, safety issues, and economic objectives. The control approach chosen should be able to meet each of the process objectives.

2. Identify the process constraints. Process constraints represent limits to normal operation. The specific limits to the operation of the process should be identified with regard to safety, environmental, and equipment constraints. The resulting control configuration must be able to effectively handle all process constraints.

3. Identify significant disturbances. A viable control approach should be able to effectively absorb the full range of process disturbances. Common process disturbances include feed temperature, flow rate, and composition changes, ambient air temperature changes, steam pressure changes and cooling water temperature changes.

4. Determine the type and location of sensors. Ensuring that adequate process measurements are available to meet the operational objectives while satisfying all the process constraints is a prerequisite for control design. The types of sensors chosen will affect the repeatability, dynamic response, and reliability of the process measurements. The locations of the sensors will determine if the desired process variables are actually being measured and can also affect their measurement delays.

5. Determine the location of control valves. The location of the control valves determines which streams are available to be used as manipulated variables in order to meet the control objectives while satisfying the process constraints. In the CPI, a control valve is usually applied using a flow control loop.

6. Apply a degree-of-freedom analysis. The total number of manipulated flow streams minus the number of control objectives and active process constraints is equal to the degrees of freedom of the process. If extra degrees of freedom are available, they can be used to improve the economic performance of the process (e.g., through process optimization).   When the process is overspecified, all the control objectives cannot be simultaneously met. One approach is to give up on one or more low priority control objectives until the remaining control objectives and constraints are controllable. It should be pointed out that constraints can change from being active to not being active as operating conditions change. For example, the condenser duty can be an active constraint to a distillation column during the summer when its cooling water temperature is high and will not be a factor for the operation (an inactive constraint) during the winter. As a result, the number of degrees of freedom of a process can change as the number of active constraints changes due to changes in the operating conditions.

7. Implement energy management. Energy management involves removing the exothermic heat of reaction or supplying the endothermic heat of reaction occurring within the process and accounting for interactions resulting from process-to-process heat exchanges and heat-integrated unit operations. If the exothermic heat of reaction is not removed, the conditions for a reactor runaway can exist. If the endothermic heat of reaction is not supplied, the reactor will not produce the desired product rate. For all distillation columns, heat must be added in the reboiler and removed in the condenser. Using product streams to preheat feeds and using the overhead stream of one column to provide reboiler duty for another column are effective ways to reduce overall process energy consumption but tend to result in more highly coupled processes. Temperature control loops are typically used to control reactors and heat recovery processes.

8. Control process production rate. When the process production rate is changed for a process based on a reactor converting feed to products, the selected manipulated variable for the production rate control must change conditions within the reactor, e.g., reactor temperature, reactant concentration, volume of reaction mixture, or pressure in a gas-phase reactor, because the products are produced from reactions that occur in the reactor. Production rates can also be set by manipulating the overall feed and relying on the controls of the various unit operations to pass the feed rate through the entire process. Likewise, the overall process production rate can be changed and the remainder of the process can follow this change eventually resulting in a corresponding change in the overall process feed rate. For more complicated process systems, selecting the best manipulated variable to control process production rate may require dynamic simulations of the overall process.

9. Select the manipulated variables that meet the control objectives. An ideal manipulated variable for a particular control objective would result in dynamic behavior characterized by a small time constant and deadtime and a large steady-state gain. As a result, it is usually advisable to locate a manipulated variable as close as possible to the control objective of interest. Chapter 12 addresses configuration selection for MIMO processes.

10. Address how disturbances will be handled. The sensitivity of the control system to each major disturbance should be considered. Opportunities for cascade, ratio, feedforward, and computed manipulated variable control should be considered in order to reduce the effects of major disturbances.

11. Develop a constraint handling strategy. Control approaches for each potential constraint should be developed. Override/select control (Chapter 10) can be applied to coordinate manipulated variable action to maintain operation within active constraints. The key is to develop constraint handling strategies that satisfy all known constraints.

12. Control inventories. Inventories include liquid levels and gas pressures. For example, outflow from or inflow to a tank can be manipulated to control its level. Fresh feed streams can be manipulated to control levels which indicate the amount of the fresh feed in the process. Fresh feed can also be used to control pressure for certain reaction systems or recycle reaction systems. Pressure control on distillation columns usually involves changing condenser duty or using the injection of inert gases or the venting of a portion of the overhead.

13.   Check component balances. Component material balances for each component in the process including inert components should be formulated to ensure that no component accumulates in the process.   This is particularly important for recycle processes. It may be necessary to add a purge stream in order to prevent the accumulation of a component within the process.

14. Control individual unit operations. The controls for each unit operation should be completed next. That is, each unit operation should be checked to ensure that it is fully controlled. For example, a temperature controller can be applied to maintain the outlet temperature of a process stream leaving a heat exchanger by adjusting the flow rate of steam to the heat exchanger. For distillation columns, control loops are typically applied to control the impurity levels in one or more products. Opportunities for cascade, ratio, and feedforward control should be considered.

15. Apply process optimization. The setpoints for certain controllers that are not otherwise specified can be set according to economic-based process optimization. For example, choosing the optimum reactor temperature can be a compromise between conversion and selectivity. In addition, when a company can sell all the product that it can produce, economic optimization can involve maximizing the product flow rate from the process. The optimization of a distillation column can involve a compromise between product recovery and utility usage. In each of these cases, setpoints to various control loops can be selected in such a way that the rate of profit generation for the unit is maximized. The selection of the optimal setpoints can be based on a simple analysis of the process or can involve detailed optimization studies using nonlinear models of the process.

14.3 Distillation Column

Process Description   Consider the design of a control system for an ethylene/ethane (C_2) splitter. The C_2 splitter produces a high purity polymer grade ethylene in the overhead and an ethane product in the bottoms. The overhead is a much more valuable product than the bottoms since it is a saleable product and ethane is recycled as feed to the furnaces where it is thermally cracked to yield more ethylene and other cracking products. The feed to the column contains approximately 70 mole percent ethylene, the overhead has a specification of less than 0.1% ethane in the ethylene product, and the setpoint for the ethylene in the ethane product is based on the economic tradeoff between energy usage and ethylene recovery and is generally set around 1% ethylene. Occasionally, small amounts of methane and sometimes hydrogen can appear in the feed. Due to the low condensing temperature of ethylene, a refrigerant is used to provide condenser duty. The major disturbances to this column are feed flow rate and feed composition upsets.

Identify process objectives. The process objectives are to produce an ethylene product with low variability while satisfying its impurity specification in the face of process disturbances. In addition, it is desired to recover as much ethylene as possible while minimizing the energy cost for the column.

Identify the process constraints. Upon further examination, it was determined that there is more than adequate reboiler and condenser duty so that as the feed rate to the column is increased, the column will eventually flood. That is, the vapor/liquid traffic will increase to the point where the tray dimensions will not support that degree of loading and the separation generated by the column will become compromised. A differential pressure across the column should reliably indicate the onset of flooding.

Identify significant disturbances. The primary disturbances are feed flow rate and feed composition changes.

Determine the type and location of sensors. Figure 14.1 shows the sensors applied to this column. Note that the product streams (D and B), the reboiler steam, and the reflux are all equipped with flow sensor/transmitters (FT) since each of these flows will be adjusted to meet the control objectives of the column. In addition, a flow sensor/transmitter should also be installed to measure the feed rate to the column since it is a major disturbance to the process. Cost and the type of service indicate the use of orifice plate and differential pressure sensor/transmitter flow indicators. Differential pressure level sensor/transmitters should also be used for the accumulator and bottom of the column since maintaining these levels is essential for reliable operation of the column. A differential pressure sensor/transmitter should also be used in order to determine the onset of flooding for the column which has been identified as a process constraint. A pressure indicator should be installed on the top of the accumulator in order to monitor column pressure. An on-line GC should be used to measure the impurity level in the ethylene product. Since the bottoms product is not a

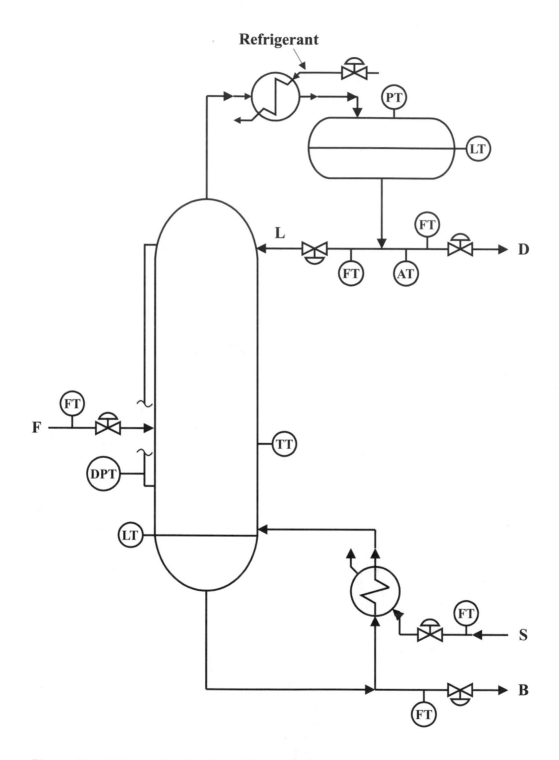

Figure 14.1 Schematic of a C$_2$ splitter with the sensors and control valves.

saleable product and it has a "soft" product specification based on the economics for ethylene recovery, it is more cost effective to infer composition using a tray temperature measurement. Laboratory samples of the bottom product taken once each 8 hours will be used by the operator to select the proper tray temperature. Using steady-state simulations of the C_2 splitter over the range of operation, the optimal location for the inferential temperature measurement was determined. An RTD temperature sensing element should be used for the tray temperature sensor due to the superior repeatability of RTD's over TC's.

Determine the location of control valves. Each of the streams equipped with a FT (Figure 14.1) should also have a control valve installed.

Apply a degree-of-freedom analysis. There are six control valves indicating that there are six manipulated flow streams. There are five column control objectives: overhead product composition, tray temperature in the stripping section, the level in the accumulator, the level in the reboiler, and the overhead pressure. In addition, the flow rate of the feed to the column can be set. Therefore, since the number of controlled variables is equal to the number of manipulated variables, the system is exactly determined. When the column reaches flooding conditions, the differential pressure measurement across the column becomes a constraint and the control problem becomes underdetermined.

Implement energy management. The flow of steam to the reboiler provides the reboiler duty and the flow of refrigerant to the condenser provides the condenser duty for this column.

Control process production rate. The production rate of this column is set by a flow contoller on the feed to the column. The operator will select the setpoint for this controller in order to maintain the level in the feed tank for the column.

Select the manipulated variables that meet the control objectives. The primary control objective is to maintain the ethylene product on specification. The secondary control objective is the bottom composition control which is directly related to the control of the tray temperature in the stripping section. Choosing which flow control loop to assign to each of these control objectives is tantamount to choosing the (c,y) pairings for a distillation column. The configuration selection problem for a propylene/propane splitter was addressed in Example 12.1. Since this is a relatively low reflux ratio column with a reflux ratio of approximately 3.5, the (L,V) configuration is a good choice for this application because the (L,V) configuration has a fast dynamic response to manipulated variable changes and is the least sensitive configuration with respect to feed composition upsets. Also, selection of the (L,V) configuration determines that the distillate rate will be set by the level controller for the accumulator and the bottoms rate will be set by the level controller for the column bottoms. Dynamic simulations of this column for appropriate disturbance tests could be used to check this analysis. Finally, the overhead column pressure is controlled by the flow rate of refrigerant to the condenser. This control configuration is shown in Figure 14.2.

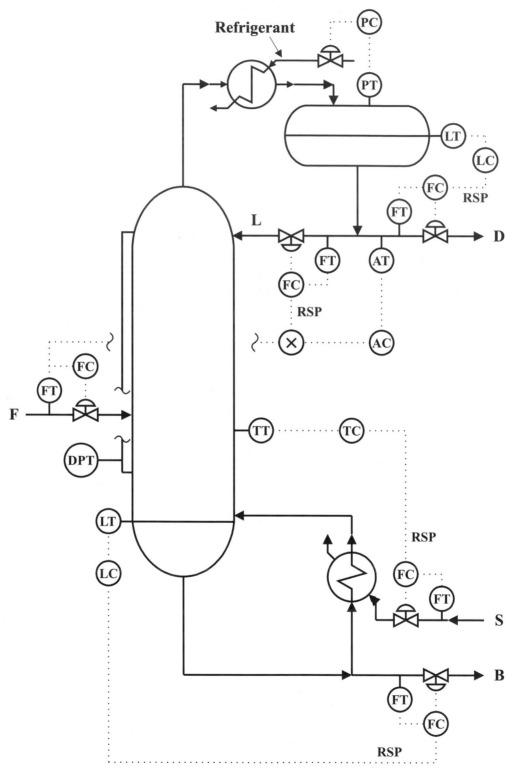

Figure 14.2 Schematic of a C₂ splitter with the (L,V) configuration applied.

Address how disturbances will be handled. The feed composition is not measured, but the (L,V) configuration is generally the best configuration with regard to this disturbance. Feed flow rate disturbances are measured and the performance of the (L,V) configuration, particularly for the overhead composition control loop, can be improved by applying ratio control, i.e., L/F control (Figure 14.2).

Develop a constraint handling strategy. The primary constraint is flooding which occurs when the feed is excessive. From the degree-of-freedom analysis, when the column encounters the flooding constraint, one control objective must be discarded. Clearly, the ethylene product purity must be maintained as well as the reboiler and accumulator levels; therefore, when the flooding constraint is encountered, one can no longer expect to maintain the setpoint on the tray temperature in the stripping section (i.e., the purity of the bottoms product). This approach can be implemented by combining the output from the tray temperature controller with the output of the differential pressure controller using a low select controller (LS). The differential pressure controller will select a larger steam flow to the reboiler than the tray temperature controller when the column is not approaching flooding conditions. When the flooding constraint is encountered, the differential pressure controller will yield a lower steam rate than the tray temperature controller. This approach is shown schematically in Figure 14.3.

Control inventories. The level controllers on the reboiler and accumulator will handle the liquid inventories. The gas inventories will be addressed by the pressure controller on the overhead.

Check component balances. When methane and hydrogen appear in the feed, they will accumulate in the overhead because the condenser temperature is not sufficiently low to condense them. As a result, methane and hydrogen buildup will decrease the condenser's ability to condense the overhead stream and the column pressure will increase. A vent line connected to the vapor space on the accumulator will provide a means to purge uncondensed light gases that accumulate in the overhead. A select controller (S) based on column pressure will determine when methane and hydrogen are building up in the overhead and open the vent to discharge them to a light gas processing unit. The select controller can compare the measured pressure with the pressure setpoint used by the pressure controller and when there is consistent offset between the measured pressure and its setpoint, the select controller will open the valve on the vent line. This select controller is shown schematically in Figure 14.3.

Control individual unit operations. Since this example is a single unit operation, there are no opportunities here.

Apply process optimization. The unassigned setpoints for this process include the setpoint for the ethylene product, the setpoint for the tray temperature controller, the setpoint for the overhead column pressure, and the setpoints for the accumulator and reboiler levels. The setpoints for the levels do not affect steady-state

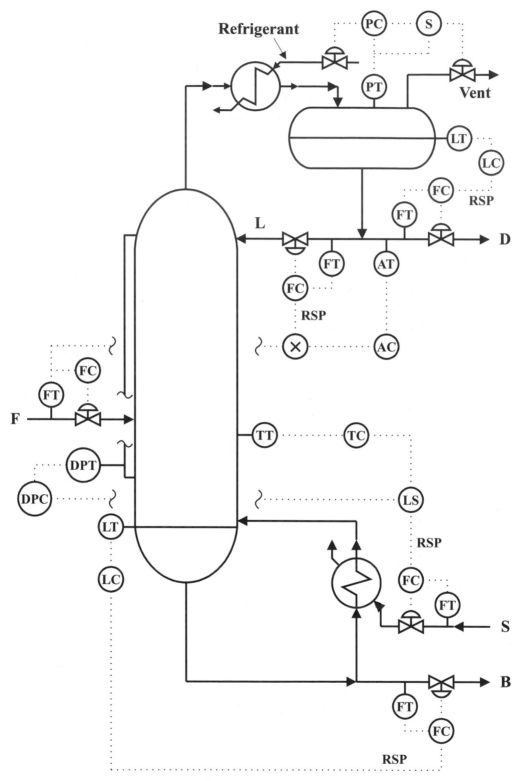

Figure 14.3 Schematic for a C$_2$ splitter with complete control configuration.

optimization. The impurity setpoint for the ethylene product is based on the product specification and the variability in the ethylene product resulting from the control system. Obviously, the closer the process is operated to the product specifications, the more profitable the operation will be.

The setpoint for the tray temperature (i.e., the ethylene content in the ethane product) is an optimization problem that requires the comparison of the ethylene recovery with the energy usage for the column. Moderate variations in the ethylene content of the bottoms product do not have a large effect on the economic performance of this column; therefore, the economic benefit from analyzing this optimization problem on-line to provide the most up-to-date optimal setpoints is low. As a result, an off-line estimate of the optimum operating point should be sufficient in this case.

The overhead pressure affects the relative volatility of the separation, and therefore, has a significant effect on the utility usage. The minimum overhead pressure is set by the temperature of the refrigerant. Since relative volatility increases as pressure decreases, this column should be operated near the minimum overhead pressure in order to obtain the most efficient separation.

14.4 Recycle Reactor Process

Problem Description. Figure 14.4 shows a schematic for a recycle reactor with a stripper[2] that separates the feed from the product. The following endothermic reaction occurs in the reactor

$$A \rightarrow B \rightarrow C$$

The reaction from B to C is much faster than the reaction from A to B; therefore, the product leaving the reactor contains primarily reactant A and product C with low levels of reactant B. The reactor heat exchanger is used to supply heat to drive the endothermic reactions. The product from the reactor is the feed to the stripper which separates A from C. Since B is lighter than A, the small amount of B in the product stream from the reactor goes out the overhead of the stripper and is recycled to the reactor. The usual bottleneck of this recycle process is the condenser for the stripper. At other times, an upper limit on the reactor heater duty can limit operation.

Identify process objectives. The overall process objective is to maintain an economically efficient production of product C in a consistent and reliable fashion.

Identify process constraints. The major constraints for this process are the limit for the stripper condenser duty and the limit on the heat duty for the reactor heater.

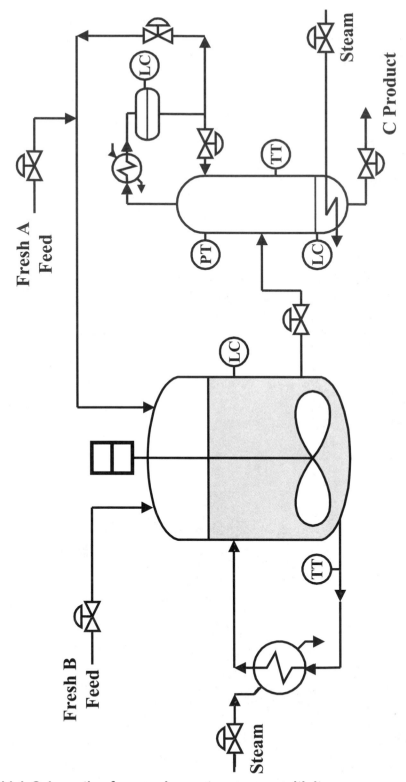

Figure 14.4 Schematic of a recycle reactor process with its sensors and valves. Note that valve symbols represent flow control loops and level controllers (LC) represent level indicators and controllers combined.

Identify significant disturbances. Disturbances for this process include steam enthalpy changes for both the reactor heater and the stripper reboiler. The ambient air temperature can significantly affect the available condenser duty which in turn can affect the reactor feed rate.

Determine the type and location of sensors. Figure 14.4 shows the sensors applied to this process. Level indicators are required for the reactor level and for the accumulator and reboiler of the stripper. A temperature sensor/transmitter (RTD) is placed in the line that delivers the reaction mixture to the reactor heater in order to measure the reactor temperature. This location was chosen because it is less expensive to install a thermowell in a process line than through the wall of the reactor vessel. In addition, because the fluid velocity should be greater in the process line than inside the reactor, the thermal resistance of the thermowell/RTD system will be lower resulting in a faster responding temperature sensor.

From an analysis of the stripper, it was determined that a tray temperature measurement in the stripping section of the stripper would be a good control point for ensuring that the bottoms product from the stripper meets the product purity specifications for the C product. Steady-state models of the stripper were used to identify the best tray temperature location. An RTD temperature sensor/transmitter should also be used for the application. A pressure sensor should also be installed in the top of the stripper in order to determine when the condenser duty constraint is being encountered. Also, orifice plate/differential pressure flow indicators should be used in each flow control loop.

Determine the location of control valves. Flow control loops, which include a control valve, are shown in Figure 14.4. Flow control loops should be installed on the fresh A feed and fresh B feed lines. Flow control loops should also be installed on the steam lines to the reactor heater and to the stripper reboiler. Flow control loops should be installed on the reactor product line, on the C product line from the stripper, on the stripper reflux line, and on the recycle line to the reactor.

Apply a degree-of-freedom analysis. There are eight flow control valves while there are six controlled variables during unconstrained operation: reactor temperature, reactor level, bottoms and accumulator levels for the stripper, tray temperature in the stripping section of the stripper and the process production rate. Therefore, this system is underdetermined since the stripper reflux rate and the recycle rate (stripper distillate rate) are not used as manipulated variables. When the condenser duty constraint is encountered, a degree-of-freedom is lost, but the system will still be underdetermined.

Implement energy management. The steam flow to the reactor heater supplies the energy to drive the endothermic reactions in the reactor. The steam flow to the reboiler supplies the reboiler duty for the stripper while the condenser removes heat from overhead vapor in order to condense it.

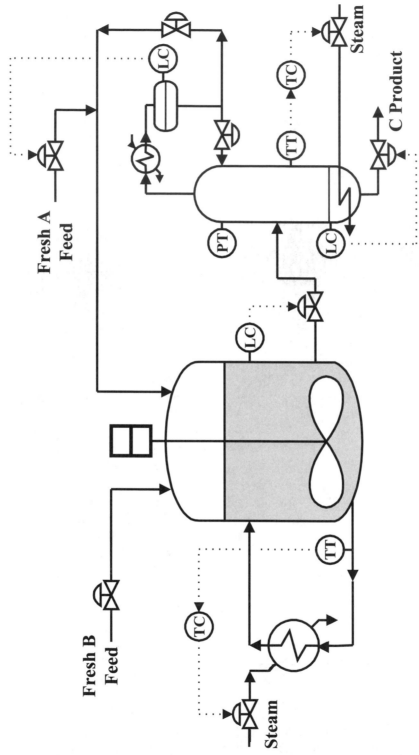

Figure 14.5   Schematic of the recycle reactor process with basic control configuration implemented. Note that the control valve symbols represent flow control loops and the level controllers (LC) represent combined level indicators and controllers.

Control process production rate. The process production rate can be set by the selecting the setpoint for the flow controller for the fresh B feed. Since virtually all the fresh B feed is converted into C product, adjusting the fresh B feed rate to the reactor is a direct means of changing the production rate.

Select manipulated variables that meet the control objectives. The temperature of the reactor can be controlled by adjusting the setpoint for the flow controller on the steam flow to the reactor heater. The reactor level can be controlled by adjusting reactor product flow controller setpoint.

Since the stripper is a low reflux ratio column, the (L,V) configuration is selected for the stripper. It is well established[2] that a flow rate for an internal liquid stream must be set externally to the recycle in order to prevent the "snowball" effect. The snowball effect can be understood by considering a level increase in the reactor. The level controller on the reactor will increase the reactor product flow rate in order to lower the reactor level. The increase in the feed to the stripper will result in a proportional increase in the distillate rate which will tend to increase the reactor level. As a result, the flow rates through the stripper and recycle to the reactor will increase until a constraint is encountered. Likewise, if the reactor level is below setpoint, the reactor product rate will be decreased and the recycle will also decrease which will continue to reduce the loading on the stripper and recycle. In order to break this feedback system with positive feedback, a constant setpoint for the flow controller on the recycle stream can be used. This leaves the accumulator level to be controlled since for the (L,V) configuration, the distillate flow rate (the recycle flow rate in this case) is normally used to control the accumulator level. In this case, the fresh A feed can be used to control the accumulator level. The unused degree of freedom is the setpoint for the reflux flow controller. This control configuration is shown in Figure 14.5.

Address how disturbances will be handled. Steam enthalpy changes can be handled by the reactor heater and stripper reboiler temperature controllers. The effect of ambient air temperature changes on the condenser duty will be addressed in the next section where constraint handling is considered.

Develop a constraint handling strategy. Two constraints should be considered: the condenser duty and the reactor heater duty. When the condenser duty constraint is encountered, the overhead pressure in the stripper increases. As the pressure of the column increases, the relative volatility between A and C decreases; therefore, an upper limit on the overhead stripper pressure must be identified and the column must be operated below this upper pressure limit. The most direct way to reduce the pressure in the stripper is to reduce the flow rate of fresh B feed. Normally, the fresh B feed flow controller setpoint is set by the operator in order to meet the desired production rate for the product C. A pressure controller can be added to the process to adjust this setpoint when the pressure in the stripper overhead is above the specified limit; therefore, a LS controller can be used to select the lower between the operator-specified setpoint and the one specified by the stripper overhead pressure controller.

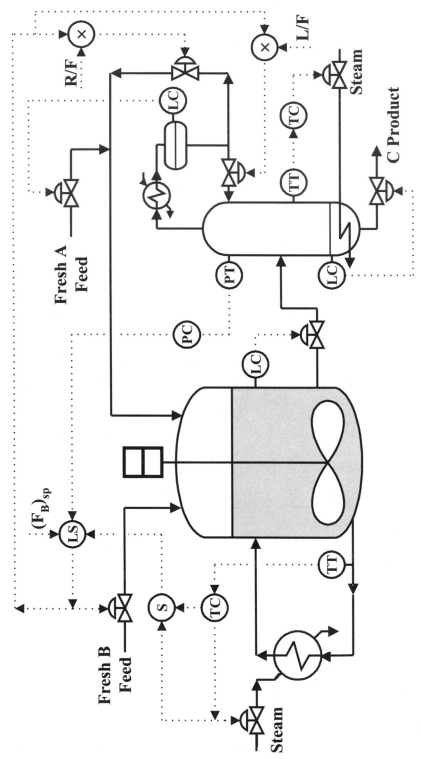

Figure 14.6 Schematic of the recycle reactor process with constraint and ratio controls added. Note that the control valve symbols represent flow control loops and the level controllers represent combined level indicators and controllers.

During the winter months when the condenser duty is at its maximum level, the bottleneck for the process is the reactor heater. When this limit is encountered, the valve on the heater steam will saturate; therefore, an override controller can be used so that when the heater steam valve saturates, a select controller will adjust the fresh B feed to maintain the temperature of the reactor at its setpoint. This override/select controller can be combined with the previous constraint controller by simply sending the output from the select controller to the low select controller which will select the lowest setpoint for the fresh B feed from among the operator specified value, the value specified by the stripper overhead pressure controller, and the value specified by the reactor temperature override controller. These constraints controls are shown in Figure 14.6.

Control inventories. The reactor level and the stripper accumulator and bottoms levels each has level controllers. There is a pressure controller on the stripper overhead to protect against high pressure operation.

Check component balances. Components A and B are each recycled to extinction except for the small amount of A that leaves with the product. Component C is produced in the reactor and removed from the process as the bottom product from the stripper.

Control individual unit operations. During constraint control the feed rate to the stripper can change significantly. Since the recycle rate (stripper distillate rate) and the reflux flow controllers have fixed setpoints, these feed rate changes can cause significant composition upsets in the stripper. In both cases, these flow rates can be ratioed to the fresh B feed rate. For the recycle rate, the ratio of recycle rate to fresh B feed rate (R/F) can be set by the operator and when feed rate changes occur, the recycle rate will be automatically scaled to the new feed rate. Likewise, the ratio of stripper reflux to fresh B feed (L/F) can be set by the operator and when feed rate changes occur, the stripper reflux will be automatically scaled to the new feed rate. In both cases, changes in the fresh B feed rate will require dynamic compensation. These additions to the control configuration are shown in Figure 14.6.

Apply process optimization. The reactor temperature setpoint and the ratios R/F and L/F are available as degrees of freedom for process optimization. Since almost complete conversion of B occurs in the reactor, there is little incentive for optimizing the reactor temperature. The value of R/F and L/F can be selected by optimizing the steady state operation with regard to utility usage while meeting the product impurity specification on the C product.

14.5 Summary

This chapter has presented a procedure for approaching the design of control systems for complex multiunit processes. The control techniques that have been studied in the previous chapters can be systematically applied using this procedure in order to develop effective control schemes for complex chemical processes.

14.6 References

1. Luyben, M.L., B.D. Tyreus, and W.L. Luyben, "Plantwide Control Design Procedure", *AIChE J.*, Vol 43, No.12, pp. 3161-3174 (1997).

2. Tyreus, B.D., and W.L. Luyben, "Dynamics and Control of Recycle Systems. 4. Ternary Systems with One or Two Recycle Streams", *Ind. Eng. Chem. Res.*, Vol 32, pp 1154-1162 (1993).

Appendix A

Pseudo-Random Number Generator

In order to apply the model for sensor noise presented in Chapter 3, a random number, x_n, is required. Considerable work has been done on developing techniques that generate random numbers that are very nearly perfectly random. For modeling noise, the requirements for a random number generator are not nearly so demanding. As a result, a simple pseudo-random number generator[1] will suffice and is given by

$$x_{n+1} = 10^P C x_n - I(10^P C x_n)$$

where x_{n+1} is the calculated random number which is between zero and unity, x_n is the previous random number which is also between zero and unity, P is the number of significant figures used in x_n, $I(y)$ is the integer value of y, and A and B are constants In order to generate a random number, four values are required: A, B, P, and x_n. A is any non-negative integer and B is any number from the set {3, 11, 13, 19, 21, 27, 29, 37, 53, 59, 61, 67, 69, 77, 83, 91}. Then C can be calculated by the following expression

$$C = 10^{-P} (200A + B)$$

The initial random number (x_0), which is known as the seed, should be between zero and unity and contain the same number of significant figures as x_n such that

$$x_0 = 10^{-P} K$$

where K is any integer not divisible by 2 or 5 such that $0 < K < 10^P$.

1. Graybeal, W.T., and U.W. Pooch, *Simulation: Principles and Methods*, Little, Brown, and Company, Boston, MA, Section 4.2.5 (1984).

Appendix B
Signal Filtering

All process measurements have some degree of noise associated with them. This noise can be caused by electrical interference, mechanical vibration, or changes in the process (e.g., variations resulting from turbulent flow). Noise is a high frequency variation in the process measurement that is not associated with the true process measurement. Therefore, a controller that is responding to the noise on a measurement will make high frequency changes to the manipulated variable that cause short term process variations in the controlled variable. The noise can increase the variability of the controlled variable about its setpoint, but the average value of the controlled variable will not change. In effect, a controller using measured controlled variable values with significant noise levels will pass the noise into the process if preventive steps are not taken. In fact, depending on the process gain and time constant, the noise level can be amplified by the controller. When derivative action is used, the feedback system is even more prone to amplifying the noise on the measurement of the controlled variable. Filtering of process measurements is an effective means of reducing the effects of measurement noise.

Sampling. The measurement of a controlled variable must be converted into a digital value by the A/D converter before it can be used by the control algorithm in the DCS. A continuous measurement (e.g., a temperature sensor) is sampled by the A/D converter at discrete points in time. After the measurement is sampled, its value is fixed at that level until the next sampling by the A/D converter. Figure B.1 shows a continuous measurement and the discrete sampled measurement. Since the sampled

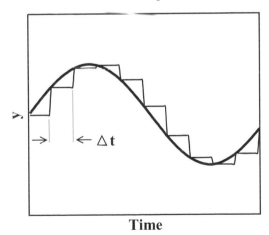

Time

Figure B.1   Comparison between a continuous measurement and the corresponding sample and hold measurement.

349

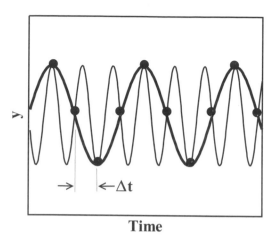

Time

Figure B.2 Signal aliasing resulting from using too large a sampling period. Thin line- the original signal. Thick line- the apparent low frequency signal resulting from signal aliasing. ● **represents the sampled measurement.**

value is fixed at its last measured value, this sampling approach is called the **sample and hold** approach or a **zero-th order hold**. The time between sample points is called the **sampling period**, Δt. The **sampling rate** is $1/\Delta t$ and the **sampling frequency** is $2\pi/\Delta t$.

From Section 7.3, both the control interval and sampling period should be less than $0.05(\tau_p + \theta_p)$ in order to approach continuous control performance. If this guideline is used, a sample and hold approach to sampling the controlled variable should provide an accurate measure of the process behavior.

Signal aliasing. Sampling a signal using a sampling period that is too large results in a loss of information for the signal that is being sampled. In other words, if the sampling period is too large, significant variation of the signal can occur during the sampling period and knowledge of the true dynamic behavior will be lost. Figure B.2 shows the original signal as a high frequency sinusoid (thin line). A sampling period (Δt), which is too large to accurately measure the original signal, is applied to the original signal yielding the apparent signal. The apparent signal is also a sinusoid, but with a much lower frequency. This phenomenon is known as **signal aliasing**. According to Shannon's sampling theorem[1], in order to prevent signal aliasing, the sampling period must be less than one-half the period of the original signal in order to accurately reconstruct the original signal.

An industrial sensor reading will contain a full range of frequencies, i.e., low frequencies representing true process changes and high frequencies from sensor noise. As a result, the sampling period selected to follow the changes in the true process will tend to cause the high frequency components of the sensor reading (i.e., those with periods twice Δt and smaller) to appear as lower frequency components due to signal aliasing. The low frequency components resulting from signal aliasing can affect control performance if their frequencies correspond to the frequencies of the process that is being controlled. The effects of signal aliasing on control performance can be handled by applying the proper filtering techniques to the sensor reading.

Filtering process measurements. The effects of high frequency noise on a process measurement can be reduced by filtering the measurement signal. Filtering can be thought of as taking a running average of the measurement readings of the last n samples. In this manner, the high frequency variations resulting from noise can be "averaged" out. The continuous form of a first order filter is given by a first order model

$$\tau_f \frac{dy_f}{dt} + y_f = y_s$$

where y_s is the unfiltered sensor reading, y_f is the filtered value of the sensor reading, and τ_f is the time constant for the filter. Using a first order finite difference approximation of the first derivative yields the equation for a digital filter

$$y_f(t) = \frac{\frac{\tau_f}{\Delta t}}{\frac{\tau_f}{\Delta t} + 1} \cdot y_f(t - \Delta t) + \frac{1}{\frac{\tau_f}{\Delta t} + 1} y_s$$

where Δt is the sampling period. This equation can be written in the following simplified form

$$y_f(t) = [1 - f] \, y_f(t - \Delta t) + f \, y_s(t)$$

where

$$f = \frac{1}{\frac{\tau_f}{\Delta t} + 1}$$

and f is the filter factor. Consider the case for which $f = 0.05$. The filter for this case can be viewed as an average of the current sensor reading (y_s) and the previous 19 sensor readings since for $f = 0.05$, 5% of the new filtered value comes from the current measurement and 95% comes from the previous readings.

The smallest control interval for normal control loops on a DCS is 0.5 to 1.0 seconds. From Shannon's sampling theorem the components of the noise with periods less than 1.0 seconds will experience signal aliasing. Since analog filters can operate at much higher frequencies (smaller sampling periods) than A/D converters on a DCS, the continuous measurement signal is typically passed through an analog filter to remove the high frequency noise before it goes to the A/D converter. Analog filters use resistors and capacitors to remove high frequency noise from electrical signals. The output of the A/D converter has a digital filter which will remove the lower frequency noise. This signal processing sequence is shown schematically in Figure B.3.

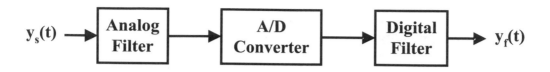

Figure B.3 Schematic showing the sequence of signal processing steps used to filter and sample a continuous measurement for use in a DCS.

1.   Astrom, K.J. and B Wittenmark, *Computer Controlled Systems*, Prentice-Hall (1984).

Index

D

E

F

W

Z

About the Author

James B. Riggs spent his childhood in Baytown, Texas in the shadow of the Humble Oil (now Exxon, USA) refinery. He graduated from Robert E. Lee High School in Baytown in 1964 and entered the University of Texas as a freshman. After he received his BSChE degree from the University of Texas in January 1969, he worked for Enjay Chemical (now Exxon Chemical) for two years before returning to the University of Texas to obtain his Masters Degree in Chemical Engineering. Next, he attended the University of California, Berkeley where he received his Ph.D. Degree in Chemical Engineering in 1977. He spent five years as an assistant professor in the Department of Chemical Engineering at West Virginia University and has been a faculty member in the Department of Chemical Engineering at Texas Tech University since 1983.

Professor Riggs became involved in process control research in the mid-1980's. He collaborated with Russ Rhinehart in this field and in 1992 they established the Texas Tech Process Control and Optimization Consortium (www.pcoc.ttu.edu). In a large part as a result of the involvement with the consortium, Professor Riggs established a research program at Texas Tech that is focused on the study of industrial process control and optimization problems. He has published a total of four books including a popular undergraduate numerical methods text, published over 60 technical papers, served as a process control consultant for industry, and holds several US patents.